THE DEEPING SECRETS

VICTOR WATSON

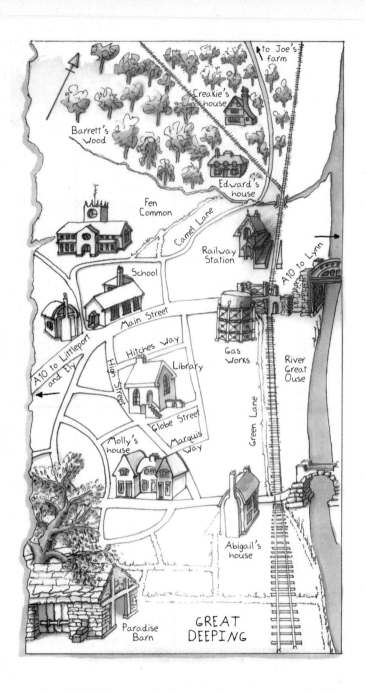

It came like something thrown by the gods, hurtling down the sky directly towards him.

Joe Temper was walking along Green Lane, beside the railway. He wasn't hurrying, and neither was the goods train that was labouring slowly on the down-line, catching him up from behind.

A girl was walking towards him – Molly Barnes, daydreaming as usual, taking a different way to her friend's house by the level crossing. Molly took no notice of the approaching train, and she seemed unaware of the aircraft diving down towards it.

The locomotive had overtaken Joe, chugging comfortably along the track beside him, when he saw the first bombs drop from the screaming plane.

At the roadside there was an abandoned flat-bed farm wagon. Its tyres were soft, buried in undergrowth. It had been sleeping there for years.

Molly's friend Abigail, standing a quarter of a mile away, had been watching for her. She too saw the first bombs fall. To her, it seemed as if Joe took flight across the lane towards Molly, felled her gently, and ushered her to safety under the floor of the wagon.

To Molly, the action was physical, with bones, bruises and bewilderment. But the effect was the same, and with extraordinary speed. She was under the wagon, and Joe had rolled in beside her and pushed her head down. She twisted her face sideways, spitting out mud and grass.

'Keep your head down!' He pressed a hard arm across her shoulders.

There was a series of overwhelming explosions, sullen volcanic roars, then a clattering and thumping of debris as lumps of mud and scraps of wood fell heavily onto the truck-bed above their heads. A metal wheel from one of the freight wagons thudded down and buried itself in the grass close by, half a hundredweight of instant death.

They crawled out into the still evening air. There was silence everywhere, stunned, deafened. There was a rich smell of fresh new grass crushed, then the smell of smoke and burning.

'Crikey!' Joe said.

Molly stared at the scene. Most of the bombs had missed the train, falling in the wet meadow on the other side of the tracks. But some had scored a direct hit on three or four wagons just behind the engine. There was a long uneven crater, and piles of scattered wreckage. A single stretch of rail – with bits of sleeper still attached – stood vertically upright. Then it collapsed slowly, caught on some telegraph wires, and brought them down too.

Further down the track, the stoker had climbed onto the top of the tender. He stood there staring, legs apart, hands on hips. The engine driver was climbing slowly down from his cab.

The bomber had gained altitude and was already out of sight.

Abigail was racing along Green Lane towards them. Her mother, who worked the crossing gates, had already rushed indoors to phone the signalman. All trains had to be stopped.

'Thanks,' Molly said. She felt breathless. 'It's a good job you were here.' She knew who Joe Temper was, but she didn't think she had ever spoken to him. He was older than she was, and in the senior class at school. She knew he lived out in Camel Fen.

'It's OK,' Joe said.

About a quarter of a mile down the line, Great Deeping station was empty. There were no passengers and no railway staff.

The porter who should have been on duty had absented himself and was standing over a mile away, by a wood at the edge of the town. Mr Creake had waited impatiently, trying to control his excitement. When he first heard the sound of the solitary Stuka bomber approaching, he started to shake, clenching his fists in his pockets and aware of his racing heartbeat.

A small voice inside him protested. *What have you*

done? What have you done? But he silenced it, as he always did. It was the voice of weakness.

He heard the distant hoot of the locomotive as it approached the level crossing. The sound came faintly across the quiet evening rooftops of the town. Everything was happening with perfect timing.

Mr Creake saw only the first of the bombs as they fell because the Stuka was flying low and the trees of the wood obscured his view. But everything was going well and he braced himself for what he knew must happen next. His excitement was so intense that he couldn't breathe properly.

For a fraction of a heartbeat, he thought it had started. But hope died at once. The explosions he heard were only the sounds of the bombs, little more than distant muffled thuds, feeble and insufficient. Rooks nesting in the tops of the trees cawed noisily as they flapped away in indignation.

The big overwhelming blast he had been anticipating did not happen. Something had gone wrong.

An object fell at his feet – a rook's egg. It exploded and splattered over his shoe, a mess of green and brown-blotched shell fragments, some pale fluid, and a small graceless creature, unhatched and featherless.

Mr Creake crushed it savagely with his foot. Then he fell to his knees, clasping his head. After a few moments, he rose and ran into the trees, stumbling with shame and failure. They would be angry with him, full of furious contempt.

Next day, people came to view the damage, walking the length of Green Lane, stopping to stare, to talk, to express their dismay.

Green Lane was a grassy track that started in the road by the level crossing. It was about half a mile long. At the other end, it went past the gasworks, through the goods yard, and out onto the road by the railway station. It was used by dog walkers and people taking a shortcut to the allotments close to the station.

Almost everyone in Great Deeping visited Green Lane that day. They saw the wrecked trucks, and the holes in the meadow where the bombs had failed to hit the train. The remaining wagons – more than thirty of them – had been towed away. Some Royal Engineers had been brought in, and they had already started work to repair the track-bed.

It was Wartime; things had to be dealt with quickly.

At first, the story the people told themselves was a bright one, full of amusement. What fools the Germans must be to send a solitary bomber on a special mission to destroy an empty freight train! Completely empty! People were cheered to know that the enemy could make such a mistake. Later, the story darkened. It became known that the empty goods train was there because of a last-minute change of plan. A trainload of high explosives had been scheduled, but there'd been a problem with the brakes. So the empty train had been sent on early, to use the time slot in the schedule. If a single truckload of explosives had been hit, it would have blown up the whole train. And that would have set off the gasworks too. Great Deeping – and everyone who lived there – would have been wiped off the earth.

One of the onlookers was Edward Barrett. He was not with the other children. He stood alone, casting a solemn eye over the wreckage. As he gazed intently at the engine, where it stood with one undamaged truck still attached, he stretched his upper lip over his lower lip, awkwardly, impossibly, so far down that almost his whole chin was covered by it.

He was always doing that – and the skin under his mouth was red and sore.

By the end of the day, the people's story was even darker – and had turned into a question. How, they asked themselves, did the Germans *know* that a trainload of ammunition was supposed to pass through Great Deeping at that precise moment?

There could only be one answer – there was a spy somewhere. An outsider must have come among them and passed the information to the enemy.

But who? And how?

What, in our *little town?* they thought. *Never! Nothing like that ever happens here.*

Young Edward Barrett felt his wet chin with nervous fingertips.

❧

Letter to Hitler – no. 17

Dear Herr Hitler,

Writing letters which I can't send might seem mad, but I have my reasons. These letters are my tribute to a great man. I belong at your feet, I am a German in my heart. I do not belong to this contemptible country. I am not alone. There are certainly others.

The day will come when I will be able to send these letters to you. For when you and your great armies ride in triumph into London, there will be nothing to prevent me from putting them into the post openly addressed to you at Westminster.

The first steps have been taken.

Yours in admiration,
The Voice of Nazi Britain

There was a new poster pinned up in the classroom. *Walls Have Ears* it said at the top. It showed two old ladies, bent over their walking sticks and huddled close together as they talked. Behind them was a wall, with a doorway, and peering round was a man with enormous ears, listening. On his arm he wore a band, with a swastika.

Until yesterday, there had been a cheerful spring poster, with tadpoles in a pond, and hazel catkins.

At three o'clock, the whole school assembled in the hall, little ones sitting cross-legged on the floor at the front, middle-sized ones sitting on benches, Molly and Abigail at the back, standing with the big ones. There were more of them this year because of the evacuees.

'God ought to have given infants square bottoms,' Abigail had whispered to Molly as they filed in.

The headmistress, Miss Redway, said she hoped they would all have a good Easter. Then they said a prayer and sang *There Is a Green Hill* with Miss Lee at the piano. That was how it should be and Molly approved. It had always been like that. Then Miss Redway spoiled it.

'Hands up,' she said, 'all those people whose fathers

12

are away in the War.'

Hands went up all over the hall, some hesitant and uncertain, some quivering with importance. One of the younger teachers put up her hand too.

'And now those of you whose father is an air-raid warden or a Special Constable.'

Five more hands.

'Now,' she said, 'who can tell us what we mean when we talk about the *front line*?'

Dennis Martin in the top year explained that it was where the fighting was, where our soldiers met the enemy and fought them.

'Good,' said the headmistress. 'Quite right, Dennis. And *where* is the front line?'

Germany was one suggestion. Italy, France, Normandy, North Africa. Texas was suggested once, and Mexico. The smallest girl in the school, in an excited whisper, suggested fairyland.

'But there is one place you have all left out.'

Everyone stared, faces were screwed up to show how hard they were concentrating.

'Great Deeping!' Miss Redway said. 'Since Wednesday, when they tried to blow up an ammunition train, the front line is *right here, in our town*.'

She paused to let this sink in. 'The enemy are among us, spying, eavesdropping, pretending all the time that they are one of us. But they are not! They are fifth columnists, agents, spies, evil wicked people from afar trying to destroy us.'

The whole school was silent now. The other teachers looked grim.

Molly scowled. She hated this. She always looked forward to end-of-term assemblies, especially this one. Easter was her favourite time of year and she wanted to enjoy it as she did every year, untroubled by fear.

'We are all fighting at the front line now,' Miss Redway said. 'I would like you to put up your hands if you are willing to be brave little soldiers.'

Many of the younger children looked uncertain, as if they thought they might be marched off to battle at once. Most of the older children did put their hands up – but not all. Someone whispered loudly, 'She's batty!'

'I don't want to be a brave little soldier,' Molly grumbled quietly, and kept her hands resolutely by her side. Abigail did the same, but with less conviction. Everyone was expected to be brave these days.

Three children from Class Five did a short play – two of them came in telling each other about a new British fighter plane; the third had a Hitler moustache and a notebook. He scribbled down what he had heard the other two say, and hurried off with a hugely triumphant look on his face.

Molly daydreamed. In the corner of the hall stood a table with a spring display – bright-green moss, primroses, cowslips, some violets, and a papier-mâché bird's nest with six small clay eggs coloured blue. The window pole leaned in the corner. The dusty blackboard seemed to be asleep. And the afternoon sunshine let itself in through the high narrow windows and illuminated two hundred heads. It had shone like that every Easter during the First World War, and the war before that, Molly supposed. All the way back to 1868, which was the date carved over the main entrance.

I won't let them scare me! Molly thought. At that moment she hated Miss Redway. She felt as if the headmistress had stolen something belonging to her.

She wished Adam had been there. Adam Swales was an evacuee from London. He lived with Molly and her mum but he had gone to spend some time in Wales with relatives. He'd been allowed to miss the last week of term. Most people didn't care if their evacuees went away for a while. Some people would be pleased if they went away for good. But Adam was different. Even Molly's mum hadn't wanted him to go.

'Are you a Nazi spy?' she said to Abigail afterwards.

Abigail nodded. 'Didn't you know?'

'All right, then,' Molly said. 'I'll be one too.'

It was wicked to say that kind of thing. But Molly *felt* wicked. They were cheating her of her Easter holiday. It should be a time of pussy willows and celandines and sticky buds, with bright chilly skies and lovely lengthening evenings. But it was being turned into something different, full of fear.

Inwardly, Molly dug her heels in. She would *not* be scared by this nonsense!

Imagine a small town high in the mountains of North Wales. A town built entirely of grey slate.

And imagine Adam Swales walking unhurriedly into the top of the town and stopping to look along the main street.

His favourite place in the whole world.

Adam had been coming to stay at his uncle's farm every year since he was three years old. The farm was two miles away, up in the hills towards Snowdon. But it was the town, not the farm, which had first made Adam want to draw pictures. He had found some paper and a pencil and knelt hunched at his aunt's kitchen table, trying – even as a small toddler – to find the best way of holding a pencil and forcing onto the paper some black-and-white sense of that extraordinary place.

There was no forcing now. Adam sat on a step at the top of the street, opened his sketchbook on the small wooden board he carried with him, and took a couple of pencils from inside his sock.

He was motionless, studying the blacks and greys of the town, slate black and slate grey. The roofs were tiled with slate; the walls were built of blocks of slate; the doorsteps and window sills were great slate slabs; the door frames and window frames were upright slate columns; the pavements at the side of the road were made of slate. The war memorial put up in 1919 was carved from slate. And he knew that, inside, most of the houses had slate floors, slate hearthstones and slate draining boards in their kitchens.

Often drab and colourless, this place was. The wettest place in Great Britain, some people said. Endless clouds streamed in from the west, rose into the mountains and poured onto the town a relentless and drenching wetness that was too concentrated to be called just *rain*.

But Adam knew that, if a sudden gleam of cloud-filtered sunlight illuminated the wetness, this mountain town would be changed into a fairy dream of impossibles. You could *not* have brilliant greys and bright blacks. But, in this town, you did.

He knew that many great artists drew self portraits every few years throughout their lives. They did it as a measure of their work, a test of time and skill. For him, this town was his self portrait.

Two girls – about his age – came up the street, talking to each other in Welsh. When they reached Adam, they stopped and watched for a moment. Adam smiled briefly at them. He was used to this.

One of them said in English, 'You an artist, then?'

Adam nodded.

The other girl said, 'You're Bronwen Jones's cousin, aren't you? Up at the farm?'

The girls watched him in silence for a moment or two. Then the first one said, 'You can draw us if you like.' They linked arms and giggled.

Adam looked up from his work. Under their headscarves they had bright, pretty faces, with soft brown hair and dark-blue eyes. But he didn't want to draw them.

He smiled and shook his head, and the two girls went off, laughing and talking rapidly to each other in Welsh.

A woman came out of a butcher's shop, got into an Austin Seven, and drove out of town. As the sound of the car died away, the London Adam became aware that the silence of the mountains was full of the bleating of a thousand sheep. But the Welsh Adam had hardly noticed it – because it was there all the time, this sound, casting a nursery-rhyme spell on the mountains and valleys.

Outside school, a fight was developing.

Abigail and Molly had never spoken to Edward Barrett. He was four classes lower than theirs. The boy was being herded and shoved against a wall in the street outside the school. There was some jeering and a good deal of laughter. He was small, surrounded by bigger children. It had happened before.

Joe Temper walked up to the two girls.

'Wotcher, Molly. You all right?'

Molly's face darkened, Abigail's brightened.

Just because he saved my life doesn't mean I have to be his friend, Molly thought crossly. Abigail, she knew, was a more generous person, more open.

'What are they doing to that little boy?' Abigail demanded.

'That's Edward Barrett,' Joe said.

'We know that,' Abigail said. 'Why are they always on at him?'

Joe looked thoughtfully at the crowd of children. So far there was no violence, only jeering. 'He's a poor scrap of a thing,' he said.

'Is it true that his dad is dead?' Abigail asked.

Joe nodded.

'Killed in the War?' Abigail's own father was missing, feared dead. Molly was immediately on her guard, watchful and anxious for her friend as she always was when the subject of dead fathers arose.

'Not in this one,' Joe said. 'Before this War started, there was one in Spain.'

Neither Molly nor Abigail had heard about the war in Spain.

'And his father's two brothers have both been killed in this one.'

The two girls took this in, slowly. Molly spoke first. 'It's not *fair*,' she said passionately.

Joe studied her for a moment, thoughtfully. 'And his grandad, *he* got killed in the first War,' he added. Then he turned on his heels and walked over to the group of noisy kids.

Abigail and Molly watched. The crowd grew silent as Joe joined them and a way was made open for him. They couldn't hear whether he said anything or not – he certainly used no force. His presence was enough, and the viciousness turned to humour, even to friendliness. Joe had been totally fearless. There had been a growing storm and he had stilled it, but it was impossible to say how. He was no bigger than the biggest of them. But they gave way to him, gladly, wanting to please.

'How did he do that?' Abigail said quietly.

Molly sniffed and looked haughty.

'*And* he saved your life,' Abigail said.

'I know,' Molly said. 'I wish he hadn't!'

'*Molly!*'

'I didn't mean *that*. I meant I wish I'd saved my *own* life!'

Joe came out from the crowd with Edward in tow, wrapping his upper lip over his lower, looking confused.

What a specimen! Abigail thought. It was an expression her mum used a lot.

Joe asked Edward what he was going to do tomorrow, the first day of the holidays.

The first day of the holidays! They were words that gave Molly and Abigail a thrill of pleasure and promise. But Edward looked as if the first day of the holidays meant nothing. Was he completely joyless?

'You can come and see my racing pigeons if you want,' Joe said.

The boy nodded. His lower lip and most of his chin were red and raw and painful.

Does he ever speak? Molly wondered.

'Can we come too?' Abigail asked.

Abigail! Molly shouted inwardly. *I'm not interested in pigeons!*

'You *will* be interested,' Abigail said to her.

And I don't particularly want to spend my precious holiday time with a boy with a squelchy chin!

Abigail, apparently, was not troubled by Edward's squelchiness and Joe didn't seem to mind who came to see his pigeons. 'OK,' he said. 'You're welcome. But not till after ten – I like a lie-in in on Saturdays. Then I got my farm jobs to do.'

'Come on,' he said to Edward. Then he turned back to the girls. 'You don't want to worry about all them spies she was on about,' he said. 'There een't any.'

Molly was startled. She hadn't said a word about spies.

'But someone told the Germans about that ammunition train,' Abigail said.

'Yes,' Joe said slowly. 'Some madman, I s'pose. Someone who thinks Hitler is bloomin' marvellous.'

'That's bad enough!' Abigail retorted.

Not as bad as a whole army of spies skulking everywhere in the town, Molly thought. An enemy on the other side of the English Channel was bad enough. And when the enemy flew its planes so low over your rooftop that you could see the pilots' faces, that was terrifying. But when the enemy might be your next-door neighbour, or the postman who delivered letters to your house every day, how were you supposed to cope with that?

Nevertheless, Joe Temper had cheered her a little. Quite a lot, she later admitted to herself.

~

Letter to Hitler – no. 18

Dear Herr Hitler,

There has been a small setback. Your brave Luftwaffe pilot found his target with perfect accuracy, but the train proved not to have explosives in it. It is of no significance: the lion in his triumphant race towards his victim is impeded by a thousand small thorns that catch in his noble fur. But they do not slow him down or prevent his ultimate triumph.

What will you do with all our churches when you are prime minister and supreme commander of Britain? The vicar came to call on me the other day. A weak and foolish man, but no danger to anyone. He came to sell me the Parish Magazine. As he stood in my living room, his head was hardly a foot away from the shoebox containing my letters to you. So close! Yet he knew nothing. That gave me great pleasure. If these letters were ever to be found, I would be executed for treason. I am excited by the possession of this secret. It is a risk worth taking because I have such important things to say. Things that will amaze the world.

I do not belong to this country. I despise the entire population, with its love of foolish traditions from the past (such as cricket), its absurd cheerfulness in Wartime, its infantile jollity.

Please, sir, believe me when I say that I do not belong to these people.

Yours most respectfully,
The Voice of Nazi Britain

❧

Adam spent the afternoon tramping about the country. He always did this when he stayed in Wales, stopping occasionally to sketch a gatepost or part of a dry-stone wall, or one of the ruined stone cottages.

There was a disused slate mine he always visited, and every year he told himself that one day he would push past the rotting wooden doors that blocked the entrance to the tunnels inside.

But he'd never done it and now it was too late. His uncle had told him that the mine was being brought back into use. His elder cousin, Gwen, had got a job there. Started in February.

He left the road, climbed a wall, and plodded over the brow of a grassy hillside. In seconds, his shoes and socks were soaked. Sheep fell silent and skittered clumsily out of reach as he approached. There was a steeper slope, with protruding rocks and ledges, and here he settled to study the entrance to the mine in the valley below him.

It was like an amphitheatre and he was the audience, looking down. Steep cliff faces enclosed an arena, a flat gleaming surface of crushed wet slate. There was a lot of mud. The original wooden doors had gone and a huge pair of metal doors stood in their place, open. He could see Gwen standing just inside, with a clipboard and a pen.

Parts of the old railway were still there, twisted, rusty, broken. A new one had been laid beside it, leading through the doorway into the darkness of the tunnels. Its rails gleamed with newness. Two-foot gauge, Adam guessed. And on it stood some trucks like no railway vehicle Adam had ever seen. They were narrow and immensely tall, with a handle at each end for pushing.

What could they be for? Adam knew that slabs of quarried slate were sometimes enormous – but they were also heavy. These high trucks would tip over, he thought, if heavy slate was stacked vertically onto them.

A lorry laboured its clumsy way up the track and into the arena in front of the entrance. It was loaded with bricks. Then Adam noticed a cement mixer standing by the doorway. Why would anyone want to build something inside a mine?

Someone came out into the light and stood beside Gwen. An extraordinary figure in such a place, wearing a dark-grey suit and a bowler hat! And from behind him came an army officer, with a cane and a briefcase.

Someone shouted, 'Hi! You!'

Do they think I'm a spy? Adam wondered. He ducked his head behind the boulder, grabbed his things, and fled quickly, slithering wetly over the soggy ground and scattering sheep in every direction.

That evening, Abigail moved in to stay with Molly. If the Germans were going to bomb the railway, Abigail's mum thought, it would be safer for Abigail to move out of the level-crossing house for the time being. There was plenty of room at Molly's because she lived in a guest house. These days, because of the War, there weren't many guests. Just a lot of empty rooms.

Abigail's mum had to stay because it was her job to open and shut the crossing gates.

'Would you like a room to yourself?' Mrs Barnes said to Abigail. 'Or would you like me to move a bed into Molly's room?'

Secretly, Molly didn't want Abigail sharing her room. She could visit it as often as she liked. And stay there for hours on end, if she wanted. Molly liked it like that. They already did everything together all through the day, and Molly looked forward to the two of them having supper together, sharing a bath together, and standing side by side to clean their teeth at the washbasin. And she hoped there would be at least one air raid, so that they could spend the night together in the table-shelter downstairs.

But she wanted to keep her bedroom to herself.

I'm not a very nice person, Molly thought. But perhaps Abigail had more tact and good sense than she was given credit for. 'Can I have the room next door?' she asked. 'Then we can tap messages to each other on the wall,' she said aside to Molly.

So that was agreed upon and Abigail moved in.

They decided to write a letter to Adam.

They wrote the first part at the kitchen table while Mrs Barnes was listening to Mr Churchill on the wireless and baby William was messily waving his spoon in the air. The middle section was written as they sat halfway up the stairs, side by side on the seventh step. The final part was done in the bathroom.

Having a bath together acted like magic and turned them into seven year olds. They did that from time to time. It was comforting.

While Abigail was in the bath, Molly knelt on the floor and did some more writing; then, when Molly got in the bath, Abigail got out and drew a picture. Finally, Abigail got back in with Molly. But the water was getting cold and they played a splashy game to warm themselves up. Some of the game spilled over onto the letter as it lay on the floor.

Afterwards, Molly found an envelope and cadged a tuppenny-ha'penny stamp from her mum. She hesitated briefly, wrote *I wish you were here* at the end of the letter, and sealed it in the envelope.

It was a patchwork letter, full of stops and starts and surprises. And bathwater stains. But what it described was patchwork too, a confusing sequence of events – an empty train deliberately bombed, an ammunition train that had *not* been bombed, and their headmistress's belief that somewhere in Great Deeping German spies were skulking about in the shadows, picking up important information and sending it back to the enemy.

In their nightclothes and slippers, Molly and Abigail went out to post the letter – not a big adventure, since the post box was just outside Molly's front door.

Mr Robertson Creake had written a letter too. He reread it carefully, folded it neatly, and took down a cardboard shoebox from the top of a cupboard.

It was a plain white box, with SIZE 11 pencilled on the lid. Mr Creake placed his latest letter inside, patting it gently as it lay there with the other seventeen.

What would happen if anyone ever discovered those letters? he wondered. He enjoyed thinking that.

In North Wales, they were sitting in the kitchen, listening to Mr Churchill on the wireless – Adam's uncle and aunt, his two older cousins, and Adam himself. Gel, the collie, was resting his head on Adam's knee.

'When I spoke to you last, early in February,' Mr Churchill said, 'many people believed the Nazi

27

boastings that the invasion of Britain was about to begin.'

Gel raised one ear as if he, too, were paying attention to the grimness of the prime minister's words.

'It has not begun yet, and with every week that passes we grow stronger on the sea, in the air, and in the numbers, quality, training and equipment of the great armies that now guard our island.'

Adam was fascinated by the way Mr Churchill's voice would sink unexpectedly to a low note. It was a darkening, like switching from an HB pencil to a 4B.

'When I compare the position at home as it is today with what it was in the summer of last year . . . I feel that we have very much to be thankful for, and I believe that provided our exertions and our vigilance are not relaxed even for a moment, we may be confident that we shall give a very good account of ourselves.'

Terrible words, those. There was a sad tenseness in the cosy room as the listeners took in what they meant. *We shall give a very good account of ourselves.* A test was coming, that's what those words meant. Something was going to happen.

The speech was finished, the wireless switched off. Bronwen, who rarely spoke, said, 'Have you noticed? Mr Churchill always says *Narsi*. Everyone else says *Nartsi*. Nartsies are bad enough, but Narsies give me the creeps!'

'Don't you worry about them,' her father said. 'If they do come, this will be the last place they'll get to.'

'Do you ever get any German bombers up here?' Adam asked.

His uncle shook his head. 'No,' he said. 'But they're havin' it bad in Swansea. And Cardiff. Terrible things have been happenin' down there. Night after night it is.'

Adam took up his pencil and settled down at the table. His older cousin, Gwen, touched him affectionately on the head. 'I remember,' she said, 'when I was about ten or eleven. I pushed you for miles in that big old pram we had. When you first came here.'

'Where *is* that pram?' her dad said.

'At the back of the shed,' Bronwen said. 'The hens like it for layin' in.'

His aunt took up the story. 'When you were about four,' she said, 'you began doing your drawings. Page after page you did! Sitting for hours at this table. And the day your mum took you back to London, d'you know what you did?'

Adam looked up, interested.

'You found an old biscuit tin and put all your drawings in it. Then you buried them in the garden.'

'Where I'd just planted my taters,' his uncle said. And everyone laughed.

It was an innocent family conversation, soothing after Mr Churchill's promise of danger to come. Adam decided to drop his bombshell.

'Gwen?' he said. 'That mine, the slate mine – what do you do there?'

The tiniest hesitation. Then, 'I do secretarial stuff, that's all. Typin', and stuff like that.'

'What do they want a secretary for in a slate mine?'

Gwen smiled at his ignorance. 'Any kind of business has secretarial jobs that have to be done.'

'I had a look at it this afternoon,' Adam said.

'Was that you lookin' over . . . ?'

Adam didn't answer her directly. 'Seemed to me,' he said, 'that it's being rebuilt for putting something *in*, not taking slate *out*.'

Gwen scoffed. 'You shouldn't go spyin', Adam Swales! Why would anyone want to put anything inside a mine? Under a mountain?'

But Adam was not deceived. 'Funny sort of trucks, too. Have you seen them, Uncle? They're tall and narrow. Like gigantic toast racks.'

'Perhaps they're for carrying gigantic slices of toast,' Gwen said.

Adam made them wait for a second or two. Then he said, 'Or gigantic paintings. You know, works of art. Big flat things.'

The silence in the room became solid, like ice.

Gwen spoke in a whisper. 'How did you know that?' she said, and then realised that she shouldn't have.

'Adam,' she said. 'It's very hush-hush. No one is supposed to know anything about what goes on in that quarry. It's a *slate* mine.'

'OK,' Adam said cheerfully.

After breakfast, Edward escaped from the kitchen and hurried to the bottom of the garden.

It was not a garden really, just a large area of rough grass with some fruit trees. Much of it was overgrown and tangled, full of ancient hiding places. At the bottom, out of sight from the kitchen window, there was a shed, built of red brick. It was mossy and old, solidly rooted.

Edward took a key from his pocket, unlocked the door and went in quietly.

The sun shone through the open doorway, lighting up the dusty silence. Edward breathed deeply as the workshop wrapped itself around him and enclosed him. Nothing had been moved since the last time his father had used it, just before he went away. Edward could remember him working in there, sawing, planing, chiselling, always busy and always quietly talking to his son.

But doubts always broke in. Could he really remember these scenes? Or had he made them up? Edward wasn't sure. He'd been three when his father had died; his only memories of him were connected with this workshop.

The chilly March sun shone on a long wooden workbench. It had been cleared and dusted, and on it stood a short length of 'O'-gauge model-railway track. In the shadowy depths of the building, stacked on shelves, there were dozens of these lengths. Edward had dared to take five and fit them together.

That had happened on a gloomy cold day in midwinter. Since then, he had taken other slight and hesitant steps. He had found an old pine box in a corner, with trucks and a turntable, a station and a level crossing, signals and a footbridge.

When he discovered the locomotive, he'd stared at it in rapture, unable to breathe – a 4.6.2 engine, with the words *Great Northern* on its nameplate, and, on the side of the tender, the letters LNER and the number 4470. The locomotive was painted in black and green, with shiny pistons and tiny, perfect brass pipes.

Edward took four trucks from the box and placed them carefully on the track, coupled them together and moved them gently backwards and forwards along the line. It was not a long journey, because the track was not much longer than the train.

One day, Edward thought. *One day!*

He put the trucks back in their box and lifted out the *Great Northern*. It was heavy and he took great care. There was something forbidden in all of this. This was not *his* train set, nobody had said he was allowed even to touch it. There would be trouble one day. Bound to be.

But he did this every day. It took some care to get all eighteen wheels correctly placed on the track. When he had done it, he pushed the engine forward. His hand and wrist braced themselves for the usual difficulty – for the loco wouldn't freewheel in the way the trucks did. There was a resistance, and when he did succeed in forcing it to move, the pistons and connecting-rods and coupling-rods all moved too. But unwillingly.

This baffled Edward. He'd expected to find a wind-up key somewhere, and a hole for it in the side of the engine. But there was no key, and no hole to put it in. And when he turned the engine upside down, he could see no clockwork mechanism in it.

There were other puzzles too – a few extra bits and pieces of brass which mystified him. What were they for? And how was this beautiful locomotive to move?

It was like a barrier to Edward. He could not get beyond it. He borrowed books from the library, and he learned about trains and their locomotives, about the history of steam power, about models you could buy and models you could build yourself. He even learned – in theory, at least, from a library book – how to drive a real engine. He practised it in his head, pretending.

His knowledge of steam locomotives was stupendous – but none of it helped with this one.

He knelt down so that his eyes were level with the workbench. He concentrated hard, transforming the short length of straight track into a graceful curve, leaning slightly inwards. The dusky background of the shed he turned into mountains, and to the rear of the tender he attached a train of ten beautiful mustard-yellow passenger coaches. Snow fell in a thick blizzard but the *Great Northern* came smoothly round the bend towards him, white smoke pouring richly from its chimney, untroubled, faithful, effortlessly taking its load through the highlands of Scotland.

It was a powerful picture, but fleeting. As soon as he had it right, it lost its substance. The locomotive remained motionless on its short length of track.

Edward sighed and got to his feet, and as he did so he heard voices in the garden, coming towards him.

It was new territory for Molly and Abigail, this part of town. They cycled along Camel Lane until they came to the last house, where Edward lived with his grandmother. There was no front garden, just a grassy bank with primroses. A path led round to the back of the house. The front door had a forlorn look, as if no one ever used it. But the back door was opened promptly when they knocked.

Mrs Barrett, Edward's grandmother, was small, no taller than Abigail and Molly. Her eyes were a deep blue, studying them intently, like a challenge. Molly could not shut out of her mind the fact that all the old lady's sons were dead, and her husband. She was like a small fist, clenched hard.

The two girls leaned softly against each other as they

stood there. 'We've come to see Edward,' Abigail said.

'He's down the garden,' Mrs Barrett said. She didn't move and the two girls felt they couldn't either, until she did.

Molly broke the spell by saying, 'Will we be able to find him?'

'If it is God's will that you shall find him, you *will* find him!'

Abigail turned, looking along the length of the back garden. 'Is he playing?' she said doubtfully.

'Playing!' Mrs Barrett said. 'No, he's not playing. He's looking for his father.'

'But . . .'

'Yes, I know. But that's what he's doing! That's all he ever does!'

They found Edward standing in the doorway of the shed, cradling the heavy model engine in both hands. As they approached, his lower lip disappeared under his upper lip, as if he was eating it.

Edward thought there should be a proper way of behaving. But if he expected the girls to wait to be invited in, he was disappointed. Abigail was inside in an instant, poking about among the contents, uttering little oohs and aahs of interest as she came across one discovery after another. Molly had the grace to look embarrassed, but she wasn't much better herself.

Edward just stood there, feeling helpless, taken over. His face was like a horror mask, weird, almost without a chin.

Abigail was in a state of rapture. She had seen model train sets before but nothing as elaborate as this. She turned to Edward, her face shining with excitement, a level crossing in one hand and a semaphore signal in the other. Then she turned her attention to the engine that Edward was still holding. 'Does it go?' she asked him eagerly.

He shook his head.

'Why not?'

Edward didn't know how to answer her. He just knew with absolute certainty that it was forbidden. The engine wouldn't go because it wasn't *supposed* to go. Even to touch the engine came close to the borderline of wickedness.

'*Gosh!*' Molly said.

In the darkest corner of the building there was a huge old lump of wood. Edward knew it was there, shapeless and shadowy, and had paid no attention to it. It looked like a big tree root after the trunk had been broken from it by a gale. But Molly had looked more carefully; it *was* made of wood, but a tunnel had been cut through it, and the wood above had been carved and shaped and painted. Plywood had been fixed to the base and railway track had been screwed onto that, passing from one end of the tunnel to the other. It was perfect, once you knew how to look at it.

'It's a tunnel!' Molly said. 'Going through a mountain!'

Edward's lower lip reappeared, red and sloppy, as his mouth fell open and gaped at what Molly had found.

The three of them spent half an hour in the shed, exploring. And Edward was happy. He really *was* happy – for just a few uncomplicated minutes. Especially when Molly looked inside an old chest of drawers and found – wrapped in tissue paper – a set of ten beautiful carriages, with proper glass windows and curtains, and little seats inside, and tables with perfect tiny tablelamps.

He began to look forward to hours of private pleasure, just looking at them. And pretending.

Abigail brought them back to earth. 'We're supposed to be going to see Joe Temper's pigeons,' she said.

Pigeons! Molly thought.

On their way out, they encountered Edward's grandmother again. She stood at the side of the house, on the path, barring their way.

They stopped when they reached her.

'Edward!' she said.

The boy waited, knowing what was coming.

'Have you read any more of your *Pilgrim's Progress* this morning?'

He nodded.

'How much?'

'Five pages.'

'When did you do that?'

'Before I got out of bed,' he said.

Mrs Barrett had a Bible in her hand. She lifted her head heavenwards with her eyes closed, then opened the book at random without looking at it. She held it in front of her with her left hand, and raised her right hand.

Abigail and Molly stared in embarrassment. Was the old woman mad?

Mrs Barrett brought down her right hand sharply, stabbing the Bible with her forefinger. Then she opened her eyes and peered down to see what her finger was pointing at.

'Rid me, and deliver me from the hand of strange children, whose mouth speaketh vanity, and their right hand is a right hand of falsehood,' she read, then looked up at the two girls, triumphantly. 'Where are you taking this boy?' she demanded.

Molly was too scared to speak. But Abigail looked at the old lady defiantly. 'Only to Joe Temper's farm,' she said. 'To see his pigeons!' Abigail had never seen the Bible treated in this way before, but she attended Sunday School every week and she was familiar with biblical quotations. 'And there is no falsehood in our right hands,' she added. 'Really there isn't.'

After a pause, Mrs Barrett nodded sharply. 'You'll have to go through Barrett's Wood,' she said to Edward. 'That's the land of your fathers!'

'Yes, I know.' His wet chin had reappeared so that he could speak, but it was impossible to interpret the expression on his face. Was he *impressed* – or *bored*, or *irritated* – by the fact that Barrett's Wood was the land of his fathers? They couldn't tell. And why had his grandmother said that?

'Be sure to have him back here in time for his dinner,' the old lady said to the girls. She turned abruptly and went into the house.

They could see Joe Temper in the road, leaning on his bike. He'd come to meet them. To hurry them up, probably.

While Edward was fetching his bike, Molly whispered to Abigail, 'She's mad!'

But Abigail wasn't so sure. 'Can you smell that cooking?' she whispered back.

Molly paid attention. There was a truly wonderful smell of steak-and-kidney coming from the kitchen window.

'Steak-and-kidney pudding,' Abigail sighed.

'Or pie,' Molly said.

'Either way ...' Abigail said longingly. A grandmother who cooked like that could not be completely bad. Or mad.

Edward's house was the last one. Beyond it, the road headed out into Camel Fen.

But first it took them through a wood. There were not many woods in the Fens around Great Deeping, but this was a real wood – half a mile across in one direction, and a mile long in the other.

The four of them cycled unhurriedly in the chilly morning sun, taking up the whole width of the empty lane. Edward's feet raced around on his little bike so that he could keep up.

Joe wore his gas-mask box on a length of string around his neck. This was uncharacteristic. At school, when there was a check-up, he was always the one without a gas mask. So Abigail – never one to hesitate if there was something she wanted to know – asked him about it.

'My dad said I could have his little old box camera. It's a Brownie. That fits nicely in the gas-mask box.'

Molly believed this was the way the school holidays ought to be – lazily passing the time, mooching from place to place with only the vaguest of plans, and her best friend beside her. That two of her companions were almost strangers added some spice. A touch of uncertainty.

Then she had a thought. 'Barrett's Wood!' she said. 'That's your name – Barrett.'

Edward nodded.

Abigail stopped pedalling at once. This had to be sorted out. She slipped one foot down to the ground and hopped her bike to a standstill. Molly wobbled and turned back on herself. Edward was in danger of crashing – ever so gently – into the side of Molly's bike, but he braked efficiently and stopped. 'Is that what your grandmother meant when she said something about the land of your fathers?'

Edward nodded again. Speaking would have interrupted his chin-chewing.

'Does the wood belong to you and your grandmother then?' Abigail asked. If it did, she felt it would change their relationship. People who owned large woods belonged to a different species.

Edward reluctantly released his lower lip. 'Yes.'

Joe had turned and was cycling back slowly. 'The Barretts used to live there,' he said. 'Rich they were, my dad tell me, in them days. The old stables are still there, in the wood.'

'Are they lived in?' Abigail asked.

'Yes,' Joe said. 'Robertson Creake lives there.'

'Mr Creake the railway porter?'

Joe nodded.

Edward's face lit up. He was suddenly transformed,

they all saw it. 'I didn't know there was a house there,' he said. Molly saw the whiteness of his knuckles as they gripped his handlebars. Some idea had taken possession of him in an instant.

'Perhaps that's where the treasure is,' he said.

'*Treasure?*'

Edward immediately regretted what he'd said. He must not deceive these new friends of his. He knew you got sent to hell if you told lies. It was clear that he must tell them the truth, accurately, at once.

'Not treasure really. Just an old sword.'

'How do you know about it?' Molly knew that when she was his age she might have made up a story like that – and then believed it and expected everyone else to.

'Granny has an old book,' Edward said. He rubbed his chin with his hand, caressing its wet roughness with his fingertips. Just to see him do that made Molly wince.

'It was during the Civil War, hundreds of years ago. One of my ancestors had to get away. Quickly. He got a message that soldiers were coming for him next morning. If he stayed, he'd be captured and executed.'

Edward stopped, in case they hadn't understood *executed*. 'His head cut off,' he explained.

'Did they get him?' This was Abigail. From the story point of view, it would be better if they'd caught him and cut his head off, she thought heartlessly. But from Edward's point of view she wasn't so sure.

'No. He got away in the night. But he had to leave his wife behind. And his little boy. He never came back.

He died before the Civil War was over and they never saw him again.'

'That's ever so sad.'

'This treasure . . . ?'

Edward shook his head. He would not allow them to carry on with this fiction, even though he had started it himself. '*Not* treasure,' he said emphatically. 'Just a sword. He left it for his little boy – but no one has ever been able to find it.'

They tried remorselessly to get more information from Edward. Where had the sword been hidden? How did anyone know about it? Could they find it – now? Tomorrow? Sometime during the holiday? But all Edward could tell them was that it was supposed to have been hidden near some mulberry trees that grew in the wood.

'Are there any mulberry trees there now?'

Edward didn't know. But Joe said, 'There *is* one. My gran used to come and collect the fruit every year for jam making.'

'Did Mr Creake know?'

'She used to give him one or two jars of the jam. That was the deal.'

The girls were excited by the idea of buried treasure. But Edward kept insisting that it was not treasure – just an old sword. And it was clear that Joe Temper was not interested in treasure, or in hidden swords. He stood patiently at the roadside, with his huge old bicycle leaning against him. When the energy of their questions finally exhausted itself, he reminded them about his pigeons.

Pigeons! thought Molly a second time.

Round a bend in the lane they came across a disused railway track that lay across the road. On either side it disappeared into the wood. The rails were dark and rusty, almost buried in the leafy undergrowth. But they could be seen clearly, bending away to their right and heading straight off to the north-east on their left. There were no crossing gates.

Again they stopped. Joe dismounted and waited patiently. There was nothing here to interest him; he crossed these tracks every day of his life.

Edward gazed along the track into the trees, longingly bringing it into active service. He saw in his mind's eye a powerful black steam locomotive, towing a freight train of such enormous length that the end of it was out of sight. He tried to make himself hear it, and smell it too, but with the others close beside him he couldn't concentrate.

Abigail told them the branch-line was connected to their own main London line, just out of sight round the bend, close to Great Deeping station. In the other direction it went through the wood and out across the Fens to the marshalling yards at March twenty miles away.

'It was used for freight,' she said. 'There were never any passenger trains along here.'

Now there was nothing here – no signals, no people, no puffing and panting of engines, no smell of steam and coal.

Molly thought Abigail was showing off a little. She knew more about railways than Molly had realised. She sighed. 'It's like your track,' she said to Edward. 'No train to run on it.'

Joe came to life at once. 'What's that about Edward's track?' he said.

So they told him about the model railway; the five lengths of track and the engine that wouldn't work.

'Can I have a look at it?' Joe said.

Edward nodded and sucked hard on his chin. No one had ever asked his permission for anything before.

A narrow cinder path ran alongside the branch-line and they heard the faint ticking of a bicycle being pedalled. The sound was coming through the trees, towards them. Cycling steadily along the cinder path came a man in railway uniform – Robertson Creake, on his way to work at the railway station.

Abigail knew who he was because he worked with her mum. Molly had never spoken to him but she too knew who he was. Joe knew him because they were neighbours. Edward had never seen him before.

As he emerged from the trees, a cinder from the pathway exploded from under one of the wheels of his bike. It shot out into the lane and hit Edward's knee.

Mr Creake braked and stopped among them. Edward stooped to rub his leg.

'What's all this then?' Mr Creake said.

There was a moment of silence – an embarrassment, as if a crime had been committed and someone was being accused.

Joe set it to rights. 'Morning, Mr Creake,' he said.

Molly watched warily. He was a striking man, good-looking in a pouchy way, she thought. Abigail was uneasy. They glanced at each other, sharing their disquiet. There was something about him . . .

'Well, you're a sloppy-looking lot!' Mr Creake said.

There was no answer to this, and so he didn't get one.

'Now if you lived in Germany, you'd be members of the Hitler Youth,' Mr Creake continued. '*That* would soon put a ramrod up your back!'

Molly watched Edward. He was swallowing his lower lip as usual, but his eyes were wide open. Was he frightened? Or was he just ashamed of being sloppy? Joe put his hand reassuringly on the younger boy's shoulder.

'We wouldn't want to join the Hitler Youth, thanks,' Joe said. 'We're all right as we are.'

'It would give you a purpose,' Mr Creake said. 'You've no *purpose*, youngsters like you! You need something to stiffen you.'

A cloud darkened the face of the sun, and all four of them suddenly felt chilly.

Joe Temper looked as if his purpose in life was nothing to do with Robertson Creake. 'Have you got a purpose then?' he asked. This question twisted the tension a little more tightly. It had not been rude – it was hard to imagine Joe ever being rude – but it *was* a challenge.

'Oh, yes,' Mr Creake said quietly. 'I have a purpose all right!'

He turned away as if he had finished. But then he stopped, and said, 'And I'll tell you this – Adolf Hitler would do this country a lot of good, Josiah Temper!'

Abigail and Molly were shocked. They had never heard anyone say anything good about Hitler. But they didn't argue. They just let him have his say. And he went on at some length about the War, and why Britain should not be fighting the Nazis at all.

And as he went recklessly on and on, Molly realised why she disliked him. It was the fact that he ignored both of the girls and addressed everything he wanted to say to the two boys. *No*, she thought, *it wasn't that he ignored them, he hadn't even* noticed *them. For him*, she thought, *I'm just a failed boy. Abigail too.*

'Do you still race pigeons?' Joe asked.

He's changing the subject on purpose, Molly thought.

Mr Creake hesitated. 'No,' he said, 'I don't. The War has put a stop to all that.'

Abigail was watching Robertson Creake's right hand. As it gripped the handle bar, the fingers kept flinging restlessly outwards, faintly tinging the bicycle bell. They were ink-stained.

'Do you remember my gran's mulberry jam, Mr Creake?'

Robertson Creake looked startled. 'Yes,' he said cautiously. 'Why?'

'I just wondered if the mulberry tree is still there.'

'Yes, it's still there.' The expression on his face was suspicious. It was obvious that he thought they were after something. So, when Joe asked if they could go and look at it, it came as no surprise to them that he refused. 'No, you can't! You keep off o' my property.'

Joe was unruffled. People in Great Deeping were often possessive about their land. 'OK,' he said.

Then Robertson Creake said, 'Well, I can't waste any more time with you. I've got a railway to run.'

He lifted himself onto the saddle of his bike, crossed the lane and set off along the path that led through the trees to the main line.

'A railway to run,' Abigail scoffed. 'All he does is move luggage about!'

'Why isn't he in the army?' Molly asked.

'Medically unfit,' Joe said. 'He's got a slight limp. Come on, young Edward, you don't want to worry about that daft old fool!'

'What *is* your name?' Abigail said. 'I thought Joe was short for Joseph.'

'Josiah's my name – but everyone calls me Joe.'

'Don't you like Josiah?'

'I like it well enough,' Joe said. 'Only Josiah Temper's dead. And I'm not!'

'What do you mean, he's dead?'

'Josiah Temper died in 1892 and there's a stone in the

churchyard that says so. But I'm here, alive and kicking.'

After a few moments of quiet cycling, Edward spoke up. 'When you die, they can put you in the same grave and use the same stone.'

A few seconds passed before they realised this was meant to be a joke – the first they had heard Edward make. He rarely spoke at all unless someone spoke to him first. Joe grinned. 'Quite right, young Edward,' he said. 'Save a lot of trouble, that will.'

Just for a moment Edward's back straightened and he held his head high. Abigail and Molly both saw it. And was that a smile on his poor sore mouth? If it was, it was so fleeting that they couldn't be sure they'd seen it at all.

Pigeons! Molly had thought. *Pigeons!* They weren't even pretty to look at.

The children were in the stack-yard, sprawled on the ground with their backs against a straw stack. On the other side of the stack, it was still the middle of winter; but where they were sitting, the sun shone straight onto them and it was as warm as June.

Brown hens moved comfortably around their feet, scratching, pecking, making occasional gentle noises of interest. Close by was Joe's pigeon loft, as big as a hen house.

'I thought they lived in a round house on the top of a pole,' Abigail said.

Molly was surprised that the pigeons were free to fly around. 'Won't they escape?'

'They're *homing* pigeons,' Abigail told her witheringly, as if she knew all about it. 'That's their point. They always come *home*.'

'Know-all!' Molly said.

The pigeons walked along the roof of the farmhouse, perched in the fruit trees among the bursting blossom buds, and stood on the tops of the stacks. In the bright spring sunshine they were croodling softly, each agreeing with the others. Plump males pestered the sleeker females. From time to time, one or two of them would rise into the air with a clatter of wings.

They were so restful, so commonplace, so *grey*. And yet Joe said that several had flown all the way back from York. Two had flown home from Durham. And one had found his way back from Edinburgh in Scotland. The birds were sent in baskets, by train, with instructions for them to be released at a distant railway station. Then they flew home and were timed to see how long they took. However, the War had put a stop to all that.

Molly watched Joe as he talked – a dark, lean figure, with his back against the stack. He was enthusiastic, quietly proud of his birds.

'That's Knight Templar,' he said.

'Why did you call him that?'

'Dunno. Liked the sound of it,' Joe said. 'He was keen to get back to his wife.'

If it had been anyone else, Molly would have been

sure they were being made fun of. But she was beginning to recognise something in Joe Temper. He was not pulling their legs.

Young Edward's sore chin was exposed as he stared in open-mouthed interest. Then the story changed. Joe told them he'd sold some of his young birds to the RAF Pigeon Service at the nearby airfield.

Abigail was suspicious. 'What for?'

'Carrying secret messages,' said Joe.

All four heads drew closer together, unconsciously becoming a conspiracy, dealing in secrets, glancing behind them.

'Secret messages? Where from?'

'From occupied France, behind enemy lines,' Joe said quietly. 'Holland, too.'

'We aren't supposed to talk about things like this,' Abigail said, hoping they wouldn't stop.

Joe shifted himself into a more comfortable position. 'Why? D'you think there's a Nazi spy in the middle of this stack? Listening to every word we say?'

'There could be.'

'He'd be bloomin' uncomfortable, then,' Joe said.

'But how do you *know*?' Molly asked. 'About the secret messages?' Her grumpiness had gone. She was hoping hard that it was true.

Joe looked left and right, and edged closer to them. 'Because,' he said, 'two or three times, birds have flown back to me by mistake, instead of their new loft at the airfield. Young ones. They do that sometimes.'

'But that doesn't mean . . .'

Joe put his fingertip to Molly's mouth to shush her. 'Dad and me, we've got orders from the RAF – what to do if one of the birds homes here by mistake. They have a metal ring on one leg, with their RAF number. And on the other one there's a little metal canister.'

'A canister?' Molly spoke the question, the other two looked it.

'A little container. With a message in it,' Joe said.

'Who sends the messages?'

'French Resistance people sometimes,' Joe said. 'Or pilots who've crashed in France. Or secret agents who've been parachuted in at night behind enemy lines.'

Abigail was sceptical again. 'Come off it,' she said. 'They use wireless. Anyone knows that!'

Joe was serious. 'Imagine it,' he said. 'You get flown in at the dead of night by an RAF plane. And you make a parachute drop somewhere in France. You *could* just radio back – but the enemy are quite likely to pick up your message on their radios. And if two or three of them do, they can get a fix on your position. Within half an hour, troops are sent to find you and you're taken away and shot.'

All four heads drew back a little as if their owners were retreating. *Shot.* The cruel finality of it seemed to be contained in the word itself. *Shot.* It was Wartime, and that's what you always came back to. People being killed. People being shot – leaving empty spaces in other people's lives.

Like Abigail's dad. Perhaps. No, *probably*.

'It's safer and quieter to take a bird in with you,' Joe said, 'and release it when you land. Sometimes they take two, in case one of them doesn't make it.'

'So they fly home with their message,' Molly said with satisfaction. 'All that way!' Her imagination could see the bird clearly, battling through clouds and rain, a blizzard perhaps, flying doggedly on until it reached the French coast, setting out across the sea knowing that if it tired there was nowhere to come down and rest.

'How long would it take?' she asked.

'Depends whereabouts in France it started. A few hours.'

Joe talked about pigeons for ages, and they were captured by his enthusiasm. Then he said, 'They're good in pies, too.'

'Joe Temper, we *hate* you!' Abigail said.

Joe shrugged and grinned.

'What shall we do now?' Abigail said. Molly sighed with pleasure. It was the loveliest question of all, the holiday question. What shall we do now? It signalled freedom. Her mood was transformed; she was happy and full of holiday.

Edward had been almost entirely silent throughout this pigeon-talk. 'Would you like to see my engine?' he asked Joe.

Joe grinned. 'I would, young Edward,' he said. 'But on the way we'll just call in on Mr Creake.'

'Mr Creake's gone to work,' Molly said.

'So much the better.'

'What do we want to go there for?' Abigail asked.

'I can show you that old mulberry tree,' he said. 'I tell you what! I'll give you a ride on the trailer of my dad's tractor. You'll like that, young Edward.'

'Can you drive a tractor?' Abigail asked.

He made a face at her. It meant: I live on a farm! Of *course* I can drive a tractor!

He left them standing and raced over to one of the big farm buildings. In the shadows of one of them stood a tractor with a long trailer fixed to the back of it. Joe turned the starting handle and there was a spluttering roar as the engine exploded into life.

As the tractor reversed into the sunshine, they could see the fumes chimneying out of the upright exhaust, and there was a sharp smell of petrol. Joe was standing on the platform with one confident hand loosely on the steering wheel and the backs of his legs braced against the metal seat. His body was screwed round so that he could look behind him as he reversed the tractor out, pushing the trailer. Then he stood on the clutch, knocked the gear stick out of reverse with the heel of his hand, and drove the tractor and trailer across the yard and stopped beside them.

'Climb aboard!' he said.

Edward wore his chinless mask. He couldn't believe this was allowed. But Joe picked him up bodily and lifted him so that he had to scramble onto the floor of the trailer. Then Joe passed his little bike up to him.

Abigail and Molly followed, then their bikes. In no time, Joe was back on the tractor.

The wooden trailer was rough on bare knees. And it was no good trying to sit. It was so bumpy that they would have slid all over the place. So they stood, clutching the sides, jubilant and breathless and the three bikes slid about in a tangle on the floor.

Molly shouted above the roar. 'Is this legal?'

But Abigail didn't care. There were special rules for farm vehicles, she knew. And special rules for Wartime. So perhaps it was.

Joe drove them – bumpily – across a small field of scrubby pasture and stopped at the edge of Barrett's Wood. Abigail and Molly jumped down from the back of the trailer. Edward stood uncertainly in the sudden silence and Molly turned to lift him down. But he jumped himself and landed firmly on his feet. He looked up proudly to see if they had noticed.

'Come on,' Joe said. 'Quietly now!'

Into the bright shadows of Barrett's Wood they went, in search of Robertson Creake's mulberry tree.

Low wooden railings separated Mr Creake's garden from the trees. The four children stood there for a few moments, taking it all in. Some washing hung on a line, but there was no other sign of life.

When Joe moved to climb over the fence, Edward looked worried. 'It's all right,' Joe said quietly. 'We're not going to commit a crime. I just want to have a look. You can stay here if you want.'

Abigail and Molly climbed over, so Edward did too. Then, with the girls, he followed Joe across the enclosure. The place was still and silent. Robertson Creake's presence was everywhere, as if he were behind every tree, watching from every window. They knew he wasn't, but there was something about him that made them think he might be.

It was not a garden really, just a grassy backyard, shadowed by the surrounding trees. There was a shed, a disused pigsty, and an empty pigeon loft. There were pigeons too, but they were wild birds, wood pigeons in the trees.

Just inside the door of the pigeon loft, there were two bins, with lids. In one there was a mixture of peas, maize and beans, in the other corn. Both were full. There was a large metal tray with fresh clean water.

Jo was surprised and thoughtful. 'He hasn't got any birds now. But he's expecting to have some soon,' he said. 'And he's had some recently.'

'What do you mean?'

'How do you know?'

Joe explained and pointed. There were fresh droppings. 'So what's he up to?' Joe said quietly.

Neither of the girls heard this remark. Molly was more interested in Mr Creake's house than the empty pigeon loft. She studied it thoughtfully – a low red-brick building of great age, with a mountainous roof, steeply tiled and covered with moss and leaf litter.

And Abigail had noticed something else. 'This yard,' she said. 'It's *round*!'

They all stopped and looked – and saw that she was right. Mr Creake's backyard was a perfect circle among the trees. They had all been in various backyards, but they had never seen a round one.

Edward was trying to work out the geography. 'Where's Gran's house?' he said.

Joe walked away from the pigeon loft and pointed. 'At the other side of Mr Creake's house is that railway line we crossed. You can see it – look! There! And on the other side of that there's a bit more wood. And on the other side of *that* is where you live.'

'I could just walk straight from here to my back garden,' Edward said.

'You could,' Joe said. 'But you wouldn't get your bike through all that undergrowth. And that,' he said, pointing, 'is the mulberry tree.'

A few yards outside Mr Creake's circular backyard, stood a tree that was clearly different from the woodland trees all around – wide, more gnarled, with tough uneven branches spreading low, almost to the ground. It looked stately, older too. And still leafless.

'*Here we go round the mulberry bush,*' Abigail sang softly.

Pity Adam isn't here, Molly thought. *This is the sort of place he would like.*

Joe wanted to take a picture of Edward standing by the mulberry tree. 'After all,' he said, 'it used to belong to your family. Still does, really.'

But Edward wouldn't do it. He was scared that Mr Creake would arrive at any minute – and he wanted to get away before he did.

Saturday morning ~ almost dinnertime

There was no sign of Edward's grandmother when the tractor and trailer stopped in the road outside her house.

Abigail and Molly started to make their way up the path, but Edward's progress was stopped by something Joe said.

'Listen, young Edward. If you keep on chewing your chin like that, you'll end up eating your whole body. There'll be nothing left. You need to stop doing it.'

Edward's right hand went up to his chin and fluttered there guiltily. Behind it, his lower lip reappeared, so painfully sore that the girls winced at the sight of it.

'Now,' Joe said. 'Where's this engine?'

Springtime was playing its oldest trick. The sun had stopped shining, the sky had clouded over, and it was suddenly colder. They went around the side of the house and down the garden to the brick shed. Joe was shown the lengths of track, the coaches, the signal box, the goods wagons. He took it all in with a cool and unhurried interest.

This is a boy who can drive a tractor, Molly thought. *You can't expect him to dance about with joy.*

Edward, however, was uneasy. Already he regretted attracting so much attention to the model train set. It was a secret of his own and he half wished he'd not allowed those girls anywhere near it.

He thought about it longingly whenever he was alone. In his head there was an entire timetable for a railway he had made up, with train services and stations where the *Great Northern* hissed and snorted triumphantly as it drew to a stop. All the stations had names. And just when the waiting passengers were sure the train was going to be late, they would hear the *Great Northern's* whistle from around the curve of the track, precisely on time.

But the train did not belong to him and was forbidden. Joe's leisurely examination of the *Great Northern* drove Edward almost mad with its slowness. He needed a quick verdict – before his grandmother came to summon him in for dinner.

'So you can't find a key to wind it up with?' Joe asked.

Edward shook his head unhappily.

'And there's no clockwork inside?' Joe turned the engine over and peered into its underside.

'No.'

'That's because,' Joe said slowly, 'this is a *steam* loco.'

'I know that, but how do you make it go?'

'I mean, it's a *real* steam loco. It works with steam, not clockwork.'

Molly and Abigail pressed in close, to look.

'See,' Joe said. 'D'you know what this is?' He pointed to a brass knob on the top of the boiler.

'It's the safety valve,' Edward said.

Joe nodded. Then, to the smaller boy's surprise, he unscrewed it. Edward had never thought to do that. He had tried to make the wheels shift but he had never dared to take anything apart.

He was horrified. And excited.

'You pour water through this hole and fill up the boiler.'

'It's a very small hole,' Edward said doubtfully.

'Here's a funnel!' Abigail said. She'd been rummaging among the bits and pieces in one of the boxes.

The funnel was a perfect fit, made of brass.

'Then you have to heat it up until the water boils,' Joe said.

'But how . . . ?'

'There should be a heater somewhere.' Again, Abigail found it – a flat brass container with three metal studs in a row, each containing a wick. The wicks were dry and black at the tip. Someone had burned them, once upon a time.

'You need methylated spirits for that,' Joe said. 'I don't suppose you've got any?'

They looked in all the shelves and boxes and corners. But there was no bottle of methylated spirits.

However, Edward's heart lifted again when Joe told him you could buy it at the chemist's.

'Have you got any money?'

Edward nodded. 'I get sixpence a week and I haven't spent anything since Christmas.'

Molly and Abigail looked at one another. Not a bad life after all, their faces said.

Then Joe explained the process – what had to be done to boil up the water and make the engine go. Edward loved the thought of it. It would be like a real engine firing up, getting ready for a long journey.

'I'll bring you some cycle oil,' Joe said. 'You'll need to lubricate the axles and the pistons.'

But there was no time for any more explanation. The light that came in the doorway suddenly darkened. Edward's grandmother was standing there.

Is she as stern as she looks? Molly wondered.

But there was no way of knowing. The old lady's arms were folded firmly and a blue-and-white duster was draped over one of them.

Edward sucked his chin into his mouth – and then instantly released it again as he remembered what Joe had said.

Mrs Barrett's head was level with Molly's shoulders. She looked straight up at Joe. 'Who are you?' she said.

She wasn't angry, or challenging, or rude, Molly thought. *She just wanted to know.*

'I'm Joe Temper,' Joe said.

'I knew your grandmother. She was a powerful hymn singer.'

Joe nodded emphatically. 'I remember,' he said. 'She used to sing hymns everywhere, all the time.'

'Thoughts of God are never out of place,' Mrs Barrett said. 'Now, *you!*' she said, turning to Edward. 'Dinner in five minutes! Inside, hands and face washed, sitting at your place – in five minutes!'

She turned and walked back up the garden.

Joe put the model locomotive back inside its box, gently, as if he were putting a baby to bed. Abigail whispered to Molly, 'Steak-and-kidney,' and Molly rolled her eyes longingly.

Edward looked as if he wanted to say something to the girls. It was hard to know how they knew, because he hadn't actually spoken. *He's scared of everything*, Molly thought. But Edward overcame his shyness and said what was on his mind. 'Is it true that you have a barn?' he said. 'A *whole* barn?'

'Is that what you've heard?' Abigail asked him.

He nodded doubtfully, as if he was ashamed of listening to such foolish rumours.

'It's true,' Molly said. 'But it's not really *our* barn.'

'We're allowed to use it though,' Abigail added. 'You can come and see it – tomorrow if you like.'

But tomorrow was Sunday and Edward knew he wouldn't be allowed. Chapel ruled on Sundays.

'Well, Monday then,' Molly said. 'Why don't you come on Monday afternoon?' She looked at Abigail for agreement. 'We're going to have our tea there.'

'And you can come too,' Abigail said to Joe.

Joe was agreeable. He turned to Edward. 'D'you want me to call for you?' he asked. 'I won't be able to get away from the farm until about half-past three. Will that be OK?'

Edward nodded. His cup was overflowing.

Molly was thinking: why have we invited them to our special place? Only Adam is allowed!

But there was no going back, it was arranged. Joe would call for Edward and they would both pay a visit to Abigail and Molly at Paradise Barn. 'Not in the tractor,' Joe said to Edward. 'My dad needs to use that on Monday. We shall have to use our bikes.'

Edward suddenly remembered the five-minute warning. He raced up the garden and, as they followed more slowly, they heard the back door slam shut.

For Molly and Abigail, the morning ended in style. They stood in the swaying trailer, holding onto the sides, as Joe drove them through the middle of the town, down the main shopping street, and even past the police station.

If there was a law against it, no one seemed to care.

It was gratifying that several of their school friends were in the street to witness their progress. It was less gratifying later, when it began to rain.

Saturday ~ dinnertime

As the rain began to fall on Great Deeping railway station, the stationmaster came out from the ticket office and shouted across the empty tracks to Robertson Creake, who was walking slowly along the opposite platform, carrying a bucket of coal.

'I'm just off to the Royal George to have a drink with my sandwiches,' the stationmaster shouted across to him.

'Right-o!' Mr Creake shouted back. But he didn't look at the stationmaster.

'You're in charge,' the stationmaster said, and turned away to set off for his dinner.

Mr Creake went into the waiting room and put more coal on the fire. When he came back outside he stood motionless for a moment or two, watching the stationmaster striding away towards the town, with his dockey bag over his shoulder and a black umbrella over his head.

There was hardly a sound to be heard except the gentle hissing of the rain. No one else was at the station. The nearest human being was old Nobby Clark who worked the signal box just beyond the road. He would come down his wooden staircase to shut the gates against traffic, and then down it again to open them when the train had passed through – but he never came onto the station.

It would have been easy to believe that Great Deeping had been abandoned by its people. That there was no one in the whole silent world except him. And that Nobby Clark in the signal box was nothing but a ghost, with no interest in anything but opening and closing the crossing gates.

Robertson Creake, despite his limp, jumped down onto the track and with four strong strides was across. He vaulted up onto the other platform and went into the ticket office. He raised the liftable part of the counter and walked through into the back, and into the stationmaster's office.

It was snug in there, with pens, ink bottles, timetables and bundles of tickets. There were a couple of old teaspoons, a kettle, some enamel tea cans, and a bottle of milk. On the desk lay a big leather-bound ledger in which the stationmaster wrote down every train and locomotive that passed through the station. On its spine, in gold, it said *1941*. Stacked at the back of the desk and lined up against the wall was a row of other ledgers, all similar, and with dates going back to 1847.

Robertson Creake opened the current volume. Inside the front cover in small print were the words *Bound & Printed by G.T. Watson, Printer, Littleport*. On the left-hand pages the details of the trains were written:

10.23 a.m. up service, Lynn to Liverpool St

or

4.05 p.m. freight, 48 wagons, Lynn to Birmingham
and on the right-hand page the stationmaster had
written any comments he thought necessary, such as:

On time

or

22 minutes late

And once

Driver took short, train delayed 9 minutes

Ordinary entries were made in blue-black ink. But
three or four times each year, the royal train passed
through to take the royal family to and from
Sandringham; for these special occasions a purple ink
had been used. And once, in the 1936 book, there was
an entire page in purple, inside a ruled black margin,
saying that the body of the dead King George V had
passed through Great Deeping railway station on its
way to London. Everyone in the town had come, lining
the railway track and crowding silently on the station,
to watch the royal train pass through.

But since the War began in 1939, an element of danger
had entered the book. Some entries had been written
in red. These denoted trains doing War work – trains
loaded with explosives, or artillery, or troops.

Robertson Creake read the entry for the previous
Wednesday. In red, it said:

7.05 p.m. Rescheduled freight train. 38 empty
wagons. Hit by enemy action.

Then, for the next three days, it said:

Track damaged by enemy action. Station closed.
No locomotive traffic.

But Robertson Creake was not interested in the past. It was the next few days he wanted to know about, especially now that the track had been repaired and services were operating normally again.

And he found what he wanted. For Monday 14th April, in the evening, the stationmaster had entered that a freight train was due to pass through:

8.45 p.m. Freight.

It was written in red, as if especially for his eyes, and Robertson Creake knew what that meant. Besides, there was no other information – nothing about where it would be coming from or where it was going to. That meant it was top secret. It was going to be a trainload of explosives, probably bound for one of the airfields.

Robertson Creake felt faint and gripped the edge of the desk. 'This time!' he muttered. 'This time!' And he said it over and over again – until he felt steady enough to close the book and walk out of the office.

He was from time to time tempted to give up his great project. How easy and pleasant it would be to do nothing, to get safely through the War by lying low and dutifully doing his job. But no, he set aside the thought. That would be a terrible weakness, a temptation he must resist.

For as long as Abigail was living in Molly's mum's guest house, they were to have their dinners at Abigail's house. This was the arrangement. 'Otherwise,' Mrs Murfitt said, 'I might forget what my daughter looks like.'

So that was where Joe Temper took them in his tractor, to Abigail's house by the level crossing.

Abigail raced into the kitchen to see what was for dinner.

'Toad-in-the-hole,' Mrs Murfitt said. 'With leeks and mashed potato and gravy.'

'The leeks and spuds came out of our garden,' Abigail told Molly, who already knew.

'What about the toad?' said Molly.

'That too,' said Abigail.

'Five more minutes,' Abigail's mum said. She was at the kitchen sink, with her back to Abigail and Molly.

'Mum?' Abigail said.

'Mmm?'

'You know Mr Creake,' Abigail said cautiously. 'He spoke to us today.'

Mrs Murfitt turned round to face her daughter. 'Of course I know him,' she said sharply. 'He's railway staff.'

But there was more to it than that, they could both see. Mrs Murfitt leaned back against the sink, arms folded, a tea towel hanging from one hand. Molly, eavesdropping, paid attention.

'He . . .'

'He what?'

'He *said* things – things about Hitler.'

'Oh, yes?' Mrs Murfitt's voice was cynical. *Now* what? it seemed to say.

'He said Hitler was a good man and we shouldn't be at war with the Germans.'

Abigail's mother nodded cautiously.

'And other things,' Abigail added lamely.

'Robertson Creake says stupid things,' Mrs Murfitt said. 'He's known for it.'

'But why?'

'Because he's stupid, I suppose. Though I do remember he had a holiday in Germany before the War. When he got home he kept telling everyone how marvellous the Nazis were and how we needed someone like Hitler in our country. He was full of it! He went back again the next summer, I think. He's a crackpot, everyone knows that. Nobody takes any notice of him. And you shouldn't either.'

She turned back to the sink. Then, with her back to the two girls, she said, 'He was my boyfriend once.' She sniffed. 'So *he* reckoned, anyway.'

Abigail was doubly shocked. It hadn't occurred to her that her mother had ever had boyfriends – except her dad. But *Mr Creake*! It was unthinkable!

Molly eavesdropped even more intently. She had noticed before how Abigail and her mum approached tricky subjects with their backs to each other. With Molly's mum, it was the opposite. They always faced each other, eye to eye, plunging headlong together into whatever emotional turmoil was coming.

'How long for?' Abigail asked.

Mrs Murfitt laughed out loud. 'About twenty-five minutes,' she said. 'As long as it takes on the train from Ely to Great Deeping. That was quite enough for me.'

Molly felt Abigail's relief. But Mrs Murfitt hadn't finished with the subject. She turned round again. 'Now listen, Abigail,' she said. 'You need to be careful with him. Just . . . just be careful. You too, Molly. You're an even bigger softie than Abigail. You should both keep away from him.'

Molly was startled. As an eavesdropper, she thought she'd been forgotten. *Am I a softie?* she wondered. She was always surprised to find out how other people saw her.

'But *why*, Mum?'

Abigail's mum rarely gave reasons and Molly was expecting none. But this time she was wrong. Mrs Murfitt tried to explain what she herself couldn't quite understand.

'He's too . . . too *cocky*,' she said at last. 'Sure of himself. He says things that no one else would dare to say. Daft things, weird things. Like about Hitler. And he is so sure he's right! He only gets away with it because everyone else thinks he's an idiot!'

The tea towel fell to the floor and Mrs Murfitt stooped to pick it up. 'He thinks he's untouchable,' she said as she straightened. 'Yes, that's it. He thinks he's untouchable. He doesn't seem to realise that nobody else takes him seriously.'

A little later, Mrs Murfitt said, 'There used to be a mulberry tree near his house. When we were little, we used to creep in and try to get some of the mulberries.'

'Who?'

'Me and Molly's mum. And one or two others.'

She paused. 'It used to make him so mad. His dad didn't mind – but young Creakey wouldn't let anyone near his place if he could help it.' She was remembering some scene from childhood. 'He was daft when we were kids – and he's even dafter now.'

The meal was placed on the kitchen table and they all three sat down. The toad-in-the-hole was a big one, in a flat pan. It was cut into four and the two girls tucked in, each wondering what would happen to the fourth part.

After a bit, Mrs Murfitt spoke again. 'Abigail?'

Abigail looked up and her chewing slowed down.

'You've been spending a lot of time in Dad's office lately.'

I didn't know she'd been doing that, Molly thought with interest. Mrs Murfitt was speaking in a different way, she noticed. Usually, the words came out of her mouth as if they had been snipped off with a pair of scissors. But now she spoke in a voice like velvet – deeper, with a slight huskiness.

'You can have it, if you like,' Mrs Murfitt said. 'You know, let it be *your* room.'

All eating temporarily stopped. Molly had an inch-long bit of gravy-dipped sausage on her fork, on its way to her mouth. But it had to wait.

Abigail was still staring at her mum. 'Do you mean *sleep* in there?' *Her* voice was different too.

'No, it's not big enough for a bed. But you can move all your stuff in there – books and comics. And all those bits and pieces that take ages to dust! It can become your own private place.'

With the mention of dusting, the scissors were back in place. Molly felt she could put the sausage in her mouth and carry on eating.

Abigail took up her chewing again – but thoughtfully. 'But I've just moved in with Molly,' she said.

'Yes, but you won't be there for long. And when you come back home . . .'

Afterwards, when the uneaten part of the toad-in-the-hole had been firmly taken away and put on the larder shelf, Abigail beckoned to Molly. They went out to the foot of the stairs and she whispered, 'Come on!'

Mr Murfitt's office was an inviting place, with a bright window facing the railway line. There were bookshelves, a desk, papers and pens, and a wooden swivel chair. On the wall were maps – all railway maps, Molly saw. One showed every railway line in England, Wales, Northern Ireland and Scotland, with every station.

So this was how Abigail had become such a railway

expert. She had been studying her dad's maps.

On the desk there was a small photo of her dad in a silver frame. Beside it lay a small green card. On the dotted line Abigail's dad had signed his name, Michael Murfitt. Inside, it said that Michael Albert Murfitt had been appointed an air-raid warden for the Great Deeping division of the Isle of Ely. *TO WHOM IT MAY CONCERN. Please give every assistance and information to the within-named air-raid warden in the execution of his duty.*

Molly supposed her father had one of those too. Both dads had joined at the same time. But they hadn't been air-raid wardens for long; within weeks they had joined the army.

Abigail slid into the swivel chair. It was too big for her and she slipped about on the shiny seat. But she seemed to belong there, and as she looked around at everything in the little office Molly knew she was reinterpreting it as *her* room now.

Molly thought back to their morning with Joe and Edward. Something had been worrying her. 'Do we like them?' she said.

'Like who?' Abigail demanded. But she knew really. Molly always did this with new friends.

'Joe and Edward,' Molly said. 'Why did we invite them to the barn?'

'Well, I like Joe,' Abigail said. She always knew at once if she liked someone. Molly took longer.

'What about Edward?' Molly asked.

Abigail was less sure about Edward. 'Well, I can't bear to look at his sloppy chin,' she admitted.

'It gives me the creeps,' Molly said. Privately she'd felt an urge to cheer him up, even to cuddle him perhaps. But a glimpse of his chin was enough to put her off.

'Joe likes him,' Abigail said. 'So he must be all right really.' Then, abruptly, she went daft and swung herself round and round in the swivel chair, shouting 'Wheeee!'

'Can I have a go?' Molly said.

Abigail got out of the chair and Molly got in it. 'It screws up and down,' Abigail said. 'So *you* have to swing the other way! Otherwise, you'll take off!'

Mrs Murfitt, downstairs, heard the laughter and the screaming. She tightened her mouth, and got on with the washing-up.

⨎

Edward waited until no one else was in the chemist's shop. Then he went in.

'Can I have a bottle of metholated spirits, please?' Edward said.

'You've spelt that wrong,' Mr Young said.

Edward was confused. 'But I haven't written it.'

'Nevertheless, you spelt it wrong. It's not *meth-o-lated*. It has a *y* in it, *meth-y-lated*.'

Edward tried again. 'Can I have a bottle of methylated spirits, please?' he said carefully.

'Methylated *spirit*, not spirits,' Mr Young said. '*Spirit*. Singular, not plural.'

Edward sighed. 'Can I have methylated spirit then?' he said.

The purchase was made. Then Mr Young said, 'I could let you have some ointment for that sore chin.'

'But . . .' Edward didn't want to spend any more of his money.

'Of course, it would only work if you stopped chewing on it.'

'I *have* stopped.'

'Oh? When was that, then?'

'This morning. I mean, I started stopping this morning.'

'Well, you'd better have this,' Mr Young said. He handed over a small round glass pot with a screw-top lid. 'It will help.'

'How much is it?'

'Nothing. It was given to me as a free sample. And I'm giving it to you as a free sample.'

'Thank you,' Edward said. He left quickly.

In spite of Molly's doubts, they were both impatient all through Sunday. Their plan to have tea in the barn (a couple of plain biscuits and half a bottle of orange squash) grew more ambitious as the long day wore on. What they now had in mind was a full-scale tea party to celebrate the start of the Easter holidays. Saturday and Sunday had just been a weekend; *Monday* was the real beginning.

Molly suggested a picnic, but Abigail said boys didn't like picnics.

'But *we* do,' Molly pointed out.

'All right then,' Abigail said.

So, on Monday morning, they separated, each with a different job – and each thinking crossly that the other had the easier task of the two. Abigail had to lug a heavy bucketful of coal and kindling across three fields to Paradise Barn. Molly's role required diplomacy, not muscles. She had somehow to get her mum to hand over some money for biscuits.

But Molly found she first had to deal with something else. When she arrived home, her mother stopped her. 'Come into the dining room, love. I want to ask you something.'

Molly dutifully followed her mum, feeling inwardly cross. She wanted to get *on*!

'Molly,' her mum said, 'I'm worried about you.'

'I'm OK,' Molly said. She was mystified and showed it.

'Are you sure?'

Molly nodded.

'You seem to be a bit glum – and I thought you would be happy to have Abigail staying here.'

Whatever else happened, Molly was anxious that her mother should not misunderstand that. 'Oh, but I *am* happy! I *love* having Abigail here!'

That was the truth. 'It's just that I miss . . .' There she stopped.

'I miss him too, Moll. *Very* much! When we sit down at the table for a meal . . . And there's that empty chair where he should be.'

There was a hug then, passionate on one side, guarded on the other. *What is she talking about?* Molly was thinking.

'But this terrible War *will* be over one day. Then he'll be home again, with us.' Mrs Barnes's voice was deep and full.

Then Molly understood. The trouble was, it was not her dad that she missed. She *had* missed him, of course, ever since he'd been home on leave last Christmas. And whenever she thought of him, she wished he was home again. His absence was a kind of presence at the back of her mind all the time. She'd got used to it.

But, to be honest, he didn't come into her thoughts very often. Perhaps once a day. Sometimes not at all.

It was Adam she missed. Adam Swales, the evacuee from London who had come to live with them last September. *Whenever Adam was there*, Molly thought, *there was something in the air – something bracing, as if someone had just rung a bright bell and you could still hear it vibrating.*

I'm not a very nice person, she thought. And she didn't explain to her mother. She distracted herself by picking up her cat and snuggling the side of her face in its soft black fur. Then, to be fair, she picked up the other one – Adam's grey-and-white three-legged cat, Tibby, who like Adam was an evacuee. But unlike Adam, Tibby had a genuine war wound.

There was nothing wrong with Adam. Except that he was in Wales.

Molly was lucky at the Co-op. People said that sweets and biscuits would have to be rationed soon. But they weren't rationed yet – and the manageress said she could have a large bagful of broken biscuits for sixpence. Molly took the glass lids off the tin boxes that stood in a row in front of the counter and used a brass scoop to help herself to broken chocolate biscuits, plain biscuits, shortbread biscuits and ginger biscuits.

She walked dreamily home, thinking about Adam.

They had invented a private game, the three of them.

None of them knew who had first thought of it. It could only be played when all three of them were walking together along the High Street. When they came to Marquis Way, Adam would turn right into it. But Molly and Abigail would carry on. Then, after about a hundred yards, Abigail would turn into Globe Street. Molly would continue alone until she reached Hitches Way; here she turned right too.

Adam would reach Lower Lane first and turn left into it. Just as he passed the bottom of Globe Street, Abigail would arrive and join him. The two of them should reach the bottom of Hitches Way as Molly emerged – at precisely the same moment.

If their timing was good, they liked to think it was a good omen.

Molly took an unofficial scrap of chocolate biscuit from one of the bags and wondered if Adam had received their letter yet.

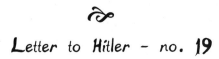

Letter to Hitler – no. 19

Dear Herr Hitler,

I met some children the other day, a disgrace to this country. They have nothing to do, no ideals to occupy their minds, no backbone in their bodies. They spend their time wandering aimlessly around the countryside. One of them constantly licked his lower lip and chin as if he wished to consume himself.

When you become Fuhrer of this country, all children must be made to join the Hitler Youth. And disordered children of all kinds must be exterminated.

The setback with the last train will be put right; another opportunity approaches; everything is in hand. I will deal with it.

Yours respectfully,
The Voice of Nazi Britain

Paradise Barn was huge and cavernous. And built against the back wall was a cabin at the top of an ancient wooden staircase. It had probably once been a hay loft, or a room where a stable lad might have slept. Adam, Molly and Abigail had been given permission to use it. It had a fireplace, a window and a wobbly bookshelf, and the children had brought in a small table, two chairs and an old unwanted bed with a mattress. It was their favourite place in the world.

They were very keen that Joe should like it. But he was not a good guest. He spent ages poking around among the old farm machinery stored in the barn before – at last! – he unhurriedly climbed the wooden stairs to the loft, which Abigail and Molly had made into their private place.

Edward was better. More polite. More admiring. Molly could still hardly bear to look at him – he had put enough cream on his chin to grease the working parts of a tractor. Abigail bluntly told the boy that you were only supposed to put a small amount on, and gave him a hanky to wipe most of it off.

Edward took the handkerchief and dutifully rubbed

his chin with it, pausing frequently to study the cream that had come off, to see if the soreness had come off with it. When he'd finished he offered it back to Abigail, who pulled a face and threw it hastily onto the fire, where it sizzled briefly.

When Joe finally came up, they sat by the fire, listening to the rain on the window and the wind blowing through the big oak tree that grew close to the barn.

Edward and Abigail sat on the camp bed, Joe and Molly on the only two chairs.

It was cosy.

And very pleasant.

Especially the broken biscuits and the orange squash.

Except that . . .

. . . well, there was nothing to *do*! Except fidget. They were all good at that.

They tried talking about spies.

And sabotage.

But after a while, there was nothing to say about that either, mostly because Molly put on her cross face and went quiet.

So they'd run out of words, apparently.

– until Abigail mentioned going to the pictures. 'Bing Crosby, Bob Hope and Dorothy Lamour,' she said. 'In *Road to Singapore*. We're going on Wednesday.'

'I *love* Bob Hope,' Molly declared – and life was restored again as the three bigger children swapped memories of Bob Hope.

Joe said he'd go to the cinema with them if they didn't mind.

Arrangements were made – where to meet, when to meet, bicycles or walking. Then the conversation died again. It was Molly who realised that young Edward had taken no part in it.

It turned out that Edward had never been to the pictures. Not ever. Not once in his whole life! It was incredible! Unthinkable! It was hard for Molly and Abigail to imagine human experience without going to the cinema at least once a week. Preferably twice.

Edward's upper lip set off downwards to find his chin. It kept doing that. Then it encountered the cream, and retreated. Like a snail drawing in its head when you touch it, Molly thought. She almost began to feel sorry for that top lip – rebuked and reminded every time it journeyed south that it wasn't going to be allowed to go there ever again.

'He could come with us, couldn't he?' Joe said. 'On Wednesday.'

Edward looked as if an angel had appeared in heaven. 'I'll have to ask my grandmother,' he said doubtfully.

'Oh, *we'll* do that,' Abigail said recklessly.

Molly looked unsure, Abigail gave her an *it-will-be-all-right* look, and Edward's face lit up.

So did the entire landscape. At that moment, the sun came out and the children suddenly knew that they had been indoors long enough.

And Molly's doubts vanished. What could be nicer than going to the pictures with a crowd of friends? (Having Adam there too, *that's* what! But she set that thought aside and cheered up anyway.)

I wonder if he's got our letter, she thought.

Adam's Uncle Hugh, working in his fruit garden, straightened himself and waited as Adam walked towards him. The sun was setting, hardly visible, a dusky red presence in the mist that filled the valley.

'Well, Adam?' he said. An early owl drifted silently through the mist. Watchful, on patrol.

Close to the path there was a row of twigs pushed into the ground. *This was something new*, Adam thought. He hadn't noticed these before in his uncle's garden. 'What are these?' he asked.

'They're my cuttin's.'

Adam was no wiser, so his uncle explained. 'They're a way of getting new plants, see? Last autumn, I cut these bits off the parent plant, and stuck 'em in the ground. That's why they're called *cuttings*. About the size of a pencil.'

'They *grow*?' Adam asked. 'As easy as that?'

'I made a slit in the ground with a spade and put some sand in the bottom. Then I put the cuttings in and trod the earth firmly around them. That's all you have to do.'

'But don't they need roots?' Adam was cautious. He was aware of his ignorance.

'They grow their own roots, *new* roots. If you're lucky,' Uncle Hugh said. 'That's what the sand is for. It *tickles* them into growin'.'

'Have *these* grown new roots?'

'Most of them have started to. I shall leave 'em there till next autumn. By then they'll have proper roots. Then I'll dig 'em up and plant 'em with the others, see?'

Adam looked disbelieving.

'Look, give me one of your pencils.'

Adam took a pencil out of his sock. Uncle Hugh took it and pushed it, blunt end down, into the ground at the end of the row of cuttings.

'That's all I did, see? More or less.'

Now Adam was sure his leg was being pulled. 'You're not trying to make me believe that a pencil could grow roots and turn into a tree!'

But Uncle Hugh didn't laugh. He just went on patiently explaining. 'No, 'course not. The wood on that pencil's completely dead, isn't it? But the cuttings I took last autumn went into the ground *alive*, straight from the parent plant.'

Adam stared at the row of cuttings, trying to make his imagination *see* the roots pushing out from the bottom of the twigs. Trying to *draw* in his mind the moment of growth. But he couldn't do it. It would be like a soldier who'd had his leg blown off, then growing another one. Impossible! No, it was even more impossible than that – it would be like a severed leg growing back into a complete person!

'Now,' his uncle said. 'Give one of them a pull. Not too hard, like.'

Adam pulled gently at one of the cuttings. It did not come cleanly out of the ground as the pencil would. It didn't move at all. He could *feel* the roots gripping the earth, just strong enough to have a hold. He still couldn't see the roots in his head, but an understanding of them came up the twig and into his hand.

'Buried treasure, see,' said his uncle. 'It's like sowin' seeds. You put something in the ground and later it gives you something back.'

Adam tried some others. It was the same with all of them, except one. One of the twigs came clean and dead out of the earth, but blackish and wet, beginning to rot.

'That one didn't take,' his uncle said. 'No roots. A bit like you.'

Adam stared at his uncle.

'It's not your fault. It's this bloody War. It's made thousands of people rootless.'

'What do you mean, *rootless*?'

'Look at you! You don't know where you belong! You've no home in London since the Germans bombed it. And you don't know whether you belong there, or here. Or in Great Dipping, or whatever it's called.'

'Deeping,' Adam said.

'You have to put down your roots, see? Otherwise, you're rootless. You don't know where you belong.'

They were interrupted then. The postman was slowly coming up the hill, walking his bike. He gave a couple of letters to Uncle Hugh and stood chatting to him in Welsh for a minute or two.

I don't know where I belong, Adam was thinking to himself. *Is that true?*

The postman got on his bike and they watched him begin the rapturous two-mile-long freewheel ride back down the winding narrow mountain road to his wife, his vegetable garden, and his supper.

'One of these is for you, Adam.'

It was a letter from Molly. Abigail too. A daft letter, full of news and jokes and craziness.

Adam knew which handwriting was which. At the end, Molly had written *I wish you were here.*

Adam made up his mind. He didn't consider, he didn't debate. He just decided.

There was trouble brewing at Great Deeping railway station. The stationmaster was nervous.

'They're coming to question us,' he had said that morning. 'Tomorrow, first thing.'

Robertson Creake had stiffened himself and spoken with indignation in his voice. 'We've nothing to hide! What are they expecting to find?'

'Dunno. Wireless equipment, I s'pose. How else could a spy get information to the Jerries?'

'Will they want to search where we live?'

'I expect so.'

There was no wireless equipment in Mr Creake's

house, except his dad's old radio. But the letters to Herr Hitler – what about *them*?

He was amazed at how quickly his clever mind thought of a plan. During his dinner hour, Robertson Creake went home, took the Hitler letters from their shoebox and wrapped them in a brown-paper parcel, bound very firmly with sticky paper and tied with string. He addressed the parcel to himself:

Mr R Creake,
Barrett's Cottage,
Camel Lane,
Great Deeping,
Isle of Ely

He couldn't post it at the Great Deeping post office; they would think he was mad, sending a parcel to himself. So he took it with him when he went back to the station, and when his afternoon shift had finished he got on the train to Ely and took the parcel to the post office there.

Edward's mother had died when he was very young; she was no more to him than a rosy memory and a couple of photographs.

They had been living in Manchester at the time. After her death, Edward had stayed for a few days with Mrs Seymour next door; then there had been Mrs Winthrop, and then a Mr and Mrs Stringer. He'd stayed at the Stringers' house for a long time. When the War started he'd been moved to an orphanage run by Miss Veronica Leighton. His grandmother, everyone said, was too old to look after such a young child.

Then one day she arrived to take him home with her. There had been a long, long train journey back to Great Deeping.

He knew at once that he'd been there before. There was nothing he could definitely call a memory, yet he found that he knew his way around the house. And before he explored the garden he knew there would be a brick building at the bottom of it.

'You were born here,' his grandmother told him. 'You lived here until you were three.'

He had learned many things while he'd been living with the Stringers and Miss Leighton. But the lesson which had come across most clearly to him was that everything a boy might want to do was forbidden – absolutely forbidden. The only things permitted were those things you were *told to do*. Nothing else was allowed.

So there was guilt in Edward's heart as he hurried down his grandmother's garden that evening with his bottle of methylated spirit.

The clouds and rain had cleared and low evening sunlight shone into the open door of the shed and onto the locomotive as he stood it on the workbench.

First he unscrewed the safety valve. That was easy because he had seen Joe do it. He found the brass funnel and used it to fill the boiler with water. Then he filled the fuel container with methylated spirit and watched the wicks swelling wetly as they drew the fuel into them.

Finally, he found his box of matches and lit the wicks. Three neat candle flames – identical triplets – leaned and stretched in unison. He slid the container into the boiler, shut the little door, and stood back to watch.

Outside, a blackbird filled the evening with song. And from the real railway about a mile away came the wailing hoot of a passing train. In Edward's shed, the only sound came from the flames inside the engine, a soft fluttering like a butterfly trapped at a window.

How long? he wondered. He glanced repeatedly out of the window to see if his grandmother was on her way down the garden.

The sun dipped down below the trees and the shadows of twilight were moving in. There was a different sound now – a low hiss, like a kettle beginning to boil. Edward took the little oil can that Joe had given him and dripped oil onto the piston-rods and – as near as he could get at them – the axles.

One kind of lubrication reminded him of another. So he applied some fresh cream to his chin.

He had only a short length of track laid out on the workbench. So he would have to hold the *Great Northern* in the air and just watch the wheels go round. He lifted it up with both hands. The water was singing now, and small blasts of steam shot out at him, tiny explosions of hot energy.

Edward spat softly onto the top of the boiler as he had seen his grandmother do when she did the ironing. His spittle bounced back at him with a brief scorched hiss.

The *Great Northern* was heavy. And hot. So he put it down and found himself some thick rags to wrap around his hand. The noise inside the boiler was urgent now. He lifted the engine again and flicked the drive-wheel with his finger – once, twice. The wheel spurted and spun for a few seconds. A third touch got it going properly.

As he watched the drive-wheels spinning round, Edward worked it out – imagining the steam coming down from the boiler, along the tiny brass pipes to push the pistons. That had to be imagined. But everything else he could *see* – the piston-rods moving in and out, releasing used steam through minute holes. And the connecting-rods shooting back and forth, driving the wheels round. It *looked* as if the wheels were driving the pistons, but Edward knew it was the other way round.

Success! – although an uncomfortable one, because his arm was beginning to ache.

Edward was thrilled. He had got his father's steam locomotive to work! A sorry kind of joy, perhaps, because he had to hold it up in his hand. But a start.

Regretfully, he put his face as close to the cab as he could get it – and blew hard. The three flames were extinguished at once, the wheels on the engine slowed, and the humming intensity of the pistons and rods began to quieten. In less than a minute the *Great Northern* was completely still.

He lowered it to the workbench with relief, unwrapped his hand, and rubbed his scorched fingers. The engine hissed softly for a while. It was wet and oily.

He'd done it! He shut the shed door, and raced joyously up the garden in the gathering darkness. As he approached the house, he jammed on the brakes, skidded on the grass – and walked calmly up to the back door as if nothing of any importance had happened.

His grandmother stood there. Her Bible was in her hand, and her finger was in the Bible, to mark her place. *'They shall be amazed one at another,'* she said. *'Their faces shall be as flames.'*

She knows what I've been doing, Edward thought. *God's told her*.

'That's from *Isaiah*, chapter 13, verse 8,' the old lady said. 'It's suppertime. Go in and wash your hands.'

Adam stood on the empty platform of the railway station. He was enveloped in soft rain, hardly more than a concentrated mist. By his feet his brown suitcase stood on the ground, in his hand was a flat leather folder, and round his neck was the cardboard box with his gas mask.

He was joined by the stationmaster. 'Got your ticket, have you?'

He inspected Adam's return ticket. Then he drew from his pocket a blank cardboard label with two eyelets and a length of string. 'Name and destination?' he said.

'Adam Swales,' said Adam.

'And you're travelling to Great Deeping,' said the stationmaster. 'I've seen that name on my map.'

He wrote the details on the card and hung it round Adam's neck. 'Daft idea. But I been told tha's what I gotta do, see?' he said. 'Makes you look like a bloody parcel!'

The previous evening at supper Adam had told them what he intended to do. With his aunt and uncle and two cousins all sitting at the table in the kitchen, his aunt had asked him if he was going to answer his letter.

But the letter had not told a clear story. Abigail's part said that the railway at Great Deeping had been bombed and – could it be true? – that Molly had almost been bombed too. And Molly's part went on and on about spies.

'No need,' he said. 'I'm going back. Tomorrow.'

Adam didn't know *why* he had decided to go back. The decision just arrived inside him, fully formed. Perhaps it was because Great Deeping seemed to have become an exciting place. Perhaps it was because of Molly's postscript. Or maybe he was, as his uncle had said, rootless and restless.

What he liked about his Welsh family was that they never made a fuss. They never put obstacles in your way, or made difficulties.

'You'll have to get the early train,' his aunt said. 'I'll make you some nice sandwiches. You'll need something – it's a long journey.' She didn't speak Welsh-English; she sounded like Adam's mum.

'See what I mean, boy?' his uncle said. 'You don't know how to stay in one place! Bronwen can give you a lift to the station on the back of the tractor, if you like.'

Bronwen had given him a quick smile.

'I can walk,' Adam said. 'You mustn't waste fuel.'

'Don't you worry about that!' Bronwen said. 'I have to take a pig to Evans the Butcher. You'll be company for him.'

'When you get there,' his aunt said, 'I want that landlady you live with to write and tell me you've arrived.'

'I can write to you myself,' Adam said.

'I know you, Adam Swales,' his aunt said. 'You might write from the north of Scotland and I'd be none the wiser if the postmark was smudged!'

At breakfast, just before she left for work, Gwen had said, 'Not a word about the slate mine, mind!'

He heard the train approaching, took the label from round his neck, and threw it into the grass that grew at the back of the platform. Then he stepped forward to meet the train as it hissed and clanked to a standstill. A small train it was, with just two carriages.

As he opened one of the carriage doors, the stationmaster said, 'Change at Conwy, and again at Chester. There you get the train to Manchester Central. From there, you travel direct all the way to Ely!' He pronounced it *Eli*.

As he slammed the door shut, Adam felt a sudden surge of pleasure, the joy of journeys. And the happiness that comes from being rootless.

They were having breakfast in the kitchen of Mrs Barnes's guest house when a large dark-blue Wolsley pulled up in the road outside. There were five people in it and they each wanted a room for one night – an army officer in uniform, three men in dark suits, and a chauffeur, also in a soldier's uniform.

'We're from the War Department,' one of them said. 'I'm Major Simms.'

Molly's mum was taken by surprise – new guests did not usually arrive at breakfast. 'I do have five vacancies,' she said, 'but I wish you'd booked in advance so I could have had the rooms made ready for you.'

Mrs Barnes knew at once why they had come but the girls were mystified. These men crowding into her house in their smart suits and military uniforms made Molly feel physically smaller, as if she were being squashed into a corner. She was glad Abigail was there.

The five visitors went up to their rooms, left their luggage, returned to the car and were gone again in hardly more than ten minutes.

'Can you direct us to the railway station?' one of the plain-suited men had asked.

As soon as they had left, Molly and Abigail started asking questions.

'They've come to investigate the bombing,' Mrs Barnes said. 'They have to find out how the Germans knew about that ammunition train.'

Molly turned pale, as if she were guilty. Abigail fidgeted. 'Can we go to the station to see?' she asked.

Mrs Barnes shook her head. 'They won't want children hanging about while they're doing their work,' she said firmly. 'But I think perhaps you had better run down to your house, Abigail, and tell your mum to expect a visit from them.'

'Why will they want to talk to her?' Abigail said.

'Well, I expect they're making investigations all the way down the line.'

'But *Mum!*' Abigail said. She was outraged.

Mrs Barnes tried to be reassuring. '*You* know your mum isn't a spy,' she said. 'And so do we. But they don't.'

Afterwards, Molly said to Abigail, 'Mr Creake likes the Nazis. He *said*.'

Abigail stared at her doubtfully. 'No,' she said. 'It couldn't be him. He works on the railway.'

Then she said, 'Anyway, Mum said he's just daft.' Finally she added, 'Besides, he would have *known* the train was empty.'

And Molly – who didn't want to think about it at all really – let it go at that.

At the railway station Robertson Creake saw the car arrive and the five men get out of it. He knew at once what this was about and he swelled with nervous self-importance. *This is my doing*, he thought.

He was summoned into the ticket office along with the stationmaster. The questioning was polite and unhurried. While two of the men were asking questions, the chauffeur made notes.

It was the officer who noticed the big leather-bound ledger on the desk. He slowly read through the recent entries and saw that some were written in red. He saw the entry for the previous Wednesday:

7.05 p.m. Freight.

Then, written the day after:

Rescheduled. 38 empty wagons. Hit by enemy action.

And for the following Monday evening – Easter Monday – the stationmaster had entered that a freight train was due to pass through:

8.45 p.m. Freight.

That too was written in red.

There was a terrible silence in the little office. Major Simms had drawn the others' attention to the entries in red. He simply pointed – and the others looked. Then, without a word, he took a fountain pen from an inner pocket and a ruler which lay on the desk. Then he wrote in the ledger across both the left and the right pages:

ENTRIES DISCONTINUED UNTIL
THE CESSATION OF HOSTILITIES

He ruled three straight lines across both pages, like a barrier. It was very neat – and very final.

The stationmaster protested. 'But that Journal has been kept since the day the station opened!' he said in dismay. '*My* predecessor kept it for forty years, and *his* predecessor kept it! I can't be the one to end it.'

The officer did not mince his words. 'There's a War on,' he said. 'Those entries reveal military secrets. If anything else is added to this book, I will have you charged with treason.'

The stationmaster almost staggered back against the wall. 'Treason?' he said. 'I fought in the last War!'

Robertson Creake made an attempt to console the stationmaster. 'Cheer up, mate,' he said. 'When the War's over, you can start the entries again.' He was stricken with what felt like a genuine pang of pity for the old man – and yet at the same time he hoped that in less than a week there would be no stationmaster, no station journal, and no station. Two opposite feelings, side by side.

One of the men in suits joined in. 'Who else has seen this book?' he asked.

It took the stationmaster several seconds to get his mind away from the terrible idea of treason. He felt as if his life was disgraced and his career done. He was heartbroken, shamed by the situation – but he did somehow manage to think about what he'd been asked. 'Only Mr Creake,' he said.

'Does no one else come into the office here?'

'No.'

'Is it locked at all times?'

'Of course not,' the stationmaster said bitterly. 'It's a ticket office.'

'Mr Creake. You have read the entries in this book?'

'I've seen them, yes.' It was so pleasant to tell the truth.

'The ones written in red – you knew what they meant?'

'Yes, of course.'

Robertson Creake was almost enjoying himself. He knew he was untouchable. If anyone was going to be in trouble, it would be the stationmaster.

There were a few more questions – Was he married? Did he ever talk to his friends about railway matters? But they were easily answered because he had never been married and he had no friends.

'Have you ever, Mr Creake, spoken to anyone about

the red entries in this book? Think carefully before you answer.'

Deliciously, innocently, and entirely truthfully, Robertson Creake said he hadn't.

'We will need to search your homes,' the senior officer said. 'Now. This morning. We have authority from the War Department. You can come with us if you like and let us in. If not, we will force an entry.'

Robertson Creake was in a state of rapture. He understood the situation completely. He was even proud of them because they were doing exactly the right thing – they were going to search his house for wireless equipment, or signs that wireless equipment had been recently removed. But he knew there was nothing like that at his house, and never had been. 'You're welcome,' he said. He truly loved this. He enjoyed being a genuine good citizen, a cooperative member of the public. He really *wanted* to be entirely innocent – so long as he could at the same time carry on with his plan. *I am innocent, wicked, important – and clever*, he thought. *Very clever.*

The senior army officer judged that the stationmaster was a foolish man, but not a spy. However, he disliked the look of Mr Creake. 'Your house first,' he said.

So the party left, with Robertson Creake squashed in the back seat of the Wolsley. Afterwards, they would search the stationmaster's house and question the signalman. And then that woman who worked the crossing gates – what was her name?

'Murfitt, sir,' said the chauffeur.

Adam's second train was a main-line express to London. So he stayed on it. His ticket was not inspected until they were halfway to London and, when the guard made a fuss, Adam had to apologise. 'You were supposed to go via Manchester Central and Sheffield,' the guard said. 'You'll have to pay the extra fare.'

But the compartment was full of soldiers going home on leave. They took Adam's part and told the guard to give the lad a chance.

They made such a noise about it that the guard gave up, and Adam continued on his way towards London.

Young Edward sat on the grassy bank at the front of his grandmother's house, watching the lane, hoping he might see Joe on his way to or from the farm.

He was used to being alone. Most of his life was spent alone. Children at school either ignored him, or made fun of him, or bullied him sometimes. Solitude had usually meant safety.

But the previous day had been like milk and honey to him. And now he sat disconsolately at the roadside, trying not to mind that Molly, Abigail and Joe had probably forgotten about him.

A dark-blue Wolsley drove by but he didn't see who was in it.

His lower lip and chin were already less sore and less

rough. But Edward continued to apply the cream because his top lip still crept downwards when he wasn't thinking about it. It was the cream that reminded him to pull it back into its proper place. *Perhaps I'll have to put cream on every day till I die*, he thought.

At one o'clock, his grandmother called him in for dinner. Stew, dumplings (he *adored* dumplings!) and mashed potatoes. Then rhubarb crumble with custard.

Afterwards, he went back to the grassy bank and sat there in the warm afternoon sunshine. He was so accustomed to dreaming in solitude that it was almost happiness to him.

Along the lane from the left came Joe Temper on his bike, slowly, effortlessly, cycling with his back straight and his arms folded.

'Wotcher, mate!' Joe said. He took control of the handle bars, cocked a leg over and hopped himself to a standstill.

Edward stood up and blushed.

'I'm off to find the girls. Want to come?'

Edward nodded, hiding his joy. 'I'll get my bike,' he said.

Then, turning back, anxiously, 'You *will* wait for me?'

'Don't you worry about your bike. It's too small for you anyway. I'll give you a ride on my crossbar.'

Edward still had to run in and tell his grandmother where he was going. But he was back in no time, half-expecting that Joe would have gone without him.

He had never ridden on a crossbar before. 'Tha's a

bit hard on your bum,' Joe said. 'But you'll only be on it a few minutes. Don't forget – when *I* lean, *you* lean.'

So, uncomfortable but happy, Edward was ridden into town enclosed in the arms of Joe Temper, who didn't seem to mind that he had to pedal twice as hard and cycle with his knees stuck out sideways.

Robertson Creake set off to walk back through the wood to the station.

After the five men had left in their Wolsley, he had stayed at home to have his dinner. But he hadn't been able to eat anything, he was too restless.

It had been a triumph at first. They had found nothing. Not a thing! They had searched every room in his house, even his attic and the spaces under the roof. They had checked and double-checked to see if there were loose floorboards or a hidden cellar. They had inspected the empty shoebox. They had got onto the roof to look for concealed aerials. They had peered into his pigeon loft and observed that it was unused and unoccupied. They had gone over his garden, examined his backyard and crept about in all his outhouses and sheds. Then they had explored among the trees, looking for signs of a worn pathway through the undergrowth that might lead to some secret hideaway where a transmitter might be kept.

Throughout it all, he had stood by, an innocent man dutifully allowing himself to be investigated. For the sake of king and country.

But they had found nothing! No wireless transmitter! No aerial! And no signs anywhere that such items had been hurriedly removed.

They haven't a clue, he told himself.

When they had done, they returned to their car. Mr Creake was not a singing man but, as he accompanied them back to the lane, he almost felt like bursting into joyous song. The kindly sun shone down on their heads through the trees, but he was too delighted with his own brilliance to notice it.

Close to the lane there was a red metal cupboard fixed to a tree. This was for Mr Creake's letters and parcels, and the milkman left his milk there to be cool in hot weather. The investigators were thorough. One of them went to inspect the mailbox while the others waited. He took a parcel from inside, addressed:

Mr R Creake,
Barrett's Cottage . . .

Mr Creake's sense of his own brilliance was extinguished at once. His traitorous heart was in his mouth. Major Simms handed the parcel to him. 'Someone must love you, Mr Creake,' he said drily.

Then they were gone, leaving Robertson Creake pale, holding his parcel, inwardly cursing the super efficiency of the Post Office. For the next few days those words kept coming back into his mind, driving him almost mad. *Someone must love you, Mr Creake.*

Edward and Joe found the girls sitting on the level-crossing gates outside Abigail's house. The dark-blue Wolsley was parked in the road outside.

Edward slipped down from Joe's crossbar, rubbing his behind. The two boys joined the two girls on the gate.

Twenty idle minutes passed by, in which time seemed to be wasting itself away. But it wasn't empty time. It contained:

~   Abigail angrily anxious about her mum and what was happening inside the house.

~   Molly thinking to herself that her mother had been right – she *was* listless and moody.

~   Joe Temper thinking that he would like another chance to rescue Molly from danger.

~   Edward wondering if they had forgotten their promise to take him to the pictures.

From a few hundred yards down the line came the sound of a crane, and there were voices shouting, giving orders. The army was at work, replacing the second of the two tracks. Within hours of the explosion, the Royal Engineers had been called in, the track-bed had been filled and levelled, and one of the lines was operating.

Green Lane had become Brown Lane.

The railway bell rang, twice. They heard the back door slam, then Mrs Murfitt came out to close the gates to traffic. She winked at them. 'They're nearly done,' she said, cocking her head towards the house. 'They're having a cup of tea.'

'I hope they've brought their own sugar!' Abigail grumbled.

All four children had a ride on the big gate as it swung across the road. A grimy black locomotive approached slowly, backing three wagonloads of sleepers over the crossing and shunting it towards the working soldiers.

Edward plucked up courage and spoke. 'I got my engine going,' he said. Then he told them how he'd done it, holding the engine in his hand because there was not enough track to put it on.

Molly scowled. She was not interested in Edward's train set. But Joe was. And Abigail felt she had a professional interest because her mum worked for the railway.

'We could lay out the track and get the whole thing working,' Joe said.

Abigail brightened. But Joe dashed her spirits at once. 'Trouble is, the grass in your garden is too lumpy and uneven. We'd have to find somewhere flat.'

But as far as Edward was concerned that wasn't the trouble at all. 'We can't,' he said. 'I'm not allowed. It doesn't belong to me.'

Molly felt bad-tempered. (What is the matter with me?) 'If you're allowed to make the engine go, why aren't you allowed to make the whole thing work? What's the difference?'

She had touched a sore point. Edward had been troubled by that very question. 'No one can be angry if I just look after it,' he explained carefully. 'But I'm not supposed to play with it.'

'And steaming up the engine for half an hour counts as looking after it, does it?' Molly said. 'Why don't you just *ask* your grandmother what you're allowed to do? That would settle it.'

But Edward thought there was a lot to be said for ambiguity. Such a direct question might settle it the wrong way. His top lip ventured miserably down towards his chin. 'If I ask, she might say no to everything,' he said.

She might even, he thought, *forbid me to go into the shed at all.*

Abigail changed the subject. 'Let's go and ask Edward's grandmother about going to the pictures,' she said. 'We said we would.'

She linked arms with Molly and Molly cheered up. But grudgingly.

They didn't go through the town this time. They set off along Green Lane beside the railway track, past the working soldiers. The metal wheel still lay embedded in the ground by the flat-bed truck where Joe had pushed Molly and himself a few nights earlier. It seemed a waste to Joe, that wheel. There ought to be a use for it.

They passed by the gasworks and the goods yard, across the Lynn road, then straight on to the station. Mr Creake was working on the opposite platform. 'If you're not intending to travel, you shouldn't be here!' he shouted. 'Or you can buy platform tickets. And that'll cost you fourpence!'

'Just taking a short cut!' Joe said cheerfully.

They didn't hear Mr Creake's reply. They had reached the far end of the platform and were swooping down the slope. At the bottom, they rode onto a narrow cinder path, running alongside the track.

There was a whistle from ahead, the 3.15 up-train from Lynn to London. It was slowing down, to stop at the station. As they watched it pass, the driver gave a royal wave to Abigail, and they all waved back.

When the train had gone, a total silence embraced them. They came to the disused branch-line going off to their left, rusty and dead. An old points lever stood, upright and white, beside the track.

Here, there was another path that branched off to the left, alongside the disused track, faithfully following the forgotten railway line.

Edward ventured a question. (Anything to distract him from the almost unbearable aches in his backside!) 'If this branch-line is never used, why is the path beside it so well worn?'

'Creakey comes this way to work,' Joe said.

The old railway track entered Barrett's Wood and led them through the trees to Camel Lane. And in no time at all they had reached Edward's house and were standing at the front door, confronting his grandmother.

Adam walked out of Euston Station and breathed the air of London.

Signs of the blitz were everywhere. Familiar buildings had been destroyed, roofscapes were different and strange, and naked walls towered above miserable craters of rubble. Glass windows were criss-crossed with tape and some of the more important buildings had walls of sandbags built up at street level to protect them from bomb damage. He overheard two women grumbling about the stink in some Underground stations now that thousands of people used them as shelters during air raids.

But the streets were still in the same places; buses and trams still moved gracefully from stop to stop; news vendors shouted their announcements to the passing crowds.

The little Welsh railway station, chilly and silent in the mountain mist, seemed to belong to a distant fantasy world.

Adam knew he had to go to Liverpool Street station to catch a train to Great Deeping. But there was something he wanted to do first.

He set off on foot to Trafalgar Square. He didn't walk, he ran. Steadily and without strain or effort, he dodged among the crowds of pedestrians – down Tottenham Court Road, onto Charing Cross Road, round the corner into Trafalgar Square, and up the stone steps outside the National Gallery.

He'd been there many times before the War – with his mum, his dad, his grandmother. And once or twice on his own. But this time the doors were locked and there were no visitors.

An old man was fixing a poster by the entrance advertising a programme of lunchtime concerts.

Adam pressed his nose against the glass door and peered inside.

'No good you looking in there,' the man said.

'Why not?' Adam asked – but he already knew the answer.

'Because there's nothing in there.'

'No paintings?'

'The old man shook his head. 'All gone,' he said.

'Where to?'

'Ah, who knows?'

I know, Adam thought. 'Is it completely empty then?' he said. 'In there?'

'Nothing in there except concerts every lunchtime,' the man said. 'To raise morale during the bombing.' He sniffed, but there was no way of knowing whether he was sniffing at Hitler and the bombing, or at lunchtime concerts. Or at life in general.

Adam walked slowly down the steps and crossed the road to St Martin's-in-the-Fields. It seemed wrong – no, not wrong, just *impossible*! – that thousands of great paintings should be hidden away in caves under a Welsh mountain. They belonged here, in London. Buried treasure, his uncle had said, but he'd been talking about sowing seeds and taking cuttings. And yet Adam felt cheered – pleased to belong to a country that had the good sense to hide its treasures in a time of trouble.

Then the sirens began to sound. People scuttled away in search of air-raid shelters.

'Cinema?' Mrs Barrett said. 'What happens if there's an air raid?'

Molly and Abigail explained. They were experts. A red sign came on the screen to tell the audience there was a raid, and then you were supposed to hurry out and run to the shelters in the school playground.

To their regret, it had never happened when they'd been there. But they assured Mrs Barrett that it was perfectly safe.

'Safe? *Safe?* How can any Christian soul be safe in such a place? There is nothing but wickedness and folly at that picture house,' Mrs Barrett declared.

For some reason it was Abigail she was looking at as she spoke. A challenging glare. So Abigail felt she ought to reply.

'*On the seventh day thou shalt worship,*' she said. '*Thereafter there shall be rejoicing all the days of the week.*'

There was a puzzled silence then. Molly watched Mrs Barrett's face. Was there a smile there? No, absolutely not. Her mouth had not moved, it was as stiff as folded cardboard.

'All right,' Mrs Barrett said. 'But you're to bring him here afterwards. Right to the door, mind! It will be pitch dark.'

She went in and the children turned away. 'She's a pushover, your gran,' Abigail said to Edward.

Edward could hardly believe his luck. 'I hope the seats are soft,' he said. He was rubbing his behind – and the others realised that Edward had made another joke. That was twice in four days.

'That bit of the Bible,' Molly said. 'Where does it come from?' She was ever so impressed.

'The Book of Abigail, chapter one, verse one,' Abigail said.

The truth dawned on them. 'You made it up?' Molly was even more impressed. 'Supposing the old lady knew . . .'

'She *did* know,' Abigail said. 'Of course she knew.'

Letter to Hitler – no. 20

Dear Herr Hitler . . .

. . . But the twentieth letter to Herr Hitler didn't get written.

For Robertson Creake suddenly lost himself. He had no idea where he was, or why he was in this room. He went hot and cold with fear and confusion. Where *was* this place? Whose kitchen was this? These objects all around him – were they *his*? The photograph on the wall, the black kettle, the ironing board in the corner – did they belong to *him*?

Then understanding was switched back on. The panic had lasted only a few seconds. *This is who I am*, he thought. *I am myself again. Yes!* And with the knowledge came the memory of his plan to blow up the whole of Great Deeping and kill four or five thousand people. He recognised himself, the old familiar Robertson Creake. Yes, he was the man he'd always been. What a relief!

But it seemed he no longer had anything to say to Mr Hitler. His head was sometimes full of voices, incomprehensible mostly. But in those few blank moments of confusion, *this* voice – his Hitler-voice – had been unaccountably silenced.

Wednesday 9th April ~ in the early hours

Abigail woke up, needing to go to the toilet.

But the five investigators were also sleeping that night at the guest house, and she was unwilling to risk meeting one of them also on his way to the bathroom. So she lay still and tried to go back to sleep. But her need was pressing.

The lino was cold to her bare feet when she got out of bed, so she monkey-walked across the floor to her door. It was better out in the passage because that was carpeted. She walked softly along in the dark towards the bathroom, hugging her shoulders because of the chilly night air.

The doors of the other guest rooms were firmly closed.

The windows were heavily blacked out because of air-raid precautions, but she stopped at one of them and parted the curtains to look out into the night.

She gazed for a few moments at the countryside in the shadowy brilliance of moonlight. There was an almost-full moon and the sky was completely cloudless. Two fields away from the edge of the town, standing dark and humpy in the transparent clearness, she could see Paradise Barn and the big tree that grew beside it.

She let the curtains fall back in place and continued along the passage. But then she stopped, frowned, thought for a couple of seconds – and went back to the window to check. Had she really seen . . . ?

It couldn't be! It was impossible!

Quickly, Abigail felt her way to Molly's room, turned the door handle as quietly as she could, and crossed over to the bed. 'Molly!' she whispered. 'Molly! Wake up!'

Molly stirred resentfully. 'What? Who is . . . ? Is there an air raid?'

Abigail was ruthless. She pulled the bedclothes off and grabbed Molly by the arm. 'Come and see,' she whispered.

Together they went out into the cold passage and shoved their heads behind the curtains.

Molly stared. Someone had lit a fire in their room in the barn. A thin column of smoke rose from the chimney, perfectly vertical, like a silver-grey strand pulled upright towards heaven. It rose many hundreds of feet into the still night air and then, at the top, spread itself out into a mile-wide layer of fine mist as light as tissue paper, with the moon shining through it.

And at once Molly knew!

'What are we going to do?' Abigail whispered. Her eyes were dark sockets staring at Molly in the moonlight.

'We'll go and see,' Molly said, suddenly decisive. 'Come on!'

'In our pyjamas?'

'We'll put our macs on over them.'

'It's probably a tramp,' Abigail protested. But Molly had already set off to the top of the stairs.

In all the adventure stories that Molly had read, when someone needed to creep downstairs at night, they always worried that a creaking staircase would waken everyone in the house. But the staircase was not the problem this time. It was Abigail whispering – more like a soft shout than a whisper, a ferocious hiss.

But no one woke up. Molly went into the kitchen and started to search for food in the larder. There were more leftovers than usual because of the extra guests. She assembled: a plump chicken leg; half a pork pie; two hard-boiled eggs; a portion of cold bubble and squeak; a hunk of bread and some margarine; and a generous slice of chocolate sponge. Finally, she found a big baking tray and loaded it all onto that.

Abigail came in with their macs and wellington boots. 'Why are we taking him food?' She was mystified.

'He'll be hungry,' said Molly. She was concentrating on pouring some milk into an empty bottle.

'Molly! It's probably some old tramp!' Then she had another thought. 'It might be the spy!'

Molly stared at her. 'It's not a tramp. And it's not a spy,' she said.

'Who is it, then?'

'It's Adam, of course,' Molly said.

A few minutes later, when they were halfway across the first field, Abigail remembered why she had got up. 'I need a pee,' she said.

Molly had no sympathy. 'You'll have to wait till we get to the barn.'

Shivering inside her pyjamas, Abigail thought to herself that the old Molly had come back. Or was it a new one?

Adam had the advantage over the girls.

He woke up with a start, hearing voices. There was a torch in the cabin and Adam picked it up and walked quietly to the door. There was a small wooden platform at the top of the stairs, like a balcony, and he stood there, peering down into the body of the barn.

But he didn't need the torch. He could see them clearly, silhouetted in the doorway against the bright moonlight – Molly holding something in front of her, and Abigail behind her, huddled and hesitating. They, on the other hand, could see nothing at all as they came in from the moon-brightness outside to the total darkness inside the barn.

'It's you!' Adam said, as if he'd known all along that they would come.

Molly felt quietly confirmed in her rightness. Abigail, who really had believed it might be the spy or a tramp, shouted happily up to him, 'We've brought your breakfast!' Her voice boomed in the echoing barn.

'I haven't had yesterday's dinner yet!' Adam shouted from above. 'I'm three meals behind.' He switched on the torch and shone it into their faces.

'Don't dazzle us, Adam Swales!' Abigail said.

Adam shone the torch to light the way up the wooden steps to the cabin. In the back-light the girls could see that he was still dressed, but shoeless.

It was warm and companionable in the cabin, with the fire burning and the curtain drawn. Adam lit a couple of candles and sat on the bed while Molly set out the food she'd brought. Abigail – no longer scared – took the torch and the chamber pot (pale green, with pink and yellow rosebuds) out onto the balcony.

Years later, Molly remembered this as one of the best moments of her life. But it would be hard to explain why, since nothing much was said, no decisions were made, and nothing of any importance happened.

Abigail came back in and shut the door, Molly revived the fire with some coal, and Adam scoffed the food. Between mouthfuls, he asked questions.

'How did you know I was here?'

'The smoke from the chimney,' Abigail said. 'It's visible for miles! It's a wonder the ARP wardens didn't come and investigate.'

'It's not against War regulations to light a fire,' Molly said.

'But how did you know it was me?'

'Molly just did. *I* thought it was the spy.'

Adam threw the chicken bone onto the fire and licked his fingers carefully and thoroughly. 'I think we should have a Council of War here tomorrow morning,' he said.

'This *is* tomorrow morning,' Abigail said.

'Later *this* morning, then.'

'We'll get Joe to come too,' Abigail said.

Abigail and Molly knew that bringing someone else in might lead to difficulties. But Adam didn't seem to mind. He knew Joe – the previous year, a group of boys at the school had made a book for identifying British and German aircraft. Joe was one of them, and Adam had done the drawings.

But he'd never heard of Edward.

'Did you come by train?'

'Only as far as Littleport. I walked from there. I didn't want to be seen.'

He must be worn out, Molly thought.

'Why didn't you come to Molly's house?' Abigail asked.

'It was after midnight when I got here.'

Abigail was sceptical. She doubted that it took so long to get from North Wales to East Anglia, even in Wartime.

'I went via London. I got there in the afternoon. Then there was an air raid and I was stuck in a shelter for ages.'

'Mum would've let you in,' Molly said, 'however late you turned up.'

'I know. But I'm going to live in hiding for a few days.'

Then Abigail asked *where* he was going to live in hiding.

'Here. In the barn.' And that's all he would say.

'How are you going to get anything to eat?'

'You'll have to get it for me.'

This irritated Abigail. She could foresee difficulties, but Molly just smiled to herself in the candlelight shadows. 'Tell us about Wales,' she said.

So Adam tried. Two girls – whose homeland was as bare and flat as a shoreless ocean – tried to imagine the closed-in skies and beautiful dark mountains of Snowdonia. But Adam was an artist, not a wordsmith.

Molly saw his frustration. 'Did you do much drawing?' she asked him. To herself she thought, *I want to go there with him, one day.*

'Tell you what,' he said. 'When we have our Council of War, I'll show you my sketches.'

'Show us now,' Abigail said.

'Not enough light,' Adam said. 'Anyway, I want *you* to tell *me* what's been happening? Who's this Edward?'

So they told him the whole story – about Edward's grandmother, the disused railway, the buried sword, and the mulberry trees. *And* – for good measure – Edward's chin.

Adam listened attentively but, if he had any thoughts about what they'd told him, he kept them to himself. 'Molly, I need you to do something for me,' he said.

'OK,' said Molly.

'You know your mum has some writing paper with the guest house address printed on it? I want you to get hold of a sheet and write to my aunt – she said your mum was to write and say that I'd arrived safely.'

'Didn't she trust you to get here?' Abigail asked.

Adam shook his head and grinned.

'You'll have to tell me what to write,' Molly said.

Later, on their way back, Abigail said to Molly, 'Are you really going to do it?'

'Yes,' Molly said.

'It's forgery.'

'I know.'

'You can go to prison for forgery.'

'I don't care! You can come and visit me.'

'In jail? OK. I'll bring you a bar of milk chocolate every week.'

'It'll be worth it, then,' Molly said.

Then Abigail said, 'And another thing. *Why* does Adam want to live in hiding?'

Molly shrugged. 'Don't know,' she said. 'I don't think he knows himself.'

Molly was right. If a teacher or a policeman had asked Adam *why* he wanted to do this, he couldn't have answered. He would have looked mulish and stupid. He was interested in the buried sword, and the solitary mulberry growing by itself in a wood – that much he knew. But was there something deeper, and harder to explain? – a desire to *prowl* perhaps, and to know what it felt like to be a spy, to live on the outside looking in? Like an artist.

He was certainly not interested in spy catching.

Wednesday morning ~ early

As daylight crept through the leafless trees, Robertson Creake cycled slowly along the cinder path beside the disused railway track, then beside the main line, and finally up the slope onto the platform at the station. He stowed away his bike, gave a friendly wave to the man in the signal box, and unlocked the ticket office.

The first train through would be the 7.05 for Liverpool Street, due in a few minutes. Mr Creake sold tickets to five or six passengers, talked about the weather, grumbled about the War, and reminded them to be careful crossing the track to the other platform.

Then the train arrived with its familiar fussy drama. Brakes squealed, doors slammed, people shouted, the engine hissed and hooted – and then the slow accelerating excitement as the engine huffed and snorted away from the platform. Finally, Nobby Clark came down from the signal box and opened the crossing gates to road traffic.

As the two gates crashed into their latches, it was like the closing of the curtains at a theatre. The action was over and the station was left deserted.

Except for Mr Creake. He had it entirely to himself

that morning; the stationmaster would not come on duty until dinnertime.

He set about his chores – cleaning, tidying, checking parcels, lighting fires in the two waiting rooms. Then, when it was all done, he went into the room at the back of the ticket office.

The stationmaster had written no more entries since the terrible warning he'd received. But the ledger was still there. The investigators had not taken it away and the entry in red was plainly to be seen. *8.45 p.m. Freight*, it said, for next Monday.

Mr Creake's head was full of voices again. One of them spoke to him as if nothing out of the ordinary was happening in his life. It reminded him that it was his job to sell advance tickets, make bookings, and answer questions about train times. And as he lit the fires in the waiting rooms, this voice reminded him how nice it would be when the warmer weather arrived and there would be no need to light fires. It spoke from a part of him that seemed actually to *believe* that nothing was going to change. But there was another voice which spoke of destruction and murder, and reminded him that what he planned to do would put an end to Great Deeping and probably most of its inhabitants. There will be no station, no railway, no advance tickets, no fires to be lit, this voice said insistently. Simply no future. This voice came from a part of his mind which was very thorough, very attentive to detail. And very proud of itself.

But sometimes there was an even lower voice that had no tone, no pitch, almost no volume. It was so faint that even the thinker was hardly aware of it. This was a lonely voice, a child's voice murmuring to itself in the dark. It went on and on, longing for something. But what it wanted could not be put into words because there was just an emptiness there. Words cannot come out of nothing, not without help. Perhaps what it really wanted was silence, and an end to all this angry longing.

There are things I must do, he said to himself. He closed the ledger and went thoughtfully out onto the platform.

The Council of War almost didn't happen at all. The problem was food.

It was to be a picnic dinner as well as a Council of War, and arrangements were made for Joe to come too and bring Edward with him. Everyone was to bring as much food as possible so that Adam could have some of it.

But before they could find the food for the next meal, the girls had to face the consequences of the last one. There had never been the slightest chance that Molly's mum – who ran a guest house and provided food for her guests – would fail to notice that a chicken leg, a pork pie and various other items had gone missing from her larder. Molly knew that really.

There was a terrible row. Abigail, who had witnessed one or two of these in the past, stood back and watched with fascination – slightly scared fascination. Molly's brother, Baby William, walked unsteadily around the table to hold Abigail's hand. He watched it all with a solemn face.

Molly's mum raged at Molly – about how it was hard enough trying to manage to scrape a living in Wartime without . . . And so on, and so on, and so on. Molly, who didn't want to confess that she'd taken the food because Adam had come home, stormed back that it was unfair and that she was always being picked on . . . But everyone knew that the outcome was inevitable – imprisonment in their bedrooms for the whole day, probably, perhaps two days. Surely not *three*?

Two or three precious holiday days would be lost. There would be no Council of War, no trip to the pictures. And Adam would starve to death.

However, they were not punished straightaway. Their sentence was deferred. The reason was that, although Mrs Barnes was sure that Molly deserved serious punishment and Abigail deserved some of it, she felt uncomfortable about punishing someone else's daughter.

In the end, they received no punishment at all. This was because the postman arrived bringing a letter from Molly's dad – the first for over two months.

Everything stopped and the atmosphere in the kitchen changed its emotional colour. All three of them sat at the big table while Mrs Barnes opened the letter. Molly and Abigail glanced uncertainly at each other.

'There's one for you,' Mrs Barnes said to Molly.

Molly fingered it, frowning. It was a strange letter, a small grey photographic copy of an original, on stiff paper. Molly had never seen a letter like it. There was a Field Post Office postmark, a printed message saying *EASTER GREETINGS*, and a shield-shaped stamp with the words *Passed by Censor*. At the bottom, there was a wavy banner with the message *Allied Forces, Land, Sea and Air*.

Molly slid it along the table to indicate that Abigail should read it with her.

Dear Molly,

I hope you are well and happy and I wish very much that I could be at home with you at Easter-time. I love you very much. Do your best to help your mum.

God bless.

Love, Dad XXX

It was not much of a letter, Molly thought. Just the sort of letter that a father who was away in the War was expected to write to his daughter. A duty letter. Tears sprang into her eyes. But what about Abigail, whose own father was missing, feared killed, and who never got a letter from her dad? And might not, ever. And crowding in on that reminder came the thought of Edward, whose parents were both dead and who would never get a letter from either of them.

These thoughts did not arrive in her head one after the other, in a tidy sequence. They were simultaneous, side-by-side, wrapped around each other. Nor did they make Molly feel happier. They just made her feel guilty for not being happy.

But Abigail saw the letter in a different light. 'He sounds sad,' she said quietly.

And Molly wondered, *Is that what it means?*

And that led to yet another thought. It seemed awful to her – shockingly wicked – that it should have been read by censors, that a simple letter from a father to his daughter should be read by strangers to check that secret information wasn't being given away! How *dare* they read her father's letter! Her dad wasn't an enemy agent!

But the arrival of the letter saved the girls from punishment. It changed the mood. Anger and disapproval had no place in that house at that time. Mrs Barnes, with wet shining eyes (crying? bright with joy? – they were not sure) made them promise never to do such a thing again.

Then they knew it was going to be all right.

However, there was still dinner to be sorted out. Under the circumstances, the girls considered Abigail's mum a better bet. She at present knew nothing about their night-time misdeeds. So they went to Abigail's house and tried their luck there. With some success, in the end.

'A picnic dinner?' Mrs Murfitt said doubtfully. 'Are you sure you don't mean a picnic tea? I've never had a picnic dinner! Do you want something *cooked*?' She was sharp-tempered and fierce as always. But not unkind.

So, at around twelve o'clock, Abigail and Molly set off to Paradise Barn, loaded with food. Boring food, to be honest, but still food. Adam probably *liked* bread and marge with cheese and pickles, and yesterday's cold mashed potato with sprouts.

Young Edward's grandmother was halfway through her morning's housework when he put the question to her.

'A picnic dinner? Did you say a picnic *dinner*? With your friends?'

Edward nodded, neck and shoulders as well as head, to show how important it was.

Old Mrs Barrett picked up a Bible. This one lived in the kitchen, soft and grubby with years of service. She opened it without looking at it, gazed up at the ceiling and jabbed her forefinger down onto the page.

Then she looked down to see what she had been directed to find. '*A day of gladness and feasting, and a good day, and of sending portions one to another,*' she read triumphantly.

It had gradually dawned upon Edward during the last few days that nobody else's parents did this – or grandparents for that matter. 'Gran, why do you do that?' he asked.

She stared at him in surprise, that he should have to ask such a question; that he didn't understand. 'It's God's way of giving me clues,' she said.

'What sort of clues?'

'To help me make the best decisions,' she said impatiently, as if it should be obvious to anyone.

'Why do you need help?' he said.

His grandmother sighed and sat down suddenly on

a kitchen stool. 'They're all dead and gone,' she said. 'Mothers and fathers and husbands and wives. And sons, too. All gone! And you – God help you! – have only me to bring you up safely! The Bible says: *Defend the poor and fatherless: do justice to the afflicted and needy.* Well, you're fatherless and needy. But I'm nearly *eighty*!'

'It doesn't matter how old you are,' Edward said. And this was true in a way. It certainly didn't matter to *him*. But his grandmother looked at him as if to say: that's all *you* know! What she actually said was, 'No, it doesn't. Because I do my best. But I need help sometimes. And who better to help me than God?'

'Other people's mums don't.' As soon as he'd said it, he wished he hadn't. It was unkind.

But Mrs Barrett only smiled sadly. 'Other people have different ways of getting the help they need,' she said. 'That's mine.'

Then she stood up. 'You shall have your feast,' she said. 'What time is Josiah Temper coming for you?'

'About twelve,' Edward said, brightening.

The weather was menacing. Low clouds streamed in relentlessly from the north-east, bitter and dark. There had been heavy snow in Yorkshire, the wireless said. People joked that the bad weather was being sent by the Germans. Some of them almost believed it. Nevertheless, the picnic dinner was a success, especially for the hungry Adam.

The others all arrived together, and there was a great noise and bustle as they crowded into the barn and followed one another up the staircase and into the cabin. Their ears were red with cold, their breath steamed, their voices were loud with excitement. Inside, they shoved each other about to get close to the fire, and took off their macs and coats. Except Joe, whose only concession to the cold weather was a red woollen scarf.

There was food in abundance, mostly because young Edward had brought a big flat basket with an entire steak-and-kidney pudding wrapped up in a cloth tied with a knot at the top. It was still warm, and the smell of it sent them into ecstasies. But the basket had bumped against his leg all the way there and left it bruised.

'You're a hero!' Adam said to Edward. Molly and Abigail exchanged approving glances. It was a good way for them to meet, they both thought.

They kept an assortment of enamel and china plates in the cabin; and a few spoons. Molly and Abigail considered knives and forks an unnecessary luxury – you could manage everything with a spoon. They had just one knife for cutting and spreading.

It took about fifteen or twenty minutes for them to scoff the lot, two sitting on the camp bed, two on chairs and one – Molly – on the floor, with her feet stretched out towards the fire.

Molly had less to say than any of the others. She was very contented. She was interested in this new arrangement of people, wondering how they would fit.

Abigail had said earlier that Adam wouldn't like Joe being there; and that Joe might be jealous of Adam. So, slipping into her eavesdropping mode, Molly watched them carefully.

But there seemed to be no rivalry between the two boys, no resentment. Nothing at all, in fact. They were not close friends, perhaps not friends at all. But they already knew each other and that seemed to be enough. Was this how boys did it? Molly was fascinated. She hated it if anyone tried to get too friendly with Abigail. (Except Adam, of course. He was allowed.)

But, with Edward, Adam was entirely different. Perhaps it was because he was younger. Adam seemed to be fascinated by the story of Edward's ancestor and his last-minute escape from capture. He questioned him closely about the buried sword (*he's got it right*, thought Edward with relief, a sword, *not* treasure) and what it had to do with mulberry trees.

Adam might have asked the younger boy why his chin was smeared with cream of some kind. But he didn't.

Then, with the food all gone and the dirty plates stacked in a corner to be dealt with later, Edward produced from his basket some more items – his steam locomotive, the bottle of methylated spirit, the oil can, the burner, and a box of matches. He'd filled the locomotive with water before he left home. *He has planned everything*, Molly thought.

'But there's no track,' Adam said.

'He's got miles of it,' said Joe. 'Back home, in his shed.'

'I'm not allowed,' Edward said. 'It belonged to my father.'

Those words, *It belonged to my father*, hung in the air with a Wartime sadness which seemed to belong to the whole unhappy world of lost and absent fathers. It was the past tense that did it – *belonged*.

The locomotive behaved perfectly – held aloft in Edward's hand at first, wrapped in his grandmother's pie cloth, and then passed from person to person as wrists began to ache with the weight of it.

The pistons elbowed back and forth at enormous speed, the wheels whizzed round, steam spat, and there was a smell of hot metal.

Afterwards, Adam brought out his sketchbook to show them the drawings he had done in Wales. The others crowded around to see but only Molly was genuinely interested in them. There was a tractor, which Joe studied carefully. But, for the rest, they were Fenlanders – what did they know about mountainsides and steep, rain-filled valleys? And towns built entirely of slate? It was just scenery.

But there was one they all liked – a strip cartoon that Adam had drawn on the train, watched by several interested servicemen.

It was a strip in six frames, three along the top of the page, three along the bottom. In the first was the title, *Dig For Victory!* In the second, he had drawn his aunt's profile as she listened to the wireless. But this was no ordinary wireless – it was shaped liked the head of Mister Churchill, with hat and cigar; and out of it came a speech bubble with the words *We must grow more food to feed our nation.*

In the third, Adam's aunt was passing on the message to his uncle. Just their heads, with a speech bubble coming from his aunt, saying *You must grow more food.*

In the fourth frame, Adam's uncle was kneeling in his garden with a pencil in his hand, looking down at six twigs pushed into the ground. *You must grow,* he was saying to the twigs.

In the fifth, there were the six twigs and the pencil, all stuck into the ground. The drawing showed under the earth too, and you could see that small roots were growing from the base of the six twigs and new leaves were coming out at the top. However, the pencil was just a pencil – and a long speech bubble, shared by all six of the rooted twigs, was saying to the pencil *You must grow!* There was a worm with a thought bubble coming from it, containing a tiny exclamation mark.

In the last frame, there was just the pencil, not growing. That, Molly thought, was the cleverest. How could anyone draw a pencil so that it looked as if it were ashamed of itself? But that was what Adam had done. Then she noticed that the worm's exclamation mark – so tiny that you could easily miss it – had planted itself in the ground and minute roots were already growing from its dot.

Molly had brought a sheet of her mother's printed notepaper and an envelope, and Adam had a stamp. So, after much consideration and disagreement about what to say, Molly wrote:

Dear Mrs Hughes,
I am glad to inform you that your nephew Adam arrived here safely on Tuesday night.
He says that he had a nice time in Wales.
Yours faithfully,
Mary Barnes

That seemed to do the trick. Abigail wanted her to add *(Mrs)* after *Mary Barnes*. But Molly refused. After all, her proper name was Mary – which meant that the letter wasn't really a forgery. But it *would* be if she added *Mrs*. What's more, everything it said was true. Molly, conscience free, felt pleased with her handiwork. The letter was folded and put in its envelope, to be posted later, on their way to the cinema.

'Cinema?' Adam demanded. 'Are you going to the pictures?'

That, of course, changed everything. Because Adam wanted to go too. But if he went with them to the cinema, he would be seen and recognised. His cover would be blown.

Yet to leave him at the barn while they all went to see Bing Crosby and Bob Hope in *Road to Singapore* was unthinkable. And for a few moments young Edward thought they were going to decide to cancel the trip. He made himself ready for disappointment.

But he underestimated his new friends. 'Go in disguise,' Abigail said to Adam.

Adam thought that was a crazy idea. 'With a beard and a moustache?' he said.

'No,' Abigail said cautiously, considering other possibilities. 'There must be a way.'

It was Joe who came up with the best idea. 'Have you got a balaclava?' he said.

As it happened, Adam did have a balaclava – a scratchy woollen piece of headwear which he loathed. Part hat, part hood, part scarf, part muffler. It was in the chest of drawers in his bedroom at Molly's house.

'My mum says even Winston Churchill would be unrecognisable in a balaclava,' Joe said.

The others agreed. It was impossible to imagine Mister Churchill in a woollen balaclava.

'Shall I get it, then?' Molly asked.

Adam nodded. 'It's khaki,' he said in disgust.

'But it will be a fantastic disguise!' Abigail said.

The afternoon seemed to go on for hours. But finally, after a crazy game of football down on the floor of the barn, Joe said he had to go home. Edward had to go too. They went back up to the cabin to pack up their dishes and pots.

'When are you going to start your prowling?' Abigail said to Adam.

'Tonight. After we've been to the pictures.'

'What are you hoping to find out?'

'You don't know what you will discover until you've discovered it,' Adam said. Then, to Molly, as she was going down the stairs to leave, he said, 'Can you get me a book about mulberry trees?'

She paused halfway down the steps, looking back at him. 'I'll try,' she said. He liked that. She was like his family back in Wales. She didn't ask questions or fuss about details. She just said she'd try – and she would.

'See you later!' Abigail shouted as they went out into the cold.

Their voices grew fainter as they moved away over the fields towards the edge of the town. Adam returned to the cabin and sat down. He opened his sketchbook, and pencilled fast to capture Molly's face, the angle of her head and shoulders, the fall of her hair, as she had turned and looked up at him from the stairs.

Robertson Creake blacked out his windows and, carrying a miserly candle, went to his airing cupboard. The War Department investigators had looked in there, searching for radio equipment, but all they'd found were his blankets and sheets, neatly folded.

From the bottom of the pile he took out one of the sheets, white and innocent, ready to be laid on a bed. But – like its owner – it wasn't entirely innocent. On one side it was white, but on the other Mr Creake had painted three thick concentric black circles with a solid-black centre.

He took the sheet out into his backyard. There was hardly a sound to be heard in the darkness. No birdsong, no distant trains moving, only the creaking of the highest branches of the trees as the cold wind drove across the countryside.

He went across to his pigeon loft, placed one foot on a ledge, and climbed onto the roof. Here, he unfolded the sheet and spread it out. But the wind caught the edges and threatened to blow it off. So Mr Creake climbed down again and went to the house for a hammer and some tacks. He returned, climbed back onto the roof of the pigeon loft, and fixed down the edges and corners of the sheet.

A bright moon, almost full, appeared briefly in a steep narrow valley in the clouds, as if watching him. Mr Creake shivered. *If it had eyes*, he thought, *the moon would have seen a wood with a big circular space in it, and in the middle of the circle a white surface with a round black target painted clearly on it.*

A rhyme came unexpectedly into his thoughts, a fragment left over from childhood. *I spy with my little eye*, Robertson Creake found himself saying.

After the trip to the cinema, they'd all had fish and chips in the cabin at the barn. The fire had been relit, the window blacked out. And, when the others had left, Adam waited until he heard the church clock strike eleven. That was when he intended to start his exploring.

It was bitterly cold and he pulled the balaclava over his head. At first, he prowled the empty streets, taking his time, getting the measure of the town at night.

No streetlights, no car lights, the houses all blacked out. The empty streets almost impenetrably dark, except when the moon came briefly out. Not a soul to be seen – except once. An air-raid warden stood motionless at the far end of the High Street. Adam slipped silently across the end of the road, unseen.

He was not expecting to find the spy who'd tried to get the train blown up. This was a game he was playing

– but Adam's games were always half serious. It's always worth looking, he believed. If you don't look, you don't see.

His plan was to explore the whole town. It was different at night, it had a different geography. The thought of prying in the dark, and seeing while unseen, appealed to him. On this first night he wanted to explore Barrett's Wood and Mr Creake's circular backyard.

He found Camel Lane, the road where Edward lived, and which led to Joe's farm. Adam had never been there before, but Joe had drawn him a map and he had memorised it. Feeling hot, he tore off the balaclava and shoved it in his trouser pocket.

He went quietly past the front of Edward's house, wondering which was his bedroom window. Then on until he came to the wood – and then, deep in the trees, the disused branch-line crossing the lane.

He turned off the road and went very carefully along the path beside the railway. *Very* carefully. He knew Molly disliked Robertson Creake, though he didn't know why.

⁂

A solitary German aircraft, a Dornier 217, was flying into East Anglia, having crossed the North Sea from occupied Holland.

The pilot had flown several missions along this route, but they had been bombing raids, with other bombers flying in formation and fighter planes in support.

Usually they had flown on to the Midlands to bomb the big industrial towns there; once or twice, he had been on a daylight mission to bomb the airfields in East Anglia.

But this trip was different. The aircraft was on a solitary mission, with very precise instructions. There were no bombs on board. This reduced the weight of the plane and increased its speed. It was important to get in and do the job, and then get safely out again – fast.

The Dornier was flying at about three hundred miles per hour at a height of around twenty-four thousand feet. It flew above the cloud layer, and the cockpit and controls gleamed strangely in the moonlight.

Behind him, the pilot knew, his gunners were silently scanning the vast empty sky in case of marauding British fighters. Unlikely at night, but always possible. When they reached their destination, one of the crew would leave his machine gun. It was his job to attend to the drop.

When the aircraft reached an appropriate point on its flight, the pilot took it down – into and through the clouds, where there was no moonlight. He almost despaired of finding his target in the thick darkness. Suddenly, in front of the plane a dazzling shaft of perpendicular light swept stiffly across the night sky. From its pin-point base on the ground far below, it swung massively across the darkness, illuminating the undersides of the clouds.

A searchlight! And a moment later two more joined it. They were looking for him.

If the engines of the Dornier had been soundless, the pilot would have been able to hear the air-raid sirens moving across the countryside ahead of him. The British Radar authorities were aware that a solitary enemy plane was flying inland at a great height. They were puzzled; it was clearly not an ordinary bombing raid. A stray bomber, perhaps? Lost? It did happen – but, just in case, the warning went out and the sirens sounded.

When Adam drew near to Mr Creake's house, he'd waited for a few moments. He walked carefully into the backyard, a strange, circular place. His feet in the blackness found some sizeable irregularities in the hard ground at the edge of the circle, changes in the contours of the earth. The first of them almost made him stumble.

Then the moonlight returned. It illuminated, as if in a dream, a tree unlike all the others. He knew at once that it was the mulberry tree. He gazed at it, sensing the character and patience of trees, understanding its great age, its weightiness. Although the trees all around it were taller, he knew at once that this one was older. Then the clouds slid back over the moon and the darkness returned. But the mulberry tree was still visible to Adam in his mind's eye, even down to its roots in the ground, maintaining its ancient hold on the earth it had been planted in.

Adam heard a door being opened in the house. *Time to go*, he thought. A spy would have stayed to watch. But Adam had come to see, not to spy; to find out what was there and understand it, not to mount watch over Robertson Creake.

On his way back into the town, he heard the air-raid warning, and a few moments later the sound of an approaching aircraft. He began to run – joyously, recklessly – through the empty streets. He didn't care that his racing footsteps could be heard echoing in the empty night. Nobody in the world knew where he was! He was invulnerable and secret. He felt as if he owned the universe.

In the street outside the Ely guest house, he slowed, then stopped. It was very tempting. He could throw stones at Molly's bedroom window and wake her up. She would come down and let him in. She wouldn't mind. *Shall I?* he thought.

As he was about to turn away, he saw the curtains move at her bedroom window. She looked down at him in the street for a moment or two, then gave a quick wave, and slipped back into the darkness of her room.

In a great mood of sudden well-being, Adam raced out of the town and across the fields towards Paradise Barn. As he ran, he realised that the sound of the aircraft was growing louder. It was losing height, flying low towards the town. The searchlights were hard at work, scissoring across the empty heavens.

Abigail had woken Molly by shaking her shoulder. It was a repeat of the previous night, except that this time Molly was pleased to be woken up. She had been dreaming that Bob Hope had been trying to kiss her. She adored Bob Hope in his films, but she didn't want him in her dreams.

As she awoke, the air-raid siren was finishing its weird up-and-down whooping and was beginning its dismal fade out. It always seemed to Molly that those final growling notes made the saddest sound in the world.

As for her dream, she would tell Abigail about it later, and they would turn it into a joke.

On an impulse, she went to her window and slipped behind the curtains. There was someone in the street below, motionless. He was looking up at her window and she could see his face, pallid and almost featureless in the enclosing darkness. She knew instantly who it was and raised her hand in a brief wave.

Then downstairs she went, following Abigail, and under the steel table-shelter in the kitchen. Blankets, cushions and eiderdowns were kept there, ready. The previous autumn, the shelter had been used nearly every night as enemy planes passed overhead.

When Abigail had moved into Molly's house, they had hoped there would be an air raid. It would be fun, they thought, sheltering together. But it didn't live up to expectations, mainly because Molly's little brother, William, was a very wide-awake nuisance. He had been a baby the year before, and had slept peacefully wherever he was put – often in Molly's arms. But he was a toddler now, with a will of his own.

He had no intention of sleeping and he had decided he liked Abigail better than anyone in the world. Molly tried not to mind. After a time Abigail began to mind too. He was a persistent and wriggly child.

Mrs Barnes pulled her dressing gown tightly around her and went out into the backyard. There was, she thought, the faint sound of a single plane somewhere up there. Then, in the distance, she saw the searchlights piercing the darkness.

Joe Temper slept on, unaware of the Dornier beginning to lose height over his father's farm.

He and his parents always ignored air raids. Their house was set in the middle of hundreds of acres of farmland, and they calculated that the likelihood of a direct hit on their home was small.

So they slept through the air raid, soundly, deeply and untroubled. Sleep was precious to farm workers who had to get up at four o'clock.

Robertson Creake had gone back indoors in search of a torch and wrapped himself in a thick ex-army greatcoat, scarf and gloves. The moment was approaching.

In his circular backyard, he looked up at the sky. As he stood there, he heard the church clock strike twelve, the sound ringing faithfully across the town and all the way to Barrett's Wood.

In the early days of the war, Mr Creake had volunteered to become an air-raid warden. The organisers had been pleased, they were short of men. They took him to their observation post at the top of the church tower, to see if he could manage the climb with his limp. He did manage it, but with difficulty. It was reluctantly agreed that Mr Creake had better not be a warden. Because of his limp.

However, he had found out what he needed to know – that from the observation post you could not see his backyard. The trees of the wood hid it from view.

So, as he paced up and down in the cold darkness, he knew that when he flashed his torchlight up into the night, it would be seen only from directly above.

He heard an air-raid siren, distant and faint. Then another, from closer. Then he picked up the sound – barely audible – of an approaching plane at a great height.

All these things are happening because of me, he thought.

Edward woke up when the siren sounded. He heard a distant one first, from Downham Market probably, or Mildenhall. Then their own in Great Deeping started up, nearer and louder.

The rule was that he should wake his grandmother. She slept deeply, and rarely heard the warnings. Then they would both go down to the cellar.

But Edward crept downstairs in his pyjamas and went outside, hugging his shoulders against the cold night air. His bare feet cringed as he walked them across the cold grass towards the shed where the train set lived.

He had expected the heavy menacing drone of many planes passing overhead. That was what he wanted to see. But instead there was a different sound – a single plane somewhere in the darkness, and coming closer.

When the searchlights were switched on, Edward stood transfixed. He knew nothing about searchlights. He had never seen them, never read about them; and no one had ever told him about them. The sight of these superhuman shafts of light filled him with amazement and terror. He had often shone a torch-beam into the darkness and enjoyed the firm weapon-like feel of it. But these lights went all the way up to the clouds! If they had been shining down instead of up, you would have thought God was looking down from heaven, searching out sinners.

As he stared, he became aware that the sound of the plane was rapidly becoming louder. He couldn't see it in the darkness, but he was certain that it was losing height and coming directly for him. At that moment there was a break in the clouds and the moon shone out, bright and clear. Edward could see the plane clearly, much closer now, flying heavily over the trees of Barrett's Wood.

He turned and ran, totally convinced that it was coming for him. There could be no doubt. Why else would an enemy aircraft come all this way and then fly low over his house?

At the door stood his grandmother, in nightdress and dressing gown. Edward tore up the garden and into her open arms.

'It's coming for me!' he shouted at her.

'I doubt it,' she said. She turned him round so that they could both look out and up above the back garden. The moonlight had been switched off again, but they could just see the plane as it ascended and banked steeply.

'He'll be safe once he's hidden in the clouds,' Mrs Barrett said.

Edward twisted round his head and stared up at her. *That* was forbidden too! Surely his grandmother was not on the enemy's side? 'He's a *German*!' he said to her.

'Yes, he is. But, for all that, I hope he gets back home safely.'

Robertson Creake, as he paced up and down, felt his right foot kick against something soft on the ground. He recoiled. A dead animal? He hated dead animals.

He risked a quick flash of his torch onto the ground. Something woollen lay at his feet, crumpled. He stooped, picked up the object and peered at it in his torchlight. He held it away from his face, as if it stank.

It was a woollen balaclava, khaki.

He froze in panic. He knew – he absolutely *knew*! – it had not been there that afternoon. Who had dropped it

149

there? Was someone still watching from the darkness of the trees? Was it a trap? He was about to commit the next crucial act in his great crime – and someone might be quietly watching him.

I will be found out, he thought in anguish. He would be hanged, or shot by a firing squad – *without* having carried out his great deed of wickedness. This was unbearable.

The German pilot knew that the universe supported Adolf Hitler and the Third Reich. He took it for granted. So, when moonlight had suddenly broken free and lit up the exact area of land that he needed to see, he was not surprised. That was the kind of luck German airmen were entitled to.

He'd spotted the wood straightaway. Then, as he concentrated, a light flashed on and off, repeatedly. It was tiny, down there in the trees. But perfectly clear. And once he had seen the light, he could also make out that there was a circular space in the middle of the wood, beside a house. In the space was a black-and-white target. It was minute viewed from this height, but clearly visible in the miraculous Nazi moonlight.

The pilot smiled at the exactness of his navigation and quickly memorised the landscape below him.

As he began a gentle descent, the moonlight was extinguished. But it didn't matter now; he had the target clear in his mind's eye. And the torchlight was still flashing. A few moments later he gave the necessary order.

A number of things that might have happened did not.

If Adam had stayed in Barrett's Wood a little longer, he would probably have seen the parachute fall. If Edward had stayed in his garden only a few moments more, he would certainly have seen it. And Joe – of all of them the most likely to work out why a parachute was falling towards Robertson Creake's backyard – hadn't even woken up.

Later, on another occasion, a number of things that might happen, *did* – fortunately.

It works out like that sometimes.

The air-raid wardens on the top of the church tower were puzzled. In the darkness they had not been able to see the aircraft. But they could tell from the sound it made that it had arrived at a very great altitude and had then dropped through the clouds and flown low. Over near Camel Farm, they thought, or Barrett's Wood, perhaps. But why would it do that?

And why was there only one?

Then it had gained height again, and now the sound of its engine was growing faint as it headed for home, flying east.

The moon was on the side of the enemy that night. Or perhaps it was the clouds. This ensured that almost total darkness was restored just as the parachute fell.

So none of the wardens saw the soft pale whisper of movement in the darkness above Barrett's Wood as it dropped silently into the trees, almost into the waiting arms of Robertson Creake.

'Some lost pilot, I s'pose.'

'That's happened before, y'know. Exactly the same!'

The distant searchlights were switched off and they could no longer hear the Dornier. Not even faintly.

There was a field telephone from the top of the tower to the Great Deeping police station, where the siren had been put up in the first War, to warn against Zeppelins. One of the wardens turned the handle of the phone and held the receiver to his ear.

After a few seconds, he said, 'I reckon you can sound the all-clear, mate! That's gone now. There was only one of 'em anyway!'

Almost immediately, the sound of the all-clear filled the night – not the dismal up-and-down whooping of the warning, but a firm wailing on a single note. Not much more cheerful, in fact, but at least it signalled that the immediate danger was over.

Robertson Creake heard the all-clear sounding. He had managed to set aside his fear and decided that if anyone was watching him from the shelter of the trees, he would have to chance it. He couldn't leave those birds unattended.

He found them easily enough. The drop had been

remarkably accurate. The parachute had caught in the lower branches of an oak tree, just outside the bare ring of his backyard. The pannier hung at head height.

He spoke softly to the birds as he detached the pannier from the harness. Within a couple of minutes he was inside his pigeon loft, with the door firmly closed behind him. Then he opened the pannier and lifted out the birds. They fluttered irritably, wanting none of this. It was dark, they should not have to be disturbed.

But they were safe. 'Two of you will be going home tomorrow,' Mr Creake said to them.

He checked their food and water, shut the loft door securely and went back to retrieve the parachute. With a few good pulls he managed to haul it down to the ground. He bundled it up loosely. He would dispose of it properly later.

No watcher had come leaping out of the darkness to arrest him. There had been no sudden burst of machine-gun fire from the trees. Robertson Creake had an idea. A rook had probably tried to use the balaclava for nest building – but it had proved too heavy and the bird had dropped it.

Yes, that's what must have happened.

'I've bin in trouble,' Joe said to the girls.

They had cycled to meet him. In the lane near his farm, they had passed Sergeant Bly from the local police station. They knew him well and had greeted him cheerfully.

He had answered them, but disapprovingly, they thought.

'What sort of trouble?' They came to a standstill and stood astride their bikes in the bright sunlight.

'Local bobby, he's bin and had a go at my dad. For letting me take the tractor into the town with you lot in the trailer.'

'I *knew* that was against the law,' Abigail said.

'Using rationed petrol, that's what he was on about. "You get your fuel coupons for farming," he kept saying. "Not to go jaunting through the town on joy rides!" He didn't half go on about it! More like a schoolteacher than a copper.'

'What did your dad say?'

'He just said he was sorry and he'd make sure I didn't do it again.'

'But did he, your dad . . . ?'

They knew that in some families the anger of fathers could be violent. But Joe grinned and shook his head. 'No, he was all right about it.'

'Did you hear the sirens in the night?' Abigail asked him.

Joe shook his head. 'They don't bother me,' he said.

The girls turned their bikes around and the three of them made their way along the lane, towards young Edward's house.

There, a surprise awaited them. They found Edward and his grandmother sitting side by side on the back doorstep, listening to the wireless that stood on the kitchen window. They might have been two children sitting together, sharing secrets. The voice from the wireless was telling them about the bombing in Birmingham. 'Considerable damage in the shopping centre . . . Midland Arcade a ruin . . . Delayed-action bombs . . . But the bombers had missed the town hall and the hospitals.'

On the step beside them was a parcel. The newcomers eyed it with interest. Greaseproof paper, squared and tied with string. Sandwiches this time then, not another meat pie. Still, it was a large parcel and that was what mattered. It was all very well Adam deciding that he wanted to live in hiding; but it was proving difficult to provide him with food. He was permanently hungry.

So they had planned another picnic – and Molly was already thinking one day ahead. What would Adam have to eat on Friday? So she asked Mrs Barrett if they could have yet another picnic the next day as well. *After dark*, she thought, *with the window blacked out, candles lit and the fire burning*. The thought of it gave her goosepimples of pleasure.

'It's Good Friday tomorrow,' Mrs Barrett said.

That silenced Molly for a moment. She had been ready for the usual grown-up objections (Why so many picnics all of a sudden? It makes extra work! You're hardly ever at home these days!). She had answers for all of them, but she had forgotten the next day was Good Friday. 'Well,' she said, 'we will spend the morning and afternoon being . . .' She couldn't finish her sentence. She didn't want to say *holy*, that didn't sound quite what she meant. Nor did *religious*.

'Being what?' Mrs Barrett said, eyes glinting.

Joe stood by with an unreadable expression on his face. He kept clear of churches as far as possible, and to him there was nothing special about Good Friday. The farm animals still had to be fed, just as they did every day.

Molly carefully remade her sentence. 'We will spend the rest of Good Friday properly,' she said.

Mrs Barrett stood up, and opened her Bible. They watched, knowing the procedure now.

Up went her head, up went her right hand, and down came the pointing forefinger. '*And he took butter, and milk, and the calf which he had dressed, and set it before them*,' she said. 'From *Genesis*.'

Beef sandwiches then, Molly thought to herself. *And a bottle of milk.*

'Butter?' Edward said, with mischief in his voice.

'Margarine,' Mrs Barrett said firmly. 'There's a War on.'

Abigail wasn't listening. She was looking intently at the open Bible in Mrs Barrett's hand. And then she said, 'Mrs Barrett, when will Edward be allowed to play with his dad's train set?'

Edward looked appalled. Who could tell what such an explosive question might lead to?

But his grandmother didn't seem to be troubled. 'Whenever he likes,' she said. 'It's *not* his father's train set. It's *his*! It belongs to Edward.'

Nobody said a word. They were silenced absolutely.

'Edward,' she said, 'didn't you know? Your father was cleaning the train set and getting it ready for *you*. It's *yours*!'

Edward was a cautious boy. He looked anxiously up at Joe, holding back his joy in case there was some kind of misunderstanding. It *couldn't* be true!

'I thought you knew, child,' the old lady said. 'I thought . . . But I should have told you, and I'm sorry. I reproach myself.'

Edward stared in disbelief. His grandmother *never* said sorry for anything (except perhaps to God). *Yet how could he have known*, he thought, *unless she told him? How did people get to know things unless they were told?*

'Your father loved that train set – so much it was almost sinful. *His* father had bought it for him, you see. When he knew he was going away, he cleaned it, and mended it, and bought a new engine from a shop in London. So that you could have it to play with. If he didn't come back.'

Old Mrs Barrett's voice had deepened, cracked almost, like the voice of a man. But it quickly recovered its usual tone, sharp, firmly in control. 'Then he went off to Spain to smite his foe,' she added.

Abigail couldn't resist it. 'And got smited himself,' she whispered.

'*Smitten*,' Mrs Barrett said sharply. 'You might as well get the word right. It's *smitten*.'

I thought she was supposed to be deaf, Molly thought crossly.

Mrs Barrett went inside and Edward went to get his bike. And when the other three were left alone, Abigail said in an intense whisper, 'Listen! That Bible! She said that quotation came from *Genesis*.'

'So what?'

'The book of *Genesis* is the *first* one in the Bible!'

They stared at her, not comprehending.

'When she opened the Bible, it opened *in the middle*! I noticed. That wasn't *Genesis*. She wasn't reading those words at all!'

They took this in, slowly. The old lady was a fraud, it seemed to mean. Then it seemed to suggest that she was a genius who knew the entire Bible by heart. They were sure this was impossible – but the more they thought about it the more the possible meanings became tangled.

Round the back of the house, Edward stood for a moment, gripping the handle bars of his bike so tightly that his knuckles turned white, telling himself that the train set was really his. He'd read about magic in stories, but now he knew what real magic was. The whole world – the whole universe! – had been transformed! *Everything* was different now, cast in a new and exciting brightness. Because the beloved train set was really his.

A lost memory came suddenly back to him. They do that sometimes, coming from nowhere, prompted by something unnoticed. And there's no way of knowing how true they are. It was a memory of himself, very small, standing on a bright sunlit beach, with his bare feet washed by the tiny waves at the edge of the sea; he was holding someone's hand, someone big.

They had gone there by train. He didn't know how he knew that, but he was sure of it.

That morning when Robertson Creake woke up he found tears on his face. A terrible sadness seemed to have taken possession of him during the night.

He wiped the tears away angrily – but he couldn't shake off the feeling. He washed, shaved, dressed, but all the time he kept wanting to cry. It was ridiculous, he told himself. And shameful. He recovered himself a little while he prepared and ate his breakfast but, afterwards, something happened that brought it back.

He saw his father.

His old dad had died ten years ago – but there he was, just for a second, looking sadly and severely at him. Robertson Creake had walked towards the landing window and seen his dead father approaching him there.

He realised in an instant that it was his own reflection in the glass. But for a moment it had *not* been a reflection, it had been his father. A visitation of the dead. The same slight sideways stoop, the same angle of the head, the hair falling over the brow in precisely the same way. And the same look in the eye.

Am I my father? he thought shakily.

He sat at the breakfast table and wrote on a tiny square of thin paper: *Monday 14th April Great Deeping 20.45.* Then he wrote it again on a second piece of paper, folded them both up, fitted them inside two small metal canisters, and went outside.

I must shake off this feeling, he said to himself angrily. *There is a job to be done! No good feeling bad about it.* But the alternative – of *not* blowing up practically the whole town – was very appealing, almost seductive. It was his duty to resist the temptation.

He went inside his pigeon loft and spoke softly to the birds. *I suppose they only understand German*, he thought to himself. *Or were they French pigeons? Or Dutch?* He didn't know.

They were fed and watered, and ready for the toss.

The concentration required to attach the tiny canisters to the pigeons steadied his nerves. Then the birds were released, one at a time, with an interval of a few minutes.

One pigeon circled uncertainly above Barrett's Wood until the second joined it. Then they set off immediately in an easterly direction, one slightly behind the other. In only a few hours, they would arrive at the German airfield. Mr Creake imagined strong military hands unfolding his messages, orders in sharp German, senior officers making decisions, a bomber pilot summoned for a briefing.

He felt sorry for the third pigeon, left alone in the pigeon loft, absolutely silent. But those were his instructions – send two birds in case one doesn't make it, and always keep one in reserve.

As he watched the two birds growing smaller in the bright morning sky, he heard the church clock striking nine. That filled him with sadness again. But the church was more than a mile from the railway and would, probably, survive. Like his own house.

As he went back indoors, another fit of weeping came over him. Wetness streamed from his eyes, his nose; he felt as if he was underwater and had just managed to lift his head above the surface. He tottered, half-drowning, gasping, sobbing without control, into his kitchen, where he sat at the table, resting his unhappy head on his arms.

But he steadied himself eventually, and sat up straight, looking at his hands. Big they were. He knew every contour, every line, every vein, the planes and curves of every fingernail. They, too, were exactly like his father's.

Mulberries were Molly's business that afternoon. And the place to go was the public library.

The library at Great Deeping was a small brick building in Globe Street. Over the arched door was the date 1868. The same year, Molly remembered, that the school had been built.

The library was open one day a week and staffed by volunteers. On duty that afternoon was Mrs Weathergreen.

The gardening section consisted of about twenty books on one of the bottom shelves. On bare knees Molly knelt on the wooden floorboards and hunted through the books. Luckily, her knees were hardened to this kind of discomfort. There was a good deal of information on how to prune roses, and how to grow bigger onions, but nothing on mulberries. Nothing at all.

Molly had a way of showing frustration. After about half an hour of fruitless searching, her body hunched up and her face took on a mulish look. Mrs Weathergreen knew the signs – she had known Molly since she was a baby. So she went over and offered help.

'I can't find anything about mulberry trees.'

Mrs Weathergreen seemed to know the contents of every book in the library. 'Try this,' she said.

It was an old book called *Tree Cultivation for the Gentlemen of Country Estates* and Molly, still kneeling, quickly found a two-page section on mulberry trees.

There was a difficulty. She wanted to borrow the book and take it to Adam, but it was on one of the reference shelves, where all the books had small round stickers on their spines. This meant that you couldn't borrow them. But the book on tree cultivation had lost its sticker – you could see the faintly discoloured patch on its spine where the sticker had once been.

Molly took the book to the desk, hopefully.

'Now,' said Mrs Weathergreen, 'because I'm the librarian today, I can decide to let you borrow this book. That would be legal. Whereas, if *you* were to pretend you didn't know that it is a reference book, *that* would not be legal. Not *very* illegal, of course. Just a tiny tiny dishonesty.'

Molly felt her face flush. *Is she a mind-reader?* she wondered.

'Molly, I've seen you in the town with little Edward Barrett. Is that why you're interested in mulberry trees?' Mrs Weathergreen never wasted words. Always straight to the point.

Molly nodded. She couldn't speak because she was being two people at that moment. One of them knew that Mrs Weathergreen was the kindest person in Great Deeping. The other was thinking crossly: *Can't I do anything without everyone knowing about it?*

'Come with me,' Mrs Weathergreen said.

She led Molly into a little office at the back of the library.

'My late husband was interested in local history,' she said. 'And one of the things he found out about was the Barrett family and their mulberry trees. *And* the buried sword. And he wrote it all down.'

From a locked drawer she took a thick bundle of typed pages, yellowing a little at the edges. And from this she selected a section entitled *The Mulberry Ring*.

'I can't let you borrow this, I'm afraid. This is the only copy, and I couldn't bear it if it got damaged. But you can memorise the main points. Or make some notes.'

Molly did better than that. She copied it out, all six pages of it. As she worked, the two Mollys went away and a third one took over. This one was a famous expert, studying a rare and valuable ancient document in a university library. Not in Cambridge – Cambridge was where Great Deeping people went on shopping trips. But Oxford, perhaps. Or Cairo. Or Peking. Molly's imagination knew no bounds.

As she passed through the library on her way out, she went over to the desk to say thank you to Mrs Weathergreen.

'Are you interested in history, Molly?' the old lady asked.

Molly nodded. Thoughtfully, because she was only just beginning to realise she was.

'I too find the past fascinating,' Mrs Weathergreen said.

But it's not really *past*, Molly thought. *It's still here, in a way.*

Tucked under her arm was *Tree Cultivation for the Gentlemen of Country Estates*, and in her coat pocket was her copy of the late Mr Weathergreen's account of the Barrett family and their mulberry trees.

Molly went out of the library, under the arch with 1868 carved on it.

When Robertson Creake reported for work that afternoon and went into the stationmaster's office, each man was seriously startled by the other.

Mr Creake was surprised. The stationmaster was seated at his desk, with a pen in one hand, a ruler in the other, and the forbidden ledger open in front of him. The stationmaster was taken aback by the expression of outrage on the porter's face – which he misinterpreted as suspicion and disapproval.

He hastened to explain. 'Don't look at me like that, Creakey! I'm not putting anything new *into* the book. I'm crossing something *out*.'

'Crossing what out?'

The stationmaster – who couldn't endure the thought that his railway colleague (whom he'd known for years) might suspect him of treasonable conduct – looked about him in case there were spies listening. 'That ammunition train,' he said in a lowered voice. 'They've cancelled it. It isn't coming on Monday. Thought it was too risky, I s'pose.'

'When *is* it coming then?'

The stationmaster had ruled a line through the entry in the book. He blotted the ink dry, closed the book, and stood it up on end beside the others.

'Dunno. Some other time in the next few days, I expect. Creakey! Are you all right? You look terrible! Do you feel ill?'

Robertson Creake nodded. He thought he was going to pass out.

'I think you'd better go back home, old chap, and lie down for a few hours. Go on! Off you go! I can manage here for a bit. My god, you do look poorly!'

Mr Creake was too shaken to cycle. Instead, he walked his bike back along the path. As he went, he composed in his head the message which the third pigeon would have to carry. *Monday 14th April Great Deeping 20.45 – this train now cancelled.*

But the ammo train would be sent some other day. What worried Creakey was how he was going to get the information to his German friends. Would they supply him with another batch of birds? Nothing had been arranged.

When it was all done and the third bird was on its way, he crouched down beside his unoccupied pigeon loft and was sick onto the grass.

'Now pay attention,' said Miss Murfitt to the whole school. 'Today we have a famous visitor. She is Professor Molly Barnes and she is an expert about mulberry trees. She is going to tell us all about them.'

A miniature school assembly was taking place in the cabin inside Paradise Barn. There were only three pupils in the school and they sat up straight on the camp bed – polite, excited, and eager to learn. All boys.

'Edward Barrett! Stop wriggling!'

'He's got ants in his pants, Miss.' This suggestion came from Joe Temper.

'Well, if he keeps fidgeting, I shall take his trousers off and have a look,' said the headmistress. She glared at Edward.

Edward wasn't completely sure she was pretending. He rubbed his chin uneasily.

'Carry on, Professor.'

'How can I carry on? I haven't started,' the professor said.

'Well, start now!'

The professor cleared her throat. 'When King James the First was king, he got very interested in silkworms.'

'Why?' This was a question from Adam Swales.

'He *liked* silk!' said the famous professor, making it up. 'Anyway, he encouraged people all over the country to plant mulberries because silkworms live on mulberry leaves. Edward's ancestor at that time had a huge garden and he planted lots of mulberry trees.'

'How many?'

'Thirty-two.' She could see they were impressed by such exact knowledge.

'He planted them in a circle.'

'Did he plant them himself?'

Professor Molly refused to be put off. 'I expect he had a gardener,' she said. 'To dig the holes. Anyway, the trees grew very well and they were called the Mulberry Ring.'

'What about the silkworms?'

'There weren't any. There are two kinds of mulberry tree – and most people had planted the wrong kind. But by the time they found out, the trees had grown big. People liked them . . .'

Edward put his hand up, blushed, and put it down again.

'Years later, the trees were cut down. All except one – and that one is still there. But it's not part of the Mulberry Ring. It's growing just outside it. No one knows why it's there. It's a mystery.'

Edward put up his hand again. This time, he got his question out. 'Is that why Mr Creake's yard is round?' he asked.

Professor Barnes said yes, and Miss Murfitt said Edward could have a gold star for cleverness.

'Years and years later, one of the Barretts rented out most of the land, including the stables and what was left of the Mulberry Ring.'

'That's where Creakey lives,' Joe said. 'In one of the stables.'

Joe was awarded a gold star too. 'That makes a change,' he said cheerfully.

'I know some more things about mulberry trees. First, their roots bleed if you cut them.'

'Real blood?' asked the headmistress.

Professor Barnes didn't even bother to answer such a silly question. She looked witheringly down her nose at Miss Murfitt and continued.

'Mulberry branches are very brittle and break off easily. The way to propagate a mulberry tree is . . .'

'Proper *what*?' Joe said.

'*Propagate* them. You take a long branch – about five or six feet – and push it into the ground. It's called a stock. After a few months, the stock grows roots and grows into a tree.'

There was silence as the class took this in. The consciousness of one of the pupils was suddenly flooded by a different geography – hillsides, rain, the sun misting through clouds, a vegetable garden, damp earthy smells. The entire Welsh character of the place and the moment was as real as if it had been all around him, like light. And, with it, the voice of his uncle.

With his mind full of roots and soft earth, Adam's thoughts turned again to Edward's treasure. 'They wouldn't have buried the sword under the mulberry trees,' he said.

'Why not?'

'Because of the roots. It's hard to dig through the roots of a tree.'

'Especially if they bleed,' said the professor.

The headmistress intervened. 'Have you any more interesting facts about mulberry trees?' she asked the professor.

'Yes. People collect the berries by spreading sheets under the tree. When they have enough, they gather them up and make jam.'

'What kind of jam?'

'*Mulberry* jam of course!'

Then Edward put up his hand again.

In this school, he was almost an infant, in a class of his own. He was quite clever at being the infants, but the others couldn't tell if this was because he was very good at pretending, or whether he thought this really was a kind of school. You never quite knew with Edward what he did and did not understand.

Miss Murfitt nodded at him.

'I've found out something about mulberry trees,' Edward said. 'And about the buried sword.'

He stuffed his hand into a trouser pocket and pulled out a crumpled sheet of paper. When he opened it the others could see that something had been typed on it.

'This was written,' Edward said, 'in 1754.'

The headmistress wasn't having that. 'Typewriters weren't invented in 1754,' she said.

Edward looked confused. He knew almost everything that could be known about steam locomotives. Yet it had never occurred to him that typewriters had a history too, and that there was once a time when no one had thought of them.

Very slowly, he explained. 'It was written down in 1754. With a pen, I expect. My father typed it out.'

'All right,' Miss Murfitt said. 'You may read it out to the whole school.'

But Edward didn't want to read it out. He was a very good reader in private, but reading in public was a different matter.

So Professor Molly read it. 'It's a letter,' she said.

My dear Niece,

You requested of me that I should inform you of the famous Barrett SWORD, which has been the daily gossip of folk hereabouts for the last one hundred years. I will gratify your wish by discovering to you all that was told to me by my Grandfather.

My Grandfather was the Grandson of Sir James Barrett, who, at the execution of King Charles in 1649, finding himself in some danger from the Officers of the Commonwealth, determined to conceal the whereabouts of the great FAMILY SWORD. He thereupon enclosed the Sword in a wooden Coffer and, accompanied by one John

Buston, Forester, carried the Coffer at Dead of Night into the grounds of the Estate. Here a Pitte was dug by the Forester, the SWORD was laid to rest in it, and the earth thrown back. The place was marked with a large Stocke which Sir James had torne from a Tree.

Sir James purposed to drawe a CHARTE to disclose the whereabouts of the Sword to his Wife, but that night he was informed that he was to be seized by the OFFICERS of the Commonwealth at dawn the next day. The Charte was not made. He found time only for a speedy and solemn Farewell to his Lady and their Small Sonne, before setting out for Ireland, where he died of a Fever.

Thus the whereabouts of the Barrett SWORD has remained a mystery.

Your affectionate Aunt, Maria Barrett

August 10th, 1754

Molly enjoyed reading the letter so much that she read it out again. She liked the words, the historical way it was written. It was a bit like poetry, she thought.

Adam looked puzzled. '*Could* a great long branch stuck in the ground grow into a tree?' he asked. He remembered his uncle's cuttings, which had been no longer than a pencil.

'It happens with willow trees, Miss,' Joe said. (*Had he forgotten he wasn't really at school?* Molly wondered.) 'If you don't believe me, you should go and see Fanny Norman's washing post.'

'What's Fanny Norman's washing post got to do

172

with it?' Abigail demanded in her normal voice, forgetting she was the headmistress.

'When she got married, her old man planted a willow post to fix her clothes line to. Then that started to grow, and now she's got a willow tree in her garden.'

Miss Murfitt remembered who she was. 'Perhaps I'll take us all on a nature walk, to see it,' she said in her best teacherly voice. 'You did very well to find the letter, Edward. It's an important historical document.' She began to applaud and the others joined in. Edward felt that he had never been happier.

Then Joe said to him, 'I reckon you could stop putting ointment on your chin now, young Edward.'

Edward looked up at him, his face radiant with relief and joy. He'd thought he would have to use the ointment for the rest of his life.

Molly took his head in her hands and studied his face. 'Try doing without it for a few days,' she said. 'And see how it goes.'

All of a sudden, they found that they were listening intently. Abigail put a finger to her lips and they stared at each other. Someone had come into the barn and was moving slowly about, downstairs. There was a short silence, and then the sound of somebody climbing heavily up the wooden stairs to the cabin.

Adam scrambled into the cramped shadows under the camp bed – and the others all sat on it. Six bare legs and two trousered legs concealed him, like a lowered portcullis.

Mrs Barrett went out into her back garden and walked down to the shed. The sun had disappeared at dinnertime and the afternoon sky was covered with an unrelenting layer of thick cloud.

In the shed she looked around her with interest. The sight of the train set brought her own son into her mind with a loving and painful vividness. Thoughts of him always brought to mind his death in a faraway war in Spain. She was bitter about that, troubled and angry that she had not been there to hold him, to cradle his head in her arms and tell him that he was safe, even if he wasn't. The same with her husband – if only she could have been there to hold him.

All those faraway deaths.

She felt the familiar weight of her Bible in her apron pocket. This one was her kitchen Bible, much-used, with a thumbed and greasy cover. It reminded her of Abigail Murfitt and the suspicious way she had peered at it. *That young person is no fool*, she thought.

She frowned, thinking about what she did with her Bibles. She knew it was a kind of trickery. But not *deceptive* tricks. They were shortcuts to understanding. They made her feel that she was always in touch with a brightness, a blessing. She saw nothing strange in this. God had spoken to Adam in the Bible, and to Noah and Jacob and Moses. So why not to her?

On an impulse she closed her eyes and with her left

hand opened the Bible at heaven knew what page. No trickery this time. A puff of flour flew from the pages as she disturbed them, and there was a faint smell of onions. Then she pointed and peered at what was there – and her heart almost froze in her body.

There were occasions when there was no trickery at all, when God spoke directly to her with a terrifying clarity – demanding, giving orders, rebuking. In the dusky light of the shed she could just make out the words: *'Beloved, think it not strange concerning the fiery trial which is to try you, as though some strange thing happened unto you.'*

It was no good asking God to speak to you and then disregarding what He said. So Mrs Barrett closed the Bible and left the shed, bracing herself for whatever terrible thing was going to happen.

As soon as his face appeared round the door of the cabin, they knew that the intruder was as scared as they were.

'Lord Almighty,' he gasped. 'It's you lot!'

He stepped into the room and pushed his ARP tin helmet back so that he could wipe his forehead.

Abigail knew her rights. 'We weren't breaking black-out regulations,' she said. 'We haven't lit any lights yet. And anyway, we've got a blind for the window!'

Mr Broadbent looked about him, breathing hard. When he wasn't on ARP duty, he was a builder's merchant. He was a heavy man; his joke with his friends in the town was that since World War One he had carried half a hundredweight of shrapnel in his body. The amount was an exaggeration, but the shrapnel was true; mostly bits of a German field gun that had been blown up in 1918.

'When I heard someone up here, I thought it was that German spy we're supposed to be looking out for. What are you doing up here, anyway?'

'We're allowed,' Abigail said. 'Mr Morton said we could come here whenever we wanted.'

'Ah! Yes. I remember now. So he did.' But he still stood there, feeling that something else ought to be said. 'All right, then,' he said at last. 'I'll leave you to it.'

At the door he turned back. 'Don't forget to black out that window before you light any of them candles!' he said sternly. It was his way of reminding them that they were just untrustworthy children and he was an air-raid warden.

This interruption dampened their spirits and spoiled the afternoon. Adam crawled out from under the camp bed, and Molly went over to the window and glared angrily out at the flat and darkening fields. Joe seemed to know exactly what Edward was feeling. 'Don't you worry about him, young Edward,' he said. '*He* was in the wrong, not us.'

Molly turned to face them. 'I *HATE* THIS BLOODY WAR!' she shouted.

There was a silence. They all stared at her. She stood

there, glaring at them, her fists clenched to her chest and shaking.

Bloody was a very bad word. In Wales it had been different. There, it was gentle and said with a caress in it, Adam remembered, but here, in East Anglia, it was like a cudgel. Boys said it often, usually in secret, to show off to one another. Everyone knew that. Men too. But you could be expelled from school for saying it out loud. And in some families, you might be beaten for saying it.

But Molly! The gentle, law-abiding Molly.

Molly's anger drained away as quickly as it had come, and her body seemed to sag a little. 'I don't care!' she said. She could see that the others were mystified by her sudden passionate outburst. 'There are other things to think about.' She knew that was a feeble reason for hating the War.

Young Edward looked scared. Joe was puzzled. Abigail just said, 'Crikey, Molly!' None of them knew what Molly meant. But *she* knew what she meant. She wanted her old life back, an Easter holiday without having to be frightened by bombs. And spies everywhere. She wanted to live like the Swallows and Amazons – there was no War in *their* lives. Molly knew she couldn't explain all that. They wouldn't understand. The War needn't stop you reading, they would say.

Adam was looking directly at her as if there was a secret understanding between them. But Molly wasn't deceived. She knew that was just as likely to mean that he was sizing her up for a sketch.

Since she'd moved house, Abigail had visited her mum every day. After breakfast on Good Friday she called on her before going to chapel.

Mrs Murfitt sat at the kitchen table, studying the railway schedules. 'Abigail,' she said, 'I want you to stay away from the railway today. *All* day. Understand?'

Abigail looked surprised. 'Why?' She was concentrating on her second breakfast. She *loved* the way her mum made porridge.

'Just do as you're told!' her mum said. 'And the others – keep them away too.'

'Mmmm,' Abigail said, licking clean her spoon.

They walked outside together and stood in the road, by the level-crossing gates. 'Ask no questions and you'll hear no lies.' Mrs Murfitt gave Abigail a shilling for the collection and sent her packing.

The morning sun, brilliant and low in the sky, was behind Abigail, and it sent a long shadow prancing ahead of her as she walked back into the town.

Molly came out of church into a perfect spring morning.

This, she thought longingly, is how Easter should always be! Every year Good Friday felt like Sunday – but not just *any* Sunday. All the shops were shut and the whole town was quiet. It was the Sunday of Sundays.

While she stood by the church porch, half aware of people talking to one another about the service, her eye fell on a gravestone close to the path.

IN LOVING MEMORY OF JOSIAH TEMPER
WHO FELL ASLEEP OCTOBER 1892
REST IN PEACE

Joe's gravestone, Molly thought. *Not a bad place to be, with the rooks nesting above in the elm trees.*

She said goodbye to her mum and set off to meet Abigail. A chilly springtime brightness was reflected from every surface. Birds were busy everywhere and a lark could be heard rising joyously from the field around the cricket pitch. Small white cauliflower clouds moved in slow unison across the perfect blue of the sky, all flat-bottomed and precisely at the same altitude. *How do they know how to do that?* Molly wondered.

She felt an old familiar joy rising in her, an exultation, intense and private. This feeling was entirely secret, probably the only thing in her life that she'd never told Abigail about.

But even on a fine spring morning there was no escaping the War. Four Hurricanes came growling over the town, low, close and intimate, making everyone look upwards. One of the pilots looked down at them and waved. It made many people feel protected and safe, but, to Molly, they were an intrusion, noisy and unwelcome.

As she came into the High Street, two young boys from school raced up to her, excited and wanting to show her something. They were in Edward's class. One of them had a younger sister in tow.

'What is it?' Molly said. 'It looks like the wing mirror from a car.'

'That's all *you* know!' one of them said. 'It's off a Spitfire!'

They raced off, happy with their trophy. The little girl followed dutifully, obliged to tag along and only half understanding what the boys were so excited about.

Molly walked home the long way round, across Fen Common. There was a small cottage where the garden gate opened directly onto the grass. A young woman was in the front garden, leaning over a pram.

Molly felt poetic and friendly, full of spring. 'It's a lovely garden for a baby to be in,' she said wistfully.

The young mother straightened. 'My husband's the one that made it so nice,' she said. 'He can make anything grow.'

Molly remembered what Joe had told them. 'Even washing posts,' she said.

'Oh, you've heard about that! Yes, it's true!' Mrs Norman smiled. 'We hadn't been married long,' she added.

The tree had a straight firm trunk, a little higher than a person, with its side shoots trimmed off. From the top a spread of young yellow-green branches had sprouted into growth. And a washing line.

'He put in that willow post a few days after we were married – and by the time the baby was born that old post had started to turn into a tree!'

Robertson Creake walked into the stationmaster's office to begin his shift.

'You feeling better this morning, Creakey?'

Mr Creake nodded, but it wasn't true. He felt washed out, exhausted, as if he'd fought a battle single-handed. 'Any specials today?' he asked.

The stationmaster shook his head. 'Except,' he said slowly, '*that* one is coming through tonight.'

'You mean . . . ?'

The stationmaster nodded. 'Red ink,' he said.

A strange quietness seemed to fall on Robertson Creake. 'What time?'

'The usual time. Tonight. Don't look so worried! The Jerries won't know the train is coming then. And, even if they do, the RAF will be ready. They won't let no bombers through this time!'

The stationmaster was a very trusting man. And a very foolish one.

Edward was on his knees in his back garden, laying out his entire railway.

He wanted to see how much track there was so that he could hold it all in his mind. There seemed to be yards and yards of it! There were points and sidings. Level crossings and bridges. Even a turntable. Round the entire back garden it went, with a main-line station by the kitchen door and a branch-line that went round the vegetable patch. Everything had been brought out of the shed – except the tunnel, which was too heavy for him.

But he wouldn't be able to run the train in the garden. There were too many humps and hillocks in the grass. Still, it filled his heart with joy. He stood a signal box close to the railway station, and concentrated on making a water-column stand up steadily on the unsatisfactory grass. It was shaped like a gallows, but instead of a rope there was a hose.

'Edward?' His grandmother had come into the back garden and was standing behind him.

He turned, looked, and stared in amazement. She was wearing a Salvation Army uniform. They had been that morning to the service at the Salvation Hall, but he had never seen her in a uniform. He didn't know she had one.

'I've shrunk,' Mrs Barrett said. The skirt came down almost to her ankles and the tunic was baggy.

'I'm going to march with the band tonight,' she said. There was a touch of defiance about her. Mrs Barrett was feeling the need to celebrate Jesus with bracing music and the thump of a drum.

In her hand she carried a silver-coloured trombone, which shone in the sun. Fully extended, it was probably longer than she was herself. She put it to her lips, and – after a few experimental squeaks – produced a beautiful upwards glissando. It faltered a little towards the top end, but her eyes shone as she took a breath. Then again, downwards this time, and flawless.

'You're going to play?'

'Of course! If I don't have an instrument they'll make me carry the collection box.'

'But what will *I* do?'

His grandmother had anticipated this. She had brought out a cardboard box, round, like a hatbox. She laid the trombone carefully down beside a railway footbridge, took the lid off the box, and showed Edward a tambourine. She blew at it to clear away the dust.

'Can you bang this in time with the music?' she said.

Edward thought he could. 'But I haven't got a uniform.'

'Nobody will mind that,' Mrs Barrett said. 'If you like doing it, we'll get you one.'

Edward smiled hesitantly. It occurred to Mrs Barrett that she rarely saw him smile.

Then a doubt occurred to him. 'Will I have to miss the midnight picnic at the barn?'

'Midnight?'

'Well, *late*,' Edward said. 'Not exactly at midnight. After it gets dark.'

'No, you needn't miss that. You can go straight to the

barn after we've finished marching – but they're to bring you back here afterwards, mind. *Not* at midnight!'

Later that day, it came into Robertson Creake's mind that if the trainload of explosives was to be destroyed, he would have to do it himself.

The moment the thought came into his head he felt steadied, and clear. This was what he was *meant* to do. *Of course!* He was a man of *action*. How wrong he'd been to be content with such a contemptible job as releasing pigeons! He should have been a solitary operator, a man of darkness who took on dangerous missions, alone and in secret. Brave, clever and resourceful. And *alone*, always alone.

But how to accomplish it?

His mind raced, working it out. Set fire to one of the trucks – no, *two* to make doubly sure. When they blew up, they would ignite the whole train. And, if the train had stopped at the usual place to take on water, the nearby gasworks would be blown up, too. Massive it would be! The biggest explosion of the War!

Petrol? Yes, of course! But petrol was rationed and he had no coupons for it. On second thoughts, petrol would be no use anyway. It was *too* combustible. It would burn itself up before it had set fire to the truck. You could set fire to dry paper or straw with petrol, but not the thick planks of a railway freight wagon – unless you had time to really soak the wood with it.

Methylated spirit? No, hopeless. Combustible, but far too feeble.

What then? There must be some way . . . *Yes!*

His blowtorch! Only last summer he'd used it to burn off the old paint before redecorating his window frames and doors. Two or three times he'd scorched the wood by mistake. And once he'd almost set the front door alight. That was the way! A blowtorch was tricky to get going, but he was good at it.

It used paraffin – and he had plenty of that. Everybody kept paraffin. Every garden shed in Great Deeping had some paraffin in it. (All those sheds would blow up too! Hundreds of small explosions inside one huge one.)

Those other voices – those doubting troubled voices in his head – were for once silent. *This* was his planning voice, his man-of-action voice.

Now, the sequence of events. The train would stop just short of the station to take on water. It always did. The water-column was only a few yards from the huge gas holder.

Perfect! He would crawl under and apply the blowtorch to the bottom of one of the trucks. But how to do it without being seen? There would be three people who would certainly see him. They wouldn't sit quietly while he set fire to their train.

One at a time. The fireman would climb to the top of the tender, to guide the water-hose. He would have to be dealt with. Then there was the driver – he wouldn't wait motionless in the cab; he would get out to see why there was a delay. And then there was old Nobby Clark in his signal box nearby. He would have to be silenced too. Three men. No, *four!* – there would be the guard in his van at the back of the train.

How could he put all these men out of action long enough for him to set fire to two of the trucks?

Chloroform! Of course!

Yes, a wad of chloroform, held firmly over the victim's face. He still had a bottle of the stuff from the days when he'd worked on the docks. Guaranteed to make anyone unconscious. But wait a minute! It took several seconds to work, almost a minute sometimes. It would knock an old man out immediately, but a young person could struggle long enough to get away or fight back. The fireman on the train would be a young man; firemen always were. The driver, too, would probably be fit and strong.

Nobby Clark was an old man. The chloroform would work on him easily. But the others would have to be knocked out first, *then* chloroformed. Then tied up and gagged.

But the guard at the back of the train – what about him? Just have to hope that he wouldn't come and investigate. He probably wouldn't, not until the train had been delayed for ten or fifteen minutes. And by then it would be too late. He wouldn't see much from his guard's van; these trains were a quarter of a mile long.

Paraffin for the blowtorch. Chloroform, and cloth pads to put it on. Rope and rags for gagging and tying.

One of Robertson Creake's many voices said to him: *What a remarkable person you must be. To have worked all that out in a matter of minutes. Inspired, but also methodical.*

Afterwards, should he run home, or use his bike? He knew he could run faster than he could cycle, but only for a short distance. His limp slowed him down. No, better to rely on his bike. He could be back at his house, a mile away from the main line, before the train went up.

He stalked off to get his garden spade, found it, and took it outside to practise aiming it at an imagined head. He would have only one chance. He could not afford to miss. He found a large turnip, wedged it into a tree at head height, and smashed it with a single slanting, over-the-shoulder blow.

The spade was an old one and it brought to mind his father. His man-of-action voice had nothing to say about that. It had gone quiet, leaving him bereft and troubled.

As Molly and Abigail were crossing the field on their way to the barn, the Salvation Army band could be heard in the distance, marching through the town. They knew exactly where it was because it always took the same route, every Sunday. And on Good Fridays. It was making its way along King George Street, back towards the Salvation Hall.

Then it fell silent, and they knew it was marching past Abigail's chapel. The band always fell silent as it passed, as a sign of respect. Nothing would be audible there but the sound of shoes softly rustling on the road and a quiet tapping on a side drum to keep them in step. Then, when they were well past the chapel, there was a dramatic double beat on the big bass drum, and the band struck up joyously – *Onward Christian Soldiers!*

The sound of the distant music gusted faintly across the darkening fields.

Molly shivered. Darkness was falling early and thick heavy clouds were being driven by a cold wind. Walking over the uneven paths was difficult because she was carrying in front of her chest a tray loaded with food for the picnic. Beside her, Abigail was struggling with a bucket of coal. They had swapped loads, twice.

When they reached the door of the barn, Molly stopped and looked back across the fields. She could see Joe, on his bike, cycling along the riverbank, an unhurried silhouette against the darkening sky. He swooped down the bank, crossed a narrow wooden plank-bridge, and set off along a different footpath towards them. The Salvation Army band had stopped playing. Everywhere was quiet. In the murky distance, she saw young Edward coming from the town, trying to run with a large basket bouncing against his leg.

He's excited about the picnic, Molly thought. When he saw Joe approaching from a different direction, Edward slowed to a walk. Not excited after all – scared of the dark perhaps, but feeling all right now he'd seen Joe.

The picnic almost went badly. Adam had shuttered the window and lit the fire. He was contentedly setting a match to the candles when he heard the others crossing the floor of the barn and climbing the stairs. But the newcomers were thoroughly fed up – even Molly. They were tired of having to supply food every day; and they were running out of plausible reasons for having so many meals in the barn.

Abigail crashed her bucket down by the fire and turned to face Adam with her arms firmly folded, ready to confront him.

'I've decided to come home tomorrow,' Adam said calmly. 'I'll arrive at the station when the *Fenman* comes in. You can meet me if you like.'

That took the wind out of Abigail's sails. 'About time, Adam Swales!' she said.

Another of Adam's impulses, Molly thought. *Or perhaps he was just hungry.* She saw that his little brown suitcase had been taken out from under the bed. 'You could come home tonight,' she said.

'There's something I want to do first.'

'More prowling about in the dark?' Abigail asked him.

'In a way,' Adam said. He wouldn't say anything else. Adam rarely explained.

Everything was all right after that. Pure delight, in fact, as everyone became companionable and good-humoured. Molly got into her favourite position on the bed, with her knees up and her back against the wooden wall. Inwardly, she was hugging herself with happiness as they all tucked into the first course. Thick bread and dripping, greasy and rich, and deeply satisfying.

She watched young Edward's chin. His upper lip did not once creep out to lick it, and there was no ointment on it – only a healthy smear of dripping, which he wiped away with the back of his hand like any normal person.

That was Joe's doing, she thought affectionately. *In just a few days, he had cured young Edward. Made him normal and set him right.*

Afterwards, they all pored over Adam's current sketchbook. There were hundreds of incomplete drawings, all done in pencil or charcoal. An elbow leaning on a table; a teapot spout; sunlight falling onto wooden floorboards; the turn of a neck or the bend of a wrist.

But mostly the pages were full of tiny images, broken off and unfinished. 'Why don't you do *proper* pictures?' Abigail asked him. But Adam just shrugged and looked shifty.

'What makes you decide to draw a particular thing?' Molly had once said to him. 'This, for example.' She'd pointed to a pencil drawing of a shopping basket with a bunch of spring onions in it.

'I just wanted to,' he said. It had never occurred to him that there was any thinking involved in it. 'It's just random.'

But Molly could see that it wasn't always random. The sketchbook he'd been using when the blitz started was full of pictures of things collapsing, falling to bits or flying into the air. Well, she thought, that was understandable.

His current sketchbook had sketches of things growing – twigs just bursting into bud, a newly planted young tree being watered, a garden spade pushed into the ground and left there. And lots of underground sketches of roots wrapping themselves around buried stones and rocks.

Why? Molly wondered.

She tried to explain her theory to him – how his mind arranged his picture-thoughts into clusters. Adam was impressed; she must be very clever, he thought, to know what went on in his mind. It had never occurred to him to be interested in his mind at all. His mind was just him.

Still, he liked it when Molly told him about himself.

The late-night picnic came to an end at last and they reluctantly gathered up coats and scarves. Adam went with them down into the barn and as far as the big outer door. As they crossed the huge shadowy space, Adam said quietly to Molly, 'I know where Edward's sword is buried.'

In the total darkness, they were nudging each other, holding each other's coatsleeves, feeling their way. 'Are you going to tell him?'

Anybody else, Adam thought, *would have said, 'Where is it? Tell me!'* But not Molly. He liked that. 'Tomorrow,' he said. 'There's one thing I need to check first.'

'Tonight?'

In spite of the darkness, she knew he was nodding his head. 'Don't say anything to him yet.'

To be companionable, Molly and Abigail planned to go with Joe as far as Edward's house. Then they would return by themselves. They had decided to take Edward home by going along Green Lane and through the station. Joe said it was quicker – but on their way back the two girls intended to come through the streets.

Alone in the barn, Adam went back upstairs, blew out the candles, poked as much of the fire through as he could, and put on his coat. A few minutes later, he set off into the dark.

⁂

Nobby Clark, sitting in his old wooden armchair in the signal box, thought he heard a noise.

Someone calling his name?

He strained his ears, heard it again, and got slowly to his feet. He opened the door and stood at the top of the wooden steps, peering into the dark.

There it was again!

He set off slowly down the steps, grumbling inwardly. Just as he reached the bottom, he heard a movement behind him, in the shadows. A strong arm was clamped around his neck from behind and he was pulled violently backwards. Before he had time to react, a pad was forced over his face, and he was breathing in some thick foul substance. He was conscious of being dragged down and under the steps of the signal box. *Is this it?* he wondered briefly. The last thing he heard was his own heartbeat, throbbing desperately. Then he became unconscious.

The driver of the freight train leaned on the narrow rail of his cab as the locomotive hissed quietly in the dark. He too heard someone calling him, trying to attract his attention. He crossed to the other side of the cab, looked down, could see nothing. 'Come here!' He was sure he heard those words with perfect clarity. He hesitated, turned round, and reversed himself carefully down the steps. His boots felt for a steady grip on the loose clinker by the track. And, as they did so, something cracked him on the back of the head, like an explosion.

He had no time for last-minute thoughts. He was instantly unconscious.

The young fireman was the most difficult. He was never still, moving all the time – from the cab to the water-column, back to the tender with the end of the hose, up the side of the tender. Never still for an instant. He was eventually dealt with, but it was messy – his ankle grabbed as he climbed, an untidy fall, his head pushed violently against the metal side of the tender. But it dazed the young man long enough for the suffocating wad to be forced over his mouth and nose.

Then he was tied up and gagged, like the other two.

After that, if there had been anyone there to watch, they would have seen the fierce light of a blowtorch weirdly illuminating the face of Robertson Creake as he crouched down and applied the flames to the underside and corner of the wagon nearest to him, the front one.

The wooden plank was singed almost immediately;

then it began to smoke, flaking and cracking into blackened squares, crisp and ugly. A small flame flickered into life. In the great darkness there was this single dazzling sphere of burning concentrated malevolence.

Robertson Creake was too preoccupied to notice that he had crossed a line, stepped beyond human understanding. He was irretrievably lost.

The four children lowered their voices when they reached Green Lane, like trespassers. Perhaps it was because of the goods train that stood motionless, facing north on the down-line beside them, intensifying the darkness. And not a sound anywhere; the whole town blacked out and silent.

Abruptly Abigail stopped in her tracks. In the darkness she turned pale and gasped.

'What's up?'

'My mum! I've just remembered! She said we weren't to go anywhere near the railway today!'

'Why not?'

'She didn't say.' Abigail was distraught, scared by her forgetfulness.

They slowed down and huddled together, sharing questions. Why had Mrs Murfitt warned Abigail? Was this the ammunition train? Molly shivered. They were standing not far from where she had been walking when the German dive-bomber had attacked.

The silent freight wagons towered beside them in the darkness, looming like a cliff, and stretching almost the entire length of Green Lane, from the gasworks to the crossing.

'Look!'

The two front trucks were on fire. They began to run towards them. The flames were coming from underneath and curling up the outer sides. Smoke was pouring upwards into the sky. Everything else was still and silent, as if the population of the whole world had crept soundlessly away and left them alone with this mysterious danger.

Questions crowded into their heads. Where was the driver? Why was no one putting out the fire? Would there be time for them to get help before the whole lot blew up?

They suddenly started talking fast, interrupting and overriding each other, making suggestions, offering solutions, defining difficulties. Out of this confusion of voices one thing became clear – there wouldn't be enough time for the nearest fire engine to get here, from Littleport. Nor the one from Downham Market. The flames were spreading too rapidly, embracing the two wagons.

Joe ran forward and climbed up the side of the locomotive to peer inside the cab. 'There's no driver!' he shouted to the others. He jumped down and began to run back – but he stopped abruptly and bent to peer beside the tender.

'There's someone here!' The others hurried to look. The young fireman was lying motionless close to the wheels of the tender.

'Is he dead?'

But Joe didn't know. 'We've got to put this fire out,' he said quietly. 'Before the whole lot blows up.'

'Why don't we just run back and tell Abigail's mum? She'll know what to do.'

'She's not there!' Abigail wailed. 'There's a gap in the schedule after this freight train – she said she was going into town to have supper with Mrs Weathergreen.'

'The man in the signal box?' Molly suggested.

It was the sensible thing to do, but Abigail knew it was no good. If Nobby Clark had not already come down to investigate, it was because something had happened to him too.

So there it was then. No one else was going to deal with this. It was up to them.

Quietly, Adam walked through the darkened streets. No one knew he was there; he was unknown and unseen.

Some cats howled in a distant garden. There was a ferocious hissing, some scrabbling, and then silence.

The door of the King George pub opened and three elderly men came quietly out, calling goodnight to the others inside. Someone laughed. Adam slipped into the shadows, pressing himself against a house front until they had passed. From behind the shuttered windows, only a few feet from him, a wireless was murmuring quietly.

When he came to the edge of the town, he braced himself. The point where the houses came to an end and the country began was where alien territory started. The emptiness of field and sky made him feel unsettled, even more watchful than usual.

Nevertheless, he went on. There was a job he wanted to do, something he had to check.

Along the lane into the wood, and across the old railway track. Then a left turn along the cinder path that led to Robertson Creake's house deep in the trees. He walked along the edge of the path where there was some grass, so that his footsteps made no sound.

He wanted to find out how close the remaining mulberry tree was to where the old circle of mulberries had been. This would resolve the only uncertain part of his theory about Edward's buried sword. Cautiously in the dark he felt his way, found the tree, roughly paced out the distance. Across the other side of the yard Mr Creake's house stood in darkness. Adam assumed Mr Creake was inside it.

A large bird unexpectedly flew past him, a pale soft silence cruising only inches from his face. An unknown woodland animal gave a tiny squeal and something scuffled in the undergrowth. Adam shivered. He would be glad to get out of this place. Then there was a new sound – a faint clicking, becoming louder. Adam felt goosepimples on the back of his neck and his hair began to stand on end. Then he heard wheels crunching the cinder path. Someone was riding towards him on a bicycle.

He raced into the trees, across the old railway, and deeper into the undergrowth on the other side. Then he stopped, ducked down, and peered back into the darkness. He expected Robertson Creake to put his bike away and go indoors. He listened with all his senses for the sound of footsteps, a door being opened and shut. But none of that happened.

Adam could see nothing for certain. But he was almost sure that Robertson Creake was still outside in his yard, watching, waiting.

Someone else on the prowl! Adam felt a surge of joy. He knew he could outwatch Robertson Creake. Even if it took all night.

$\approx$

'If we can draw the train forward, we could use the water from the water-column,' Joe said.

But that was no good. The undersides of the two trucks were already burning fiercely. 'You wouldn't be able to squirt it underneath,' Abigail said. 'It's not like a fireman's hose.'

'Well, what are we going to *do*?'

'Can't we get help?'

'There's no *time*!'

'Edward, can you really drive an engine?' This was Abigail.

'Yes. I think so.' (Did she really *mean* it?)

'This one?'

'*Well?*'

It dawned on Edward that nodding his head in the dark was no good. 'Yes,' he said.

'We could uncouple the two front trucks and tow them away from the rest of the train.'

'But they'll still blow up.'

'Only those two – not the whole train.'

'Tow it further down the line, you mean?' Joe was beginning to think they might just be able to do it.

They considered, agonising. It seemed like something that children couldn't do.

Then Abigail. 'It's no good!' she said in distress. 'There's the Ferry Inn, right beside the line – we might blow it up!'

She was right. The inn – popular with fishermen before the War – was close to a small cluster of cottages, crowded together between the river and the railway, about half a mile north of the station.

An anguished silence then. 'The branch-line,' Molly said.

They seized upon her idea. There was no time for discussing the details. The disused branch-line it would have to be.

And the risk? No one mentioned it.

'Joe,' Abigail said. 'Do you know how to shift a points handle?'

'I reckon so.'

'You'll need the key!'

'What key?'

'To unlock the points.'

'OK,' said Joe. But he sounded uncertain, so Molly – acutely aware of how urgent this was – took over the questioning. 'Abigail, do you know where the key is?'

'It'll be somewhere in the signal box.'

There was a necessary division of labour.

Abigail would have to go up into the signal box and look for the points key. She dashed off at once into the darkness, half-stumbling over the rough stones, hoping desperately that she would, after all, find Mr Clark there, alive and well.

Meanwhile Joe – because he was the strongest and knew about machinery – went to uncouple the two burning trucks from the rest of the train. He found that the train had continuous braking and screw-couplings. But he set about it systematically, feeling his way in the darkness towards understanding how the fitments worked.

He could feel the heat of the flames on his back as he crouched in the space between the second truck and the third.

Edward would drive the engine. He had recognised the class of locomotive at once – a Class V2 2–6–2. He'd been close to one often enough, but always at a station. He'd never been beside one at ground level. The drive-wheels towered above him, the top of each one at least two feet above his head. Even the lowest of the steps up to the cab was level with his stomach. But Molly was behind him and she lifted him up until he found a place for his feet. The next moment he was on the footplate and staring around him in the half-darkness.

Molly climbed up behind him.

It was true that Edward did know how to drive an engine. But what he knew was book knowledge. This was different. He was almost overwhelmed by the size of everything. The locomotive seemed to have been designed for giants. But he quickly found the regulator handle and brake valve – and he thought those were the only two controls he would need. He knew that a good driver should cut off the pressure before starting, to prevent the wheels from skidding on the rails. But he didn't know how to do that and there wasn't time for him to work it out.

Abigail came running through the darkness just as Joe completed the uncoupling. 'There's no one in the signal box!' she gasped.

'Did you find the key?' Joe asked her.

It wasn't an ordinary key. It was a heavy T-shaped metal tool, about the size of a kitchen tap. 'What do I do with it?' Joe said.

But Abigail didn't know exactly. 'There'll be a hole or something. You'll have to fit it in and turn it.'

'Abigail, are you coming with us?' Molly asked.

'I can't! Someone's got to open the gates to let you through!'

None of the others had thought of that. Abigail was

off again, racing along the track, her feet finding the regular solidity of the sleepers as she ran in the darkness.

As soon as Joe climbed up onto the footplate, Edward braced himself. He released the brake and set his hand to the regulator handle. It was a lever, immensely long, but it moved easily. At first nothing happened; he moved it further. There was a series of deep resolute blasts from the funnel, which set Edward's heart racing with excitement. The great locomotive began to move.

Edward was driving a train!

He turned round in the dark to share his delight with Joe. But Joe was clinging to the rail of the cab and leaning out, trying to see. Neither Molly nor Edward was tall enough to see through the small grimy window meant for the driver.

They drew the two burning trucks away from the rest of the motionless train and in less than a minute they had left the gasworks behind. As they came level with the signal box, they saw Abigail racing up the steps, stumbling once in the dark. She had closed the crossing gates to traffic on the main Lynn road by the station. She gave them a quick forlorn wave as they passed. Molly caught sight of her at the top of the steps, re-entering the signal box to start telephoning.

The next minute they had crossed the main Lynn road and were steaming through the unlit station. Then out into the darkness and over the river bridge.

In the signal box, Abigail knew what she had to do. She found the phone and contacted the next signalman down the line. 'Mr Jacks?' she said.

'What the . . . ?'

'Listen!' she said. But Mr Jacks wouldn't listen. 'Who are you? Why are you using this phone?'

'Mr Jacks, *please listen*! The munitions train is on fire and . . .'

'Who *are* you?'

'I'm Abigail Murfitt. Mrs Murfitt is my mum.'

The tiniest pause. Then, 'OK, Abigail. What is it?'

Abigail quickly told him.

When a train is moving, the driver is in charge. But when it's motionless, the guard is responsible. It occurred to Fred Sharples after a time that this stop to take on water was taking longer than it ought.

He jumped heavily down from his van at the rear of the train to see what was going on. He stood watching in disbelief as – about a quarter of a mile ahead – the locomotive was towing away the two leading trucks of his train. And were they flames he could see, flickering in the darkness? Surely not!

He set off in hopeless pursuit, running heavily along the trackside, but when he reached the head of the train there could no longer be any doubt. He stood with his hands on his hips, bent at the waist, in despair, gasping for breath. In the distance he could see the locomotive steaming away from him through the empty shadows of Great Deeping station, briefly reddened by the passing flames.

Then he saw two bodies lying in the dark. One of them groaned as he approached.

'Stop now!' shouted Joe. 'We're close to the junction!'

But Edward couldn't stop the locomotive. For some reason, the brake handle did not respond. So he adjusted the regulator to reduce speed and that slowed the engine down.

Joe could faintly see the white handle of the points-lever in the darkness. He jumped out, a terrible jarring jump which shook his whole body from his ankles to his neck.

He raced ahead of the engine, gasping breathlessly, stumbling forward with the effort. He saw at once how the handle had to be pulled but, as he'd expected, the lever was firmly locked. Finding the place where the key had to be fitted was not difficult, even in the dark. In it went, and Joe's strong hands turned it. There was a rusty grating of metal, then a slippage. He stood up, grasped the handle firmly, and heaved.

There wasn't much time. Edward's engine was very near now, hissing, clanking, almost looming over Joe. There was a smell of burning wood.

The points had probably not been greased for thirty years. Joe tried again, bracing his feet and legs and forcing his whole body to work as a human lever against the metal one.

And he did it. The muscles in his strained and stiffened body felt a shift in the mechanism. Something gave, and there was a grinding thump and clang as the points shifted and slotted sideways into their new position.

Joe fell backwards as the engine and the two burning trucks went past. Fat blasts of exhaust thundered out of the chimney. He caught a glimpse of Molly's white face. He had thought he would get back into the engine once the points had been changed, and go with them. But he could see now that that was impossible. It was too high, moving too fast. He could jump down from a moving footplate, but getting back up was not possible, especially in the dark.

The wheels of the engine squealed as the points directed them into the bend and off the main line. The locomotive with its two burning trucks was on the branch-line.

They're on their own now, Joe thought as he watched them go.

Molly stuck her head out and peered ahead. She could sense rather than actually see the line in front of them, curving into the trees which closed in on either side. There was all kinds of undergrowth growing over the track, and the track-bed and the sleepers were buried. But the rusty metal rails were still there, an inch or two above the woodland litter. They received the locomotive and faithfully guided the metal flanges of the wheels. But in thirty years of disuse they had lost their exact and perfect gauge. There were small twists and slight dips, so that the big locomotive swung and swooped heavily as it moved.

As they plunged into the thicker darkness of the trees, Molly stuck her head out and looked back at the trucks. She could hardly see them because of the tender; but she could see that the flames had spread rapidly. Some were leaping upwards, lighting up the trees where they met overhead, and making sinister leaping shadows as they passed. She knew that the wooden outsides of the trucks were now burning rapidly.

Edward was in a condition of pure concentrated purpose. They were past the points now, so he dared to speed up the train a little. They approached the road-crossing in the middle of the wood, and passed smoothly over it, clanking and hissing.

The plan was to get the train safely through Barrett's Wood, away from all houses. But Molly suddenly knew that they had come far enough. They had to get away from it at once. She had no idea where this knowledge came from. Perhaps it was an instinct, some deep recognition of danger. Or perhaps her mind had worked it out using knowledge which she didn't know she had.

Whatever it was, she knew they had to get away. Now!

Robertson Creake crouched among the trees beside his house, hugging his body with his arms. *Surely this is far enough away*, he thought. An anxious joy seized him as he waited. *If only I can get through this*, he said to himself.

He was resolved, almost calm. One of his voices had murmured to him that he should give up the Germans after this. He should abandon all thoughts of being a celebrated Nazi hero. He might live for another forty or fifty years, this voice said – and in all that time he need never do another bad thing! Not one! A lifetime of spotless goodness. He would deceive everybody. That way, he would have knowledge of *both*. There would be years of innocent goodness – and one great gargantuan wickedness to look back on in secret.

He would have done it! He would be an evil hero in his own eyes.

But there was something strange. He realised that he had heard for several minutes the distant sound of a train moving, the faint puffs of a locomotive. This was odd. Then the sound changed completely. Whatever it was that he could hear was *coming towards him*, the noise changing its character as it passed through the trees.

It wasn't possible! But then he saw a yellow-and-red flickering light in the thick darkness of Barrett's Wood. On the branch-line! The line that hadn't been used for thirty years! It was impossible, inconceivable!

It had come in pursuit!

The engine and its two trucks came in sight, passing along the track across the front of his house. The flames had a good hold now, he saw. Yet where was the rest of the train? How could it be that only the two trucks that he'd set alight were being drawn along the branch-line towards his house?

It was beyond his comprehension.

Then Robertson Creake did a foolish thing. He should have run as fast as he possibly could, or hidden behind something, or thrown himself face down on the ground. But instead he walked forward, across his backyard, towards the branch-line. He could see now that two children were about to jump down from the cab of the engine.

He walked on, like a man under sentence.

It's creepy, this, Adam had thought – *the two of them, each watching silently*. But he knew he couldn't move until Mr Creake had gone away. *I must just stick it out*, he told himself. He couldn't see anything, but he knew – he just *knew* – that Robertson Creake was still in his backyard.

But then came the sound of a train. *Strange*, he thought. *Hadn't they told him the line was disused?*

What he saw next bewildered him completely. It was strange, bizarre, utterly beyond reason. A powerful locomotive coming through the trees, towing two blazing trucks! It didn't make sense.

When the engine and the two burning trucks had passed safely over the points and onto the branch-line, Joe straightened his aching body. Abigail was running towards him from the signal box, racing along the pathway beside the main line.

She was clearly intent upon following the others along the branch-line. Joe knew it was foolish but he joined her anyway. 'Nobby Clark has been knocked out,' Abigail told him breathlessly as they ran. 'I found him under the steps.' She was glad that Joe didn't trouble her with questions. She'd opened and closed the crossing gates, phoned one of the signalmen and told him what was happening. She'd had enough of doing things on her own. Now she wanted to be with the others.

Then they felt the blast of the explosion – heard it, saw it, *felt* it.

They stopped abruptly. Abigail stood with her hands clenched to her face, staring at Joe. There was more horror here than she had room for.

Molly hadn't hesitated. She'd grabbed Edward, shouting something which he didn't hear, torn his hand from the regulator handle, and pushed him to the right-hand side of the footplate. It was too narrow for the two of them to jump off side by side, and she daren't push him ahead of her in case he fell under the wheels. So she jumped herself, but never slackening her grip on his wrist. The sudden pain in his arm made him yell as he came out behind her, jerked violently, half falling and half jumping.

The line ran through a shallow cutting here, barely a yard deep – but enough to lessen the shock of their jump. Molly staggered upright and yanked Edward to his feet, dragging him almost through the air. At a speed which she knew she was not capable of, she ran – and made Edward run – into the trees. There was one big one, an enormous oak, solidly rooted, and they raced towards it.

Just as they got to it, a great clump of pressure lifted them off their feet, heaving into their backs. Molly used it to swing them both round to the other side of the oak. They found then that there was suddenly no air at all, nothing to breathe. They were inside an unnatural vacuum of heat.

Then they were gasping again. Molly felt the oak trunk shuddering at her back as she enclosed Edward with her arms and pressed his head and face into her.

The noise was beyond all imagining. And the things that Molly saw in the red darkness were impossible. The entire front wall of Robertson Creake's house shot inwards at enormous speed. Then the mortar between the bricks of the back wall dribbled out from between them, and for a second they hung together with nothing to bind them. Had she *really* seen that? Then they crumbled, and at the same moment the roof fell in, obscuring everything else with a mountain of spilling tiles and rafters and plaster.

The cardboard box and the letters to Herr Hitler were incinerated in an instant. Atomised into oblivion.

When the worst of the exploding roar was over, Molly looked fearfully around her. In the aftermath – the immediate seconds of time following the blast – the dark sky was full of flying and falling objects. Great flowering petals of flame flew above, flickering darkly, then dying. Smaller trees – uprooted entirely – fled through the sky, and some went at ground level, as if they had discovered the power to scuttle away out of danger. A voluminous billow of smoke fattened, rose, and poured itself upwards. Millions of tiny sparks flew up into the darkness.

One of the casualties was the last surviving mulberry tree. It was dislodged entirely and thrown headlong so that its roots were exposed, embedded in a vertical wall of hard earth.

Then came a strange humming silence of falling clotted objects, huge chunks of metal and wood, clods of earth and stone, tree roots. Molly knew the sounds they must all be making as they fell, but in reality she was deafened and heard almost nothing.

There was a bitter smell of smoke and gunpowder and burning. The air was dry and scorched, as if it had been burned of all life. Small black flakes of burnt debris fell softly down.

Edward had twisted his face free of Molly's grip and was shouting something. It seemed he wanted to get away. Molly heard nothing – but she knew they must not move yet. Cautiously she peered round the tree trunk. There was a crater deep enough to build a house in. Nothing in it was recognisable except that at one end there was the smoke-box and chimney of the engine, hissing fiercely and pointing upwards as if it had tried to lift itself free of the blast, and failed. Several yards away, upside down, was the front bogie with three of its wheels still intact, one of them freewheeling sadly round.

The night blew up in Adam's face. He saw it before he heard it. And he heard it before he understood it. And as he began to understand, an unseen wall of air stopped his breath and blasted him backwards, half-running, half-staggering, almost off his feet. With him went a hurricane of branches, old leaves, twigs and other debris, in a furious whirl of fragmenting chaos.

Then something heavy and sharp hit Adam's head. He managed to slow down, still driven by the explosion. He knew he was losing his balance, swaying sideways. He had a vague sense that he had come out of the trees. Then his legs gave way and he collapsed to the ground. The last thing he was aware of as he lost consciousness was the feel of soft wet grass on his knees.

Abigail followed Joe along the cinder path – blindly, at a run. Through the trees, across the lane, and into the wood on the other side.

She raced into the arena of ruin and took in the situation almost at once. In the stinking smoky darkness, strangely lit by burning debris, she saw Edward break away from Molly and race towards the crater. He was shouting something but she couldn't hear clearly.

Abigail knew without thinking what their roles were. So did Joe. He raced after Edward, she towards Molly.

Joe caught up with Edward, wrapped his arms around him from behind and stopped him from going any closer. Then he turned him round so that he could look straight into Edward's desolate face. The smaller boy started yelling incomprehensible things about water and steam pressure – and then Joe realised that Edward thought *he* had blown up the engine, and that his driving had been at fault in some way. Had he not understood about the munitions? Or only half understood? 'There were bombs in the trucks!' Joe said. '*They* blew it up, not *you*!' But Edward was deafened and Joe had to say it again and again, shouting.

The younger boy stared at the older one as understanding dawned in him. His mind understood what Joe was saying, and he understood that he should feel comforted. But his heart was broken – that such a beautiful locomotive (*his* locomotive, which *he* had driven) should be destroyed in this way.

As she ran to Molly, Abigail caught sight of something from the corner of her eye, and veered towards it. It lay on the ground, dark, long. Not a tree trunk. Abigail stood beside Robertson Creake and looked down into his eyes. But his eyes were not seeing her. Blood was oozing silently from a hole in his chest.

Then Abigail understood. And Molly, running up, saw and understood what Abigail knew.

They knelt down in the flickering darkness. As they stared down at the dead face, Molly realised with a sharp excited hurt that something unknown had come into their life. Then, as an afterthought, she realised it wasn't a hurt at all, just a difference.

'We've seen a dead person,' Abigail said. But Molly could hear nothing. She was numbed and deafened, and all she knew was that Abigail's mouth was moving.

Then Abigail started to shake. She had thought of her father, almost *seen* him. Was this what had happened to him in France? Had he lain on the ground in the dark, bleeding? Had a stranger found him, staring upwards like that, seeing nothing?

The thought had come into her mind uninvited, as if it had been deep inside her all the time, waiting. From now on, it seemed to Abigail, nothing in the whole world would ever be the same. *She* wouldn't be the same, ever.

Edward was racing towards them, with Joe just behind.

'We must keep Edward away from this.' Molly thought she was speaking normally.

Abigail nodded, wondering why Molly was shouting at her. They took on their responsibilities at once and hurried towards the young boy, to intercept him, to stop him from seeing Mr Robertson Creake, dead.

And at that moment there was a break in the clouds and the moon came out, floating free and full, illuminating the desolation with a sharp and exact clarity.

When the explosion came, Mrs Barrett had been working in her kitchen. She felt and saw the solidity of God's great world being cracked and forced outwards, opened up and shattered. Her hearing was stunned and the glass in the kitchen windows dribbled in a strange humming silence in fragments to the floor.

Dazed and almost unable to keep upright, she hurried across the hall into the sitting room. Just as she opened the door the ceiling fell down in a cloud of ancient plaster, filling the air with gritty dust and grey wooden laths.

She hurriedly shut the door and went outside, coughing painfully and expecting the whole house to collapse at any minute. She stared about her in amazement and confusion. The house stood firm but a huge fire was billowing in the middle distance through the trees that separated her back garden from Robertson Creake's. Mrs Barrett supposed it must have been a bomb – but why would the Germans want to drop a bomb there?

Then she saw a figure, black against the brightness of the fire, staggering among the trees. It seemed to be a boy and her heart leapt into her throat. *Please, Lord, no!* she cried inwardly.

Almost at once, however, she knew that this boy was taller and older. This was not Edward. But where *was* Edward? She must find him.

She set off recklessly towards the inferno. But the unknown boy had now come out of the trees and was standing at the bottom of her garden, and swaying about. Then he collapsed – and Mrs Barrett knew what she must do.

Her heart was sick within her, but her sorrow for the young men of her family who had died at war and far from home directed her. She knew she could not abandon this boy. She must simply hope that wherever Edward was someone else would be caring for him. She hurried down the garden towards the boy, knelt on the wet grass beside him, and peered at his face. He was unconscious and in the bright flickering darkness she could see he was someone she didn't know. Blood was oozing through his hair and down the left side of his face. She couldn't see clearly – but there seemed to be a deep injury to his head.

She untied her apron and used it as a bandage, hoping to stop the flow of blood. The boy groaned as she did it, and when she had finished she laid his messy and disordered head on her lap and began to tell him repeatedly that all would be well.

Her deafness was wearing off and she could hear the distant sound of a fire-engine bell coming faintly across the fens. *Good*, she thought. *The firemen would know what to do.*

She continued to talk to the boy in her lap, gently, urgently, like a prayer. As she knelt there, the darkness suddenly lifted and she was bathed in moonlight. Mrs Barrett saw this as a good sign. *God always has a full moon around Easter-time*, she thought.

The explosion set the dogs barking. Every dog within fifteen miles of Great Deeping protested its indignation. The night was filled with yapping and howling.

On the main line, beside the gasworks, a line of abandoned trucks packed with high explosives stood silently, with no locomotive. The driver was the first to regain consciousness. His head was sore and he felt nauseous. The young fireman's injuries were more extensive; he came round quickly but was unable to move. Nobby Clark, the signalman, was the last to be found; he kept coming round, then passing out again.

The guard was nowhere to be seen. He had dutifully set off back along the line to lay detonators on the track to warn any following train of danger ahead.

In the darkness the children had felt as if the rest of creation had moved away and left them entirely unaided and alone. But even before the explosion there were people who were alerted and concerned. The air-raid wardens on the church tower saw the distant light from the burning trucks and immediately contacted the fire service. The local siren sounded and the Littleport fire engine was on its way. Later the engine from Ely, and another from the nearby airfield, also came.

When Mr Jacks the signalman received Abigail's message, he first contacted every other signal box on the line, then the police.

Everyone in Great Deeping heard the explosion, a single massive thump of noise and vibration. Fragments of ceiling fell down, broom handles leaning against walls fell sideways, cats crouched under chairs. Someone later said the spout had fallen off a perfectly good teapot. In several houses, window catches were dislodged and the top halves of the windows slid down. One old lady woke to the sound of something whirring downstairs and found that her wind-up gramophone – long seized up – had freed itself and was softly running down.

People ignored the air-raid warning and came out into the dark streets, wondering.

An ambulance from the RAF hospital at Ely joined the other vehicles as they crowded along Camel Lane towards the place of the explosion. Sergeant Bly the policeman, with his uniform pulled over his pyjamas, had somehow managed to get there quickly enough to direct the vehicles.

In addition to the three injured railway staff, the ambulance men found:

~ a young boy, temporarily deafened, covered with cuts, scratches and bruises, and in a state of shock;

~ a girl, older, also deafened, scratched and bruised, white-faced and silent;

~ another girl, uninjured, not deafened, but equally shocked and confused;

~ an older boy, uninjured, breathless, but able to tell them what had happened;

~ another boy, unconscious and bleeding from a head-injury;

~ an elderly woman, uninjured but in a state of shock, who kept telling them that God had restored her hearing;

~ and a man, killed.

The survivors were all taken away to hospital.

There was no fuss, no delay. There was a War on, and things had to be dealt with. Again.

A small team of investigators came down from London, the same people who'd come the first time. Their task was straightforward. They didn't talk to either Molly or Edward because they were kept in hospital for several days. But Joe and Abigail were released after only one night, and they were able to tell the investigators the whole story – from the moment when they'd walked along Green Lane to the moment of the explosion.

But they couldn't explain why Adam had been there. 'He likes going about after dark,' Joe said – and the questioners had to be content with that because Adam himself was still concussed, and couldn't be interviewed.

The young fireman had seen the man who had attacked him and recognised his face. And when Joe told them that Robertson Creake had sometimes kept carrier pigeons, the case was clear-cut.

The investigators completed their enquiries and went back to London. Their findings were supposed to be secret – but everyone in Great Deeping quickly knew the full story.

Concussion affects people in strange ways. *Severe* concussion – which is what Adam had – confused his sense of time.

In the next few weeks, nights no longer followed days in an orderly way. Sometimes it seemed to be night-time, sometimes it was daytime – but none of it made sense. He had no idea of Wednesday following Tuesday, or of Tuesday following Monday. The daily hospital sequence of breakfast, dinner and supper was lost entirely. His head-injury – with thirty stitches and a thick bandage – healed steadily, but the confusion in his mind took longer. When he had to get out of bed he felt dizzy and sick, longing to lie down again and go back to sleep.

Visitors came to see him but he remembered them strangely, overlapping one another. His mother came, he knew. Several times. Still in her WAAF uniform, snatching days from her duties on the coast of Kent. The hospital was an Air Force one and the doctors were all RAF officers. So Mrs Swales, in her uniform, had to stand to attention whenever an officer-doctor passed through the ward. His father came too, catching an afternoon train from London and returning in time for the nightly bombing raids.

Adam's London grandmother came too. She was severe and angry. She hadn't seen Adam since the day he'd been evacuated. 'We sent him away to the country so that he'd be safe from bombs,' she grumbled. 'And he gets himself blown up in the middle of a wood!'

Abigail and Molly visited several times. Joe cycled over twice, and once young Edward came too, with Molly's mum.

Adam's visitors chatted and laughed gently, questioned him about the food and the nurses, teased him about the startling haircut around his head-injury. They talked to the other patients – all wounded airmen – as much as they talked to Adam. Words, words, cheerful words. But none of the visitors said anything about what had happened on the night of the explosion. They'd been given strict instructions not to talk about it.

But once, when she was his only visitor, Molly told him everything. In an intense low-voiced conversation she told him what she had done that night, and then made him tell her what he had done. Adam asked her questions, listened attentively, sorted it out in his head, watched her eyes, longed for pencil and paper (also forbidden). Other patients and visitors in the ward fell silent from time to time and glanced at them – the boy on one elbow leaning sideways towards the girl, she close to him, impatiently tucking her hair behind her ears.

This conversation helped. But it left Adam convinced that there was something else. Something he had to tell her. Or was it something *she* had to tell *him*?

In the wider Wartime world, normal life was slowly restored. Two of the three railway staff recovered quickly, but the older man – Mr Clark, the signalman – took a good deal longer. He was off work for a month.

Enemy planes continued to pass over the town at night, the siren sounded the air-raid warning, and people moved, grumbling, into their shelters. Occasionally, convoys of army lorries drove through the town, sometimes carrying troops, sometimes tanks or heavy guns. The War Department began to call up older men, in their mid-thirties. The male population of Great Deeping fell further and there were more unhappy goodbyes at the railway station.

News of the War came in from all sides. The local and national newspapers reported the Great Deeping explosion, but only briefly and without naming either people or places. There were no headlines. The children were national heroes, but anonymous. It was a security issue, they were told, and the enemy must not be allowed to learn anything from what had happened.

'Do they read our newspapers then?' Abigail asked in surprise. Yes, she was told – there was almost certainly a German intelligence unit whose job was to read British newspapers to see what they could learn from them.

But details of what had happened could not be kept secret from Great Deeping and the surrounding farms and villages. From Ely to Lynn the children were the subject of much talk – amazed, proud and gleeful. 'Would you believe it?' people said. 'They're only little 'uns!'

People talked about Robertson Creake too. 'I never did like his eyes,' they said. 'He never looked you straight in the face.' He had a mean mouth too, they recalled. Kept himself to himself. Mr Creake's many small kindnesses – helping passengers with heavy luggage, advising them about train times, and helping elderly travellers in and out of carriages – were not forgotten. Quite the reverse – they were especially remembered and became part of the puzzle.

Mrs Barrett stayed in Molly's mum's guest house for a week. Molly was dismayed when she learned that this was the plan. *She'll bring God with her*, Molly thought crossly. *We'll have the Bible morning, noon and night!*

Mrs Barrett *did* bring God with her – she said grace before every meal. But mostly what she brought was some fresh cooking. Mrs Barnes refused to take rent from the old lady, and Mrs Barrett refused to be barred from the kitchen.

The explosion seemed to have restored her hearing. This was very important to her – she saw it as a miracle. But to the girls it was her rabbit pies that were miraculous.

One day there was a funeral in Great Deeping. Only two people attended the service and prayed for the soul of the dead man. But almost the entire population stood in the streets to watch his coffin carried by. Some turned their backs as it passed. A young man spat – but was quietly rebuked by the people nearby.

After that, the attempted sabotage that might have

destroyed Great Deeping receded into the background. People's amazement and disbelief faded into acceptance and thankfulness. They didn't forget, but their lives moved on and they had to think about other things.

Abigail had moved back with her mother at the railway cottage. Molly had expected to be inconsolably wretched when this happened – but she found it made little difference. They still spent most of their waking hours together anyway, Molly wanting everything to be as it used to be, and Abigail mysteriously changed.

The back seat on the top deck stretched across the entire width of the bus.

Edward, kneeling sideways, had one hand out of the window holding a small silver Spitfire. Its red propeller was spinning in the passing wind. The tiny plane was on a perilous mission – a journey of immense distance, all the way from Great Deeping to the hospital at Ely. If you adjusted it to scale, it was a flight of hundreds of miles. Hugely dangerous. Every time the bus stopped, the wind failed, the propeller came to rest, and the pilot glided his plane inside the bus and landed it tidily on the arm rest, for refuelling.

Molly and Abigail were on the lower deck, with a schoolfriend.

Beside Edward on the long seat were Mrs Barnes and Mrs Murfitt, talking seriously. Their words came faintly to him, as if they were in another room, with the door closed.

'You can never tell what they're going to do next.'

'I *told* them not to go near the railway that day. And what did they do . . . ?'

Their voices were low and throaty, an emotional leftover from the turmoil of anger and fear they had both been through. The children had heard this conversation a dozen times – a useless exchange because it always led to the same conclusion. *Well, if they hadn't, none of us would be here.*

'Everyone keeps saying how proud we should be to have such children.'

They might one day feel pride, perhaps. But what they'd felt at the time was anxiety, relief, anger – and a strong undercurrent of fear. Adam's parents had come down and the story had had to be repeated, again and again, so that they too could take in its enormity.

Edward thought they might talk about it for ever. So he'd stopped listening.

But the tellings and retellings gradually healed the rawness, and the danger which had come so close began to seem a little more distant. The War had that effect too. It didn't stop just because of one incident in an East Anglian town; news of defeats, bombings, and the sinking of ships came in with such speed that single local events got crowded out and were diminished.

'You never know what's going on in their heads.'

Inside Edward's head, the pilot was preparing to take off again.

'I suppose we'll get over it.'

'We'll feel better when Adam's out of hospital.'

In a lower voice: 'Abigail's not herself. She's gone so *quiet*!'

'She *would* be! Think what she might have found when she . . . She knew that.'

Edward heard the conductor ring the bell, twice, and felt the enormous vehicle cough itself into gear and rev up. The Spitfire took off again and headed in an elegant loop towards the open window.

'It's a terrible thing, war.'

'It's made our children into heroes.'

Edward stole the word at once. That's what his Spitfire pilot was – a *hero*! The little plane was out of the window again, its propeller spinning joyously as it continued on its mission. And its pilot sat at the controls, hunched in complete and concentrated attentiveness.

Adam woke up one afternoon to find his Uncle Hugh sitting beside his bed.

'You've been in the wars!' his uncle said. 'We've been really worried about you! Your auntie. And Bronwen and Gwen.'

'You've come from Wales? Just to visit me!'

'None of this would've happened if you'd stayed with us. What d'you want to live in a place like this for? There's nothing here!'

Adam grinned. He was very happy to see his uncle.

'I came out of Eli station and I asked someone the way to the RAF Hospital. And he said "Go up that hill and bear right." I said, "What hill? I can't see any bloody hill!" '

There it was again, that *bloody* – familiar and comfortable, with no hurt in it.

'There's nothing here, boy! It's as flat as your auntie's ironin' board!'

His uncle talked almost without stopping. He brought with him Adam's other landscape – the mountain farm, winding narrow roads worn deep, wet rocky walls covered in orange and yellow lichens.

And the ugly-beautiful town in the mountains, built of slate.

'Your mum and dad have been worried crazy about you,' Uncle Hugh said. 'Ringin' up your auntie and me every night. So I thought I'd better come and see for myself, like.'

He pulled out his pipe and tobacco pouch, realised that smoking wasn't allowed, and shoved them vaguely back into his pocket.

'I had a couple of hours in London this morning,' he said. 'Went to look at the Houses of Parly-a-ment – they've been bombed, y'know.'

Uncle Hugh paused, took his pipe from his pocket again, sighed regretfully and put it back. 'Bastards!' he said thoughtfully. 'And you were right about that converted mine.' He lowered his voice. 'The paintin's.'

'I knew I was right,' Adam said. 'All the paintings have gone from the National Gallery.'

'We're not supposed to know, but everybody does. Buried treasure. It's what I said to you – bury your treasure in times of trouble.'

That reminded Adam. 'How are your cuttings?'

'Funny you should say that, boy. I was thinking of them on the train. I got plans for a new fruit garden! They're doing fine. All of them taken nicely. Except those two which rotted. There's always one or two that go rotten.'

Then Adam remembered. Cuttings taking root. That was it! *Yes!* He crossed his fingers, hoping he would remember long enough to tell the others.

Next day, his friends arrived together, all four of them. They were back at school now. But it was a Friday afternoon and they'd got special permission to leave school early. Adam heard the ward sister talking to them in the corridor outside.

'Only *two* visitors at a bedside. There are four of you.'

'Oh, *please*!'

'And you've only got fifteen minutes until the end of visiting time.'

'We're children. We count as half.'

'We only paid half fare on the bus.'

There was a relenting smile. Adam could hear it in the sister's voice.

'All right! But be very quiet. And only fifteen minutes, mind.'

'Yes, sergeant!' Abigail meant it to be a joke, but it didn't work because the ward sister *was* a sergeant.

In they came, sitting on his bed, surrounding him, other visitors staring.

There was a lot of whispered talk then at other bedsides, as patients explained to their visitors. 'See those kids? They're the ones . . .'

'No! The train that blew up? Really?'

'And the boy – he's the one who drove the engine.'

'The big one?'

'No! The little one!'

'Never! What that little squit? He's not big enough to reach the steering wheel!'

'They don't have steering wheels, engines.'

'Get away! How do they go round bends if they can't be steered?'

The newcomers whispered eager questions to Adam, giving him no chance to reply. Molly slipped half a bar of chocolate under his pillow.

Abigail said less than the rest. That's how it was with Abigail these days. The least injured, the most shocked.

Then, at last: 'I know where Edward's family sword is,' Adam said. 'But you won't be able to get it.'

He signalled to them to close in around him.

'Your ancestor dug a hole and marked it with a branch broken off a nearby tree. Correct?' He was looking at Edward.

As he talked Adam noticed the younger boy for the first time. *Really* noticed him. Edward the pure-chinned, Edward the engine driver, who – unlike the rest of them – had ancestors.

Edward nodded. The others waited impatiently.

'What *kind* of tree was it?'

But they didn't know. How could they? Just a tree. Any kind of tree that happened to be there!

'But *what* kind of tree happened to be there?' Adam said.

They had no answer. So Adam prompted them. 'Professor Molly?' he said.

Then Molly realised. 'A mulberry tree?' she said.

Then they all began to understand. The mulberry ring! All those mulberry trees had been close by.

'What happens when a mulberry branch is stuck into the ground?'

Again, it was Molly, the mulberry expert, who knew the answer. 'It grows roots and turns into a new tree,' she said. Then she began to fill in the historical details. 'No one went to find the buried sword,' she said slowly, 'so the branch was just left there, stuck in the ground – and it grew into a tree! And *then*, when the trees in the ring were cut down later, the younger one was left. It wasn't part of the ring.'

She looked questioningly at Adam. 'Yes!' he said. 'It's the one that's still there! And the sword is under it!'

But they had some news for him. It *wasn't* still there. It had been blown out of the ground by the explosion.

Then there was a lot of excited talk about how big the hole was, and could they plan a digging party?

'But the military police won't allow us near the place,' Abigail said. 'We've been to look, lots of times.'

'And *I* won't allow you near *this* place either,' said the ward sister, 'unless you leave now!' She had come up behind them, unnoticed, keeping a watchful eye on the other visitors shambling towards the exit.

So the four children left, chattering eagerly about rooting trees and buried treasure.

'That's where he lay,' Molly said, remembering the night.

'*He* was no loss to anyone, at any rate,' said Abigail.

The military policemen had gone away at last and the four children ignored the 'Keep Out' notices. They approached through the trees at the bottom of Edward's garden and walked slowly towards the crater. It was enormous, far bigger than they'd realised. About twenty feet deep and at least sixty feet across. The remaining bits of the locomotive had all been taken away; all that was left was a faint burnt smell of explosives. A section of the derelict railway track had vanished entirely.

Grass will grow over the crater, Molly thought, *in time. And one day children will run down its sides and play in it. Or it might fill up with rain and become a pond.*

Around it, there was desolation. They had seen scenes like this in films about the other war, the Great War. Nothing grew. And the trees that had once stood there had been blasted into nothing or smashed off at ground level, leaving sharp irregular stumps. There was a massive scatter of bricks and other masonry that had once been the old stable where Mr Creake had lived. The pigeon loft and other outbuildings had gone.

Further from the centre of the explosion some of the bigger trees had survived. One of them was the oak that had saved Molly and Edward. Not far off was the mulberry, upended and uprooted, lying on its side with its roots exposed. In the middle-distance the bluebells had bloomed under the trees, as they did every year.

Joe and Edward had gone towards the smaller crater left by the mulberry tree. But the two girls had been drawn to the spot where they had found Robertson Creake.

'He was no loss to anyone,' Abigail said again. She spoke as if there were a different conversation going on in her head.

'Let's go back to the others,' Molly said.

They squatted at the edge of the hole and watched the two boys digging for buried treasure. Edward's hands were already hurting but Joe was used to this kind of work.

'I'm changing my name,' Abigail said. She sounded tense, expecting disapproval.

'*Can* you do that?' Edward said with interest.

'Well, I'm going to anyway,' Abigail said. 'My middle name is Sarah – and from now on that's who I'm going to be. So you might as well start getting used to it.'

'Sarah?'

Molly disliked this idea at once. *Abigail* belonged to her; *Sarah* would be a stranger. 'Your mum won't let you,' she said hopefully.

'She'll have to. I shan't answer unless she calls me Sarah.'

'Sarah,' Edward said, to try it out. 'Sarah.'

'You'll never get everyone at school to stop calling you Abigail,' Molly said. 'The teachers won't.'

Abigail thought for a moment. 'Well, next term, we'll be at a different school – and I'll start off there as Sarah.'

The boys' conversation headed in a different direction, but Molly was still thinking about Sarah-Abigail – and hating it.

'I'll still be at the same school,' Edward said sadly. 'And Joe.'

But Joe shook his head. 'I'm leaving,' he said. 'I could have left last year, if I'd wanted.' Joe's last year of schooling had been patchy; sometimes he had left school, sometimes he attended.

'To work on the land?' Abigail asked. This was not unusual.

'Nope! I'm going to join up.'

'To be a soldier? But you aren't old enough!'

'I will be, come Christmas. I'm going to join a Boys' Regiment. Until I'm eighteen. Then I'll be a proper soldier.'

'But you're a farmer – people working on the land don't have to fight!'

'I'll come back and be a farmer when the War's over.'

Shall I change my *name?* Molly wondered. *Shall I make everyone call me Mary?* But quickly she answered herself. *No, I don't need to.* But how she wished Abigail wouldn't change hers!

Later she said, 'How deep is it now?'

Joe eyed the hole, estimating its depth. 'About three feet.'

'Would Sir What's-his-name have dug three feet down?' Molly said.

'He was trying to hide something,' Joe pointed out.

Molly wasn't satisfied. Her imagination was at work, thinking the past into really happening. 'But he was in a hurry,' she insisted. 'He needed to get away. He wouldn't have had time to dig a deep hole.'

'And it was in the middle of the night,' Abigail added. 'They were digging in the dark.'

Molly was warming to her subject. '*And* he expected to be digging it up again after only a few weeks.'

'He didn't know he was going to die in Ireland and not come back,' Abigail said.

Molly felt herself turning into a professor again. 'If he only buried it about one foot deep,' she said, 'the sword will be in the roots of the tree, not deeper down in the hole.'

'So we should be digging *up*, not down,' Abigail said.

The mulberry tree's roots were beside them, embedded in a slab of dark brown soil, almost as hard as a wall. When they started to dig into it, sideways, loose earth and stones fell at their feet and into the hole they had already dug. Some of it fell into their boots.

It was uncomfortable work and Professor Molly was beginning to lose her confidence.

Then, suddenly, '*Look!*'

A flat chunk of dark soil had fallen clear, and behind it – like a fossil lying in a split rock – was the outline of a sword among the tree roots. It was like magic, a vision, as if history was coming back to visit them. The blade was narrow, round-ended, about a yard long. Dark brown, almost black, and very rough. The hilt was a spherical design of metal guards, a cage to protect the hand that held the weapon. The earth around it – dark and powdery – dribbled softly away. *A wooden box gone rotten*, Joe thought.

He reached to pull the sword out straightaway but the girls stopped him. So it was Edward who touched it first, putting his hand up to the blade.

But he drew back. Where he touched it, the sword fell away in thick rusty flakes.

Edward's grandmother had come through the trees at the bottom of her garden and walked up to them, unheard, with some jam tarts on a plate.

'It will fall to bits if we try to move it,' Edward said sadly.

Mrs Barrett thought to herself, *Life is letting him down again*. She climbed awkwardly down into the hole and the four of them stood aside so that she could inspect the sword in the soil.

They half expected her to quote from the Bible, but this time something different sprang to her mind. 'If we had a camera . . .' she said.

When they realised what she meant, Joe tore off through the trees, vaulted the fence and raced across the field towards his father's farmhouse. 'Save me one of those tarts!' he shouted as he went.

While they waited, Edward said, 'Gran, who does the mulberry tree belong to?'

'Me. When I'm gone, it'll belong to you.'

'Crikey!' Abigail said.

'What about the crater?'

'That too. It all belongs to us. Mr Creake paid me rent every month.'

'Does the railway line belong to us as well?'

'No, but the railway pays me five shillings a quarter for rent,' Mrs Barrett said.

I own a stretch of railway, Edward thought. *But it's broken.*

'This tree is not quite dead,' Mrs Barrett said. It was true. Some of the roots were still in the ground. The tree was clinging to life and had thrown out a few summer leaves. 'Dying – but not dead yet.'

Then Joe came back, breathless and sweaty. He jumped down into the hole with his Brownie camera and took three pictures. 'No more film,' he said.

They successfully removed the hilt of the sword entire, in one piece, a complicated sphere of metal guards. Molly imagined a leather-gloved hand inside it. But the blade disintegrated into shards of rust.

Edward was trying not to show his disappointment. Perhaps he had dreamed of a bright and perfect weapon shining in the sunlight, made of gold, with a bejewelled handle.

It was impossible to know how to comfort him, Molly thought. *Too young to be joked into cheerfulness; too big to be cuddled.*

'Never mind, mate,' Joe said. And that was all. Edward looked up at him and knew he had to be brave about this. Molly watched them, with interest and approval.

Abigail saw there was something else jammed among the roots of the mulberry tree. Saying nothing, she reached forward to pull it free, wondering if it too would crumble into nothing.

It was a package, flat, made of a shiny material, with a hint of oiliness when she rubbed a bit of it clear with her thumb. It must have been buried with the sword.

'What have you found?' Molly asked.

Abigail showed them. Mrs Barrett inspected it closely. 'Oilskin,' she said. 'Or leather perhaps.' She unwrapped it and the first flat layer broke off in her hand. She unfolded a second, and a third. They too cracked apart where they had been folded. But, further in, the layers opened as they were meant to.

Inside the wrapping was a single page of stiff paper, folded, and sealed with wax. Perhaps not paper at all.

Mrs Barrett broke it open, read the first few words and passed the letter to Edward. 'This belongs to you,' she said.

They crowded around Edward, trying to see what was written on it. A round elegant handwriting, with loops and swirls and extra capital letters.

Edward, in my moſt hertie wiſe, I commend me unto you . . .

They tried to make sense of this but they couldn't. The spelling was wrong and there were fs all over the place.

'Into my kitchen!' Mrs Barrett said. 'We'll work this out over a cup of tea and some biscuits.'

'Molly will be able to read it,' Joe said. 'She's the historical one.'

Molly was less confident; the last ancient text she had read had been retyped with a typewriter, which had made it easier. Still, she knew those fs weren't fs at all; they were a stretched-out way of writing an s – and that was a start.

While Mrs Barrett made tea in the kitchen (smelling of fresh putty, with newly glazed windows), Molly studied the letter in the living room (smelling of its newly plastered ceiling).

'*Can* you read it?' Edward said eagerly.

So Molly began. She didn't change the words much, but she tried to read it so that it made sense to everyone.

'Edward, in my most hearty wise, I commend me unto you.

'Whereas I am informed that my enemies grow daily nearer, albeit it is great pity of my hasty departure hence, yet, since it hath pleased God to send us such hap, we must be contented. Therefore, I pray you, my little son, be of good cheer though your father be suddenly gone away. Look to your mother and be comfortable unto her, and take upon yourself the burdens of the household, as far as may be.

'May God in his mercy bless you. And so fare you well.

'Barrett's Manor. 9 April, 1649. By the hand of your loving Father, Robert Barrett.'

The sword had not survived but the message had. One sentence especially spoke across the centuries, as clear as a silver bell ringing in darkness – 'Therefore, I pray you, my little son, be of good cheer though your father be suddenly gone away.'

'We told Edward we'd get his railway set up, so that he could run his steam train,' Abigail said.

Molly agreed. They had almost promised. 'But where?' she said. 'His back garden's too bumpy.'

They walked on slowly.

'The barn . . . ' Molly said thoughtfully, like a question.

'*Yes!*' Abigail said, with something like her old eagerness.

'But he has *tons* of stuff!' Molly said. 'How could we get it there?'

'We'll ask Joe. He'll know how we can do it.'

So they consulted Joe – and in a matter of minutes it was arranged. Edward was to have a train day, on Saturday. And Adam came out of hospital the day before, on the Friday afternoon – triumphantly brought home in an RAF jeep.

When Molly and Abigail got there after school, they found Mr and Mrs Swales there too. They had managed to get leave on the same day and had travelled together to Great Deeping.

Most of Adam's scar was now hidden under his hair, but about an inch and a half of purple still ran down beside his left eye. 'It will always be there,' he said cheerfully. 'My war wound.'

There was a greetings card from North Wales, with a picture of a woman in a long dress and a pointed hat, seated at a spinning wheel. 'That's my auntie,' he said, showing it to the girls.

'Adam,' his mother said, 'don't tease.'

Tibby – pressing tirelessly against Adam's ankles and purring in ecstasy – seemed pleased to have him back. 'He's been a bit peaky since you went into hospital,' Mrs Barnes said.

Abigail's mum – not a cat lover – looked critically at Tibby. 'He's certainly not a hundred per cent,' she observed.

But how could a cat with only three legs ever *be a hundred percent*, Molly thought. And then she knew with the instinct of long friendship that Abigail was having the same thought. They glanced at each other and one of them snorted. A fit of giggles followed.

Joe used the farm tractor to transport the railway set, and the girls helped to load and unload. Adam – still recuperating – was forbidden to take any part in this. So he stayed in the barn and helped young Edward lay out the lengths of track.

The result was deeply satisfying. The floor of Paradise Barn was flat, dry and spacious. The track visited every remote corner, twisting and curving, crossing over itself and dividing into loops and sidings. There were three level crossings (Abigail was in charge of them), two signal boxes (Adam), numerous signals, two road-bridges, a large town station and a small country station. There were sheds and a turntable (Molly, with not much to do), and one long delicious straight stretch of track that emerged from the mountainous tunnel (in Scotland) and turned into an elegant sweeping curve.

Edward was the driver. He charged the *Great Northern* with water, filled the burner with methylated spirit, trimmed the wicks, lit them – and waited patiently for the steam pressure to build up. The black-and-green locomotive, with its shiny pistons and brass pipes, had been lovingly polished in readiness.

Eight handsome carriages – with imaginary passengers sitting at the tiny tables – stood on the track, already coupled, waiting to be connected to the locomotive. On another line, a freight train stood ready.

There were a few derailments at first. But at last the beautiful passenger train had a long and perfect journey, all the way from Great Deeping to Kyle of Lochalsh in the north-west of Scotland, a graceful run, smooth and elegant. Abigail had found Kyle of Lochalsh on her father's railway map. Steam spat, pistons gleamed as they moved, wheels clattered over joins in the track. Edward had said he would control the points, but when it came to it he just wanted to listen and watch, to find different positions for the best view – the most realistic view – of his father's locomotive (*his* locomotive!) as it steamed by.

Then he remembered something. He took out his Dinky-toy Spitfire and gave it to Molly. So she became an RAF pilot and swooped low over the train, keeping watch, checking that all was well.

The *Great Northern* did three magnificent and faultless runs, two with the passenger coaches and one with the freight wagons.

'It seems a shame to pack it all up,' Joe said.

'But we needn't,' Molly said.

'It can stay here all summer,' Abigail added.

Joe knew what Edward was thinking. 'Not the engine,' he said. 'You'd better take that home with you.'

Molly woke, to find Adam standing beside her bed.

'I'm going out. Want to come?'

He was wearing shorts and sandals, nothing else. It was a warm night. Molly nodded and sat up. 'What are we going to do?'

'I'll need a couple of things from your mum's garden shed,' he said.

'What things?'

'A saw and a spade.'

Molly thought for a moment. 'I had that idea too,' she said. 'Only I wasn't going to do it in the middle of the night.' She rubbed her eyes. 'You won't need a spade,' she added.

'Why not?'

'There are molehills in Edward's back lawn.'

'So what?'

'Molehills are soft. Easy to push something into.'

'What about the mole which lives there?'

Molly yawned, feeling the agreeable superiority that country people have when townspeople show their ignorance. 'Moles don't live inside molehills,' she explained kindly.

247

Adam grinned. 'Get dressed then,' he said.

Two minutes later, they were walking carefully downstairs, along the passage and across the kitchen to the back door.

The cool night air felt delicious on their skin. Adam waited while Molly went into the garden shed and found a pruning saw. It folded up, like an oversized pocket knife.

Out in the street, Molly said, 'Let's get Abigail.'

It wasn't far to the house by the level crossing. Molly went quietly into the garden while Adam waited in the road. There were always tools lying about in Mrs Murfitt's garden. Molly quickly found a long-handled hoe and, with the metal end in her hands, she tapped the wooden end against Abigail's bedroom window.

She had to repeat the action several times. Then the curtains were parted and a face appeared at the window, looking down eagerly. Molly almost let the hoe fall into the coldframe. She beckoned excitedly, and Abigail nodded and disappeared from her bedroom window.

'Where are we going?' she whispered a minute later.

'To Barrett's Wood,' Molly said.

Abigail didn't ask why. 'OK,' she said.

'Let's race!' Adam said.

But Molly wouldn't agree to that. Adam hadn't been long out of hospital – and, besides, there was no point in racing because everyone knew she was the fastest runner in Great Deeping. Adam would never be able to outrun her. Nor would Abigail.

'Let's run together,' she said.

She set the pace, a little faster than a jog. Through the empty moonlit streets of the silent town they ran.

When they came to Marquis Way, Adam turned right into it. But Molly and Abigail carried on. At Globe Street, Abigail turned right. Molly continued, alone now, until she reached Hitches Way; here she turned right too. They would all meet again at the bottom, in Lower Lane. Silently Molly ran, in the middle of the road to avoid doorsteps, shoe scrapers and empty milk bottles. She thought of Adam and Abigail, each alone, in the other two parallel streets.

It was like running inside a dream.

Adam reached Lower Lane first and turned left into it. Just as he passed the bottom of Globe Street, Abigail emerged from it and joined him. Neither of them spoke. Adam was concentrating, Abigail grinning. The two of them reached the bottom of Hitches Way just as Molly emerged to join them. Their timing was perfect.

All done without a word; they were like highly skilled pilots performing a well-rehearsed manoeuvre. They ran side by side, in unison, in step. Molly gripped the closed-up pruning knife as if it were a baton carried in a relay. *I could go on like this for ever,* she thought.

They turned into Camel Lane, but when they drew near to Edward's house they slowed to a walk. Silently they followed the lane into the wood, across the abandoned railway track, and left along the cinder path that ran beside it – *the path that Robertson Creake would never use again,* Molly thought morbidly.

'Are you scared?' Abigail asked Molly.

'Not with you two here,' Molly said. 'Are you?'

Abigail shook her head happily.

For Molly, Abigail's name change had been like having a small stone in your shoe, or a piece of grit in your eye. But today she's more like her old self, Molly thought, and her spirits lifted. Then – because she was Molly – she wondered if she was deceiving herself.

The path ran alongside the old railway line and brought them to the very edge of the crater and the arena of desolation around it. They looked briefly into it, then turned aside and went in search of the smaller hole where the mulberry tree had been upended.

They stooped and peered into the dense branches of the fallen tree. The night was bright and they could clearly see the one branch that was still alive. Its leaves were fresh and vigorous, black in the moonlight.

The old tree had not grown any straight branches, only crooked ones. They found one that would do, but then they had a minor disagreement. Molly thought it needed to be about five or six feet long; Adam thought about six inches. They compromised at around three feet.

'So *that's* what this is all about!' Abigail said.

Molly and Adam held the bough steady while Abigail sawed it. They pulled it free of the tree and Molly held it on the ground, upright.

She was looking at its leaves, imagining it into a young tree. Adam was looking at the sawn-off bottom end, imagining it growing roots.

'It's rootless,' he said. His uncle's voice somehow got into his own, and the word *rootless* came out as a miniature Welsh melody.

Molly wanted to hear it again. 'What did you say it was?' she said.

This time Adam realised. 'It's rootless, boy-o,' he said. *Very* Welsh this time, slightly overdone.

They made their way around the giant crater and through the trees, past the spot where Adam had been when the trucks had blown up. He said nothing about it, however, and in no time they emerged at the bottom of Edward's back garden.

Old Mrs Barrett's bedroom was at the back of the house. She awoke, sleepily aware that she had heard sounds outside. She got out of bed and crossed to the window. She saw in her garden – down near the bottom, two kneeling, one stooping – three figures in the moonlight, pushing something into the grass.

Spirits, she thought contentedly. *Three spirits sent from heaven!* As she went back to her bed, she knew that in the morning there would be a different explanation. But, for now, it felt as if she had seen a vision.

The three friends didn't want to go home and back to bed. Not yet. As the sky lightened in the north-east, they wandered about in the wood, and Molly and Abigail gave Adam a lesson about birds and birdsong. Teaching aids were bursting into song all around them. Then they followed the disused railway track back to the main line and so on to the station, deserted in the coming dawn.

Even in the signal box, no one was on duty.

At a distant farm out in the fens, a cock crowed. Somewhere in the town a dog barked, and from the dairy almost two miles away came the sound of milk bottles being loaded, clear in the enormous stillness.

'Let's go back along Green Lane,' Molly said.

Through the goods yard and by the gasworks they went, slowly now, growing tired. And so to the grassy road that ran alongside the main line.

No trains were there this time, no sign of life of any kind, no sounds at all.

Then they became aware that there *was* a sound – the faint grumble of a distant aeroplane. They looked up. At first they couldn't see it, but from somewhere at an immense and unimaginable height, a plane was passing over.

There had been no air-raid warning, no siren. 'One of ours,' Adam said.

Watching over us, Molly thought.

The plane was flying at such a great altitude that the light of the coming sun caught it a couple of minutes before sunrise reached ground level. It was like a distant brilliant bird in the clear blue sky. A slim pencil-perfect vapour trail marked its flight, spilling behind it into a woolly skein of pink.

Adam turned to Abigail. 'Are you really going to make everyone call you Sarah?' he asked her.

Abigail shrugged. 'I probably won't bother,' she said.

Good! Molly thought happily.

The characters and incidents in this story are entirely fictional, and Great Deeping is a fictional town located a few miles north of Ely, about halfway between Littleport and Southery.

However, the idea for the story came from something that happened in fact. In June 1944 an ammunition train of fifty-one wagons was approaching Soham station in Cambridgeshire when the engine driver, Benjamin Gimbert, noticed in the darkness that the truck behind the engine, containing forty 500-lb bombs, was on fire. He stopped the train just outside Soham station so that the fireman, James Nightall, could jump down and uncouple the first two trucks. Their plan was to separate the burning truck from the rest of the train and tow it away from the station buildings and out of the town. This they did, but as they passed the signal box, Mr Gimbert leant out of the cab to shout to the signalman, Frank Bridges, to stop the mail train which he knew was almost due. But at that moment the bombs exploded. Soham station was destroyed and six hundred buildings in the town were damaged. The fireman was killed instantly, and the signalman later died of his injuries. Mr Gimbert, the driver, survived and eventually recovered.

It is not difficult to imagine what would have happened if the exploding truck had blown up the rest of the train. In recognition of their extraordinary courage, Benjamin Gimbert and James Nightall were awarded the George Cross.

I remember this incident well; I lived about ten miles away and my grandmother's house was in Soham. But I have also made use of an excellent account – to which I owe a debt of gratitude – on the www.soham.org.uk/history website. It was there that I came across the incident of the seized-up gramophone brought back to life by the explosion.

Victor Watson lives in an eighteenth-century cottage with his wife (who is a great help), two cats (which are no help at all) and a tortoise (which has been trying for forty years to escape). His children and grandchildren are helpful too (mostly).

He has taught many courses on children's literature and produced a number of books on the same subject. One of them is called *The Cambridge Guide to Children's Books in English* – a very fat book about children's authors. Now (at last!) he is writing children's books himself. The first, called *Paradise Barn*, tells the story of how Adam, a London evacuee, makes friends with Molly and Abigail in his new home, and helps to solve a wartime murder mystery. *Paradise Barn* was short-listed for the Branford Boase Award, a prize given annually to the most promising book by a first novelist.

CATNIP BOOKS
Published by Catnip Publishing Ltd
14 Greville Street
London EC1N 8SB

This edition first published 2011
1 3 5 7 9 10 8 6 4 2

Text copyright © Victor Watson, 2011
Map copyright © Suzy Durham, 2011

The moral rights of the author and illustrator have been asserted.
All rights reserved. No part of this publication may be reproduced,
stored in a retrieval system, or transmitted in any form or by any
means electronic, mechanical, photocopying, recording or otherwise,
without prior permission of the copyright owner.

A CIP catalogue record for this book is available from the British
Library.

ISBN 978-1-84647-118-6

Printed in Poland

www.catnippublishing.co.uk

KU-102-064

HOW TO USE THIS BOOK

Increasingly teachers in ordinary schools can expect to find in their classes children with disabilities who may have special educational needs. This book is designed to help such teachers. Some may find it helpful to read the whole book but others may prefer to select specific information.

The book is divided into two main parts. Part 1 covers various needs which may apply to any child with a disability in an ordinary school. Part 2 contains information about specific disabilities listed in alphabetical order. Each entry in Part 2 is sub-divided into three sections:

1. description of the disability
2. educational implications of the disability in terms of
     a) learning difficulties
     b) considerations for classroom management
3. additional points.

In many instances readers will find it helpful to refer to information in Part 1 after reading an entry in Part 2. For example, an understanding of Cerebral Palsy may be enhanced not only by the specific entry in Part 2 but also by reading about other related disabilities and sections in Part 1 concerning curriculum, communication and design needs. Cross references have been indicated and reading a combination of sections may be helpful when considering the needs of an individual child.

Appendix A gives a summary of the Education Act 1981. With the passing of this Act all teachers have become directly involved in the education of children with special educational needs and the summary outlines the implications of the Act and emphasises the importance of active participation by parents. The reader's attention is also drawn to Appendix B which gives further information on specific disabling conditions, Appendix C which supplies more general information and Appendix D which gives the names and addresses of organisations which can supply further information on children with special educational needs.

Illustrations

FOREWORD

It is now seven years since the publication of our report on children with special educational needs. The report expressed the view that many (though not all) children with special needs may be successfully educated in ordinary schools; and this remains my view. Successful placement of these children largely depends on the training given to teachers; and our report stressed that, if children with special needs are to do well in ordinary schools, they must be taught by teachers who understand their needs, and have the requisite skills and confidence to meet them. I therefore warmly welcome this book which I hope will contribute to a greater understanding of the needs of children with disabilities among teachers in ordinary schools. Other professionals may benefit from it as well. I am particularly pleased that the emphasis of the book is laid on the implications of disabling conditions in the classroom, and that it is written in non-medical language. I hope this approach will help to remove some of the medical mystique surrounding disability, which has often proved daunting to teachers.

I recommend this book to teachers, student teachers and all concerned with the education of children with disabilities in ordinary schools.

Mary Warnock

Mary Warnock

INTRODUCTION

Since the implementation of the Education Act 1981, RADAR has received a considerable number of enquiries from teachers who have been asked to take into their classes a child or group of children with special needs resulting from a disability. They are not seeking information about medical conditions but about the educational and social implications of those conditions in an ordinary school. A medical label often does not help a teacher very much, particularly as there is usually a wide range of abilities and disabilities under each one. The type of questions asked are:

> Will he have learning difficulties?
> Will he be incontinent?
> Will he use a wheelchair?
> Will he be able to eat school meals?

We have therefore produced these general guidelines for teachers to provide a helpful background against which they will be able to consider the individual requirements of each child with special needs resulting from a disability. I believe the book will help all those in education currently concerned with placing children with special needs in mainstream classes. Entire books could be written on each section but I hope, within the limitations of space, most of the major issues have been raised and practical advice and information given.

I am sure the book will be useful not only to teachers with designated responsibility for children with special needs but by all classroom teachers at both primary and secondary level, administrators, careers officers and medical and para-medical personnel working with children with disabilities. It can be used both as a basis for training and for self-help.

This guide offers a basic introduction to some of the special needs of children with disabilities. It has not been possible to include every disability but those most frequently encountered among children have been covered. Readers are recommended to seek further information about specific conditions from the relevant voluntary organisations (listed under Appendix D) and to extend their understanding by means of training courses and discussion with special school colleagues.

A lack of familiarity of the needs of children with disabilities causes many teachers to feel anxious about accepting them into their classes. This book shows that such fears are unfounded; it suggests practical ways in which difficulties may be overcome and problems anticipated and prevented; to the benefit of both teachers and children.

George Wilson

Director

ACKNOWLEDGEMENTS

The authors would like to thank the members of the Working Group, appointed by RADAR's Education and Training Committee, under whose guidance this book was prepared. The members of this Group were:

Elizabeth Rowe – chairperson
Wynn Evans
Guy Gray
Kit Hartley
David Hutchinson
Bert Massie
Barbara Riddick.

We also wish to thank all those who gave so much of their time and expertise to assist in the compilation of the book and we are particularly indebted to the members of RADAR's Education and Training Committee for their support and encouragement. In addition, we would like to thank the many teachers, voluntary organisations and the staff of the Department of Education and Science who generously assisted us.

We would like particularly to thank the following:

Robin Attfield
Diana Ernaelsteen
Pat Fitton
Frances Hasler
Fred Heddell
Paul Jamie
Gordon Mitchell
Lillian Ramsay
Winifred Tumim.

RADAR gratefully acknowledges the financial support of the Department of Education and Science and also of

The Nancy Balfour Trust
Lord Barnaby's Foundation
Emerton Charitable Trust
The Allen Lane Foundation
The Whitaker Charitable Trust

which has enabled us to undertake this project.

Judith Male
Claudia Thompson

CONTENTS

PART ONE

PART TWO

APPENDICES

PART ONE

CHAPTER 1

EDUCATIONAL
AND CURRICULUM NEEDS

INTRODUCTION

This section gives pointers for consideration in order to achieve successful integration of children with special needs. Inevitably, general terms are used but it cannot be overemphasised that all children with special needs must be considered on an individual basis. Like all others, they require a balanced curriculum which allows elements of both success and challenge.

1.   TEACHING CONSIDERATIONS

Many children with special needs have three main difficulties with regard to curriculum and learning:

    (a)   the effect of not receiving and absorbing all the information offered;

    (b)   the effect of finishing work more slowly and therefore not completing a task before starting the next one;

    (c)   the effect of their inability to transfer learning from one situation to another.

The following points are suggestions to help overcome some of these difficulties. Many of them relate to good teaching practice in general and are of benefit to all pupils but they may need to be carried out to a greater extent with some children with special needs:

    i.   preparation of learning materials may require more careful thought, incorporating, for example, smaller steps in learning, more opportunities for review and longer to practise skills;

    ii.   summaries of work are often useful and are particularly helpful to children who may be struggling to keep up because of hearing or sight problems or inability to take notes at speed. An oral summary at the beginning and/or end of the lesson will assist the child and written summaries, where practical, will help to reduce the problem of note-taking, leaving the child more time to concentrate on learning. Summaries may also be used to provide a helpful way of ordering information;

    iii.   where possible work should be presented in a recognisable sequence, with correction and review procedures incorporated, as some children with special needs require additional help to acquire and apply new concepts. Many commercially produced materials divide the currıculum into blocks, each of which introduces and reviews new material. Similarly many schoolbased programmes devised by remedial departments and specialist teachers use the same techniques. This offers greater flexibility to the classroom teacher, enabling him* to give help to individual pupils at appropriate points in the learning sequence. You may like to discuss different methods of presentation of learning materials with the appropriate specialist adviser and with colleagues;

iv. part of teaching techniques is to provide opportunities to practise using new skills or information. This is of particular value to children with special needs who may need longer to master new skills. Wherever possible, encourage them to present the information in their area of greatest strength, eg. orally, in writing or visually. Often typed sheets provide a legible and consistent method of presenting information to older pupils. Inevitably, additional practice takes time but with careful consideration of teaching methods many children with special needs will be able to keep pace with the rest of the class. If a child consistently experiences difficulties, additional support may be required and ultimately the placement of the child may need to be reconsidered;

v. where children have difficulty in transfering information from one situation to another conscious planning of cross-curricula links is helpful;

vi. where work is marked and time extensions are given to children with special needs, it is important to keep within the time limit expected of the rest of the class. Again it is a matter of finding the correct balance for each child. The method by which the pupil's work is to be assessed should be considered in the initial arrangements and timetable (see also chapter 11);

vii. as with all children, children with special needs, respond well to success in their work. For some children very great efforts will be required to achieve the desired results and the way you present and mark work will help to encourage them.

2. PRACTICAL SUBJECTS

Additional planning may be required to allow children with special needs to gain access to practical aspects of the curriculum, including science, home economics, craft, design and technology. Environmental factors play an important role in permitting access but the attitude of those involved is more crucial. Some children, eg. those with poor co-ordination, those in wheelchairs and those with

*The male pronoun is used throughout the book and should be taken to apply to both male & female.

sensory disabilities, may need adaptations to equipment to help them gain access to the curriculum. An occupational therapist will be able to advise you on ways in which equipment can be made more stable and additional help may be available from support teachers or a teacher's aide (see section 5 below). With proper supervision and equipment, many children with special needs can take part in practical lessons. The use of groups where two or three pupils work together on a task allows children with disabilities to participate whilst elements which they cannot carry out personally may be done by other members of the group. This helps to eliminate the impression of a child with special needs being treated in a special way. At the same time, try to ensure that he takes an active part in the task and is not always left to take notes of what the others are doing (see also chapter 9).

3. TIME AND TIMETABLING

Timetabling is always a balancing act between areas of priority. When a child needs additional time for certain elements of the curriculum (eg. careers advice, typing or self-care) a balance must be struck between the special needs of the child and the opportunity to participate in the widest possible general school curriculum. In the end, a compromise based on the individual needs of the child must be reached but this consideration is one of the most important if a child with special needs is to receive maximum benefit from placement in an ordinary school.

Some children with special needs are slower than average in performing a variety of tasks and this needs to be taken into consideration before the child starts school. Extra time may be required in the following areas:

(a) learning

(b) communicating – eg. writing and typing

(c) movement between lessons (of the child and sometimes of equipment)

(d) toileting needs

(e) additional requirements – eg. physiotherapy, speech therapy.

In an already crowded day, management of time has important implications for a child's educational needs. The five areas outlined above are discussed in more detail below:

(a) Learning

Some children with special needs require extra time to absorb and apply information. This is discussed in more detail in section 1 above. Children with some disabilities eg. asthma and heart conditions may have no apparent learning difficulties associated with their condition but the disability may indirectly result in a reduced learning ability and tiredness and sometimes have a substantial effect on the child's learning over a period of time.

15

(b) Communicating

Some children with special needs require extra time for communication. This is also discussed in more detail in section 1 above and in chapter 2.

(c) Movement Between Lessons

Movement between lessons may present difficulties for those using wheelchairs, calipers or other mobility aids. It is usually a greater problem for secondary schools with larger buildings and sites. If the child is consistently late for lessons, arrangements for him to leave the previous lesson a few minutes early may be considered (see Homework below). Whatever arrangement is made, try to keep it consistent so that everyone knows what to do and the child knows what is expected. There may be occasions, eg. when the class is doing a test, when the arrangements have to be changed in which case it is helpful to notify the teacher taking the next lesson so that the child is not unduly penalised. The distances between classrooms and staircases are other points to take into account when planning the school timetable so that long distances across large sites are avoided wherever possible. Trolleys are of immense help in moving around any large piece of equipment, eg. a typewriter or computer.

(d) Toileting Needs

A few children with disabilties may need to use the toilet more frequently than normal. Some, especially those in wheelchairs, may take longer than normal. Often these needs can be accommodated during break-times but occasionally they may interfere with lessons. Wherever possible try to encourage a regular routine and if toileting needs become a problem seek advice from the child's parents and the medical services. Meeting such needs is basic to successful integration and it is important to ensure that the appropriate help and facilities are available when the child needs them. (See also chapter 7).

(e) Additional Requirements

The two most common additional requirements of children with special needs are physiotherapy and speech therapy. If these are needed, they are essential to the child's health or communication needs and should not be underestimated. The problem for the school is fitting them into an already crowded timetable with the minimum of disruption. A multidisciplinary approach in developing programmes for individual children should include class teachers so that therapy (of various types) may be integrated into the main curriculum of the child; for example many children with spinal injuries have physiotherapy programmes which require them to stand for part of the day to help prevent deformities and improve their general health. Whilst this could be done at lunch-time the child could also stand during certain lessons provided he is given the correct equipment to enable him to participate in the lesson eg. a tray on the front of a standing frame allows the child to place a book on it and take part as normal in the lesson.

Similarly co-operation between the physiotherapist and the teacher can lead to innovative and imaginative ways of incorporating physiotherapy exercises into PE.

Sometimes it is impossible to incorporate therapy into the main curriculum and lessons have to be given up to allow time for therapy. Where this occurs very careful consideration must be given to the implications for the child's education and future career choices.

4. HOMEWORK

If homework is set, it is important to ensure that children with special needs are expected to attempt the same work as all others. If a child appears to be struggling with homework, it may be helpful to discuss this with his parents to establish the reasons. Homework is often set at the end of a lesson and if a child leaves early to get to the following lesson on time, a system should be devised to ensure that he is aware of the work expected, eg. he should know that he must check with one of his friends before he goes home. Alternatively, homework may be set before he leaves the class.

5. CLASSROOM SUPPORT

Some children, although severely disabled, are appropriately educated in ordinary classes. If such children require special assistance in order to learn, this may be supplied either in the form of a support teacher or a teacher's aide. Teacher's aides have different titles in different education authorities but their role, ie. to allow the child access to the curriculum, is broadly similar. Although teacher's aides usually have little or no formal training their experience with individual children can provide an enormous source of help to the class teacher and can make the difference between successful and failed integration. Some teachers are initially a little concerned about having another adult in the classroom and others do not know that this resource is available; but once they realise how much help an aide can offer, any doubts are usually quickly overcome. If a child with special needs takes up too much of your time and prevents you from giving enough attention to other pupils, an aide may be the best way to solve this problem as she* will relieve pressure on the teacher thereby allowing him to spend more time with the whole class. It is important for both the teacher and the aide to know the precise function of the aide and how this will be carried out in the classroom. The role will depend to a great extent upon the needs of the individual child or children allocated to the aide but may include, for example:

　　additional explanations – eg. for children with hearing difficulties

　　setting up equipment – eg. a typewriter

　　preparing work in alternative ways.

---

*Teacher's aides and welfare assistants are usually (but not exclusively) women, hence the female pronoun is used in reference to them.

The aim is to relieve the class teacher of this responsibility to allow him to spend more time with the class as a whole. It is up to the teacher to determine how best to use the aide. In order to be useful the aide needs to be well-informed and therefore you will probably find it helpful to include her in pre-class discussion on the content of the lesson and identify areas (eg. specific vocabulary or a summary of work) where she will be of most value to the child. As the aide becomes more familiar with the child she may be able to make helpful suggestions on methods of presenting work etc. You may also find that she can be of assistance to other children in the class and in this way she will be less clearly identified with one child.

6. ENVIRONMENTAL FACTORS

Advice about aids and adapations may be obtained from an occupational therapist or orthotist who can be contacted through the school medical service. Lighting and background noises need particular attention for children with sensory disabilities and special consideration should be given to seating arrangements for all children with disabilities to ensure that they are both comfortable and in the best position to assist their learning eg. close to the teacher, blackboard or any equipment they might need. Correct chair and desk heights are extremely important and children should have a firm base on which to work and where possible be able to place their feet flat on the floor (See also chapter 8). For children with muscular problems, the correct positioning of the shoulders and arms makes a great difference to their ability to write/type and seating arrangements should be carefully considered to allow optimum use of their hands.

All children, including those with special needs, have a range of attitudes and aptitudes. Their success in the classroom will depend to a great extent on their willingness to participate and help themselves. It will also depend on their ability to make use of compensatory senses, their sequencing memory and comprehension and upon their social ability to work with others. You may find that preparing for a child with special needs involves additional consideration of both your classroom and planning and presentation of teaching material. However, teachers who have experience of childern with disabilities in their classes often comment that the close attention given to the individual needs of these pupils frequently benefits the whole class.

CHAPTER 2
COMMUNICATION NEEDS

INTRODUCTION

Children whose special needs are in the area of communication, principally difficulties in speaking and writing, may be severely disadvantaged and are likely to need special help.

Communication difficulties in speech may be caused by physical problems, eg. deafness, lack of control of the muscles of speech (as in some children with Cerebral Palsy); or an abnormality of the mouth, tongue or throat. Alternatively, language difficulties may result from problems in organising information which may be manifested in vocabulary, syntax and ordering of words and phrases (as in children with Aphasia/Dysphasia).

In some instances speech can be developed through speech therapy in which case a programme is devised by the speech therapist often in conjunction with the teacher. This may include both regular sessions with the speech therapist and also co-ordinated training within the classroom. Where speech cannot be developed, or only to a very limited extent, children may need to use alternative forms of communication, often employing aids. Such alternatives are usually slow and less versatile than speech. They also severely reduce the opportunities a child might have to initiate coversation. Despite these problems, people with severe communication difficulties have successfully completed training courses and gained employment. Communication systems are constantly improving and allow people with speech problems to express their feelings of frustration at failing to understand or be understood in conversation. Such problems usually relate to people speaking too fast and lacking patience to understand.

Rhythm and intonation are important in speech and children with speech difficulties may need to learn to use rhythm and breath control to develop good communication. This is normally carried out under the guidance of a specialist teacher or speech therapist. Some children with speech difficulties rely heavily on written language. An aid may be needed to replace handwriting and hence response may be slow.

All children with special needs in the area of communication, in speech or writing, require individual consideration and, on the advice of a specialist teacher or speech therapist, may use one or a combination of the following communications techniques.

1. VISUAL DISPLAY AIDS

Visual display aids give an indication of the meaning of the message through a visual display usually consisting of pictures or symbols or sometimes words. The

19

Fig. 1

The basics of Blissymbolics

Blissymbolics is a graphic, meaning-based communication system. Some of the symbols are *pictographs:* They look like the things they represent.

house   man   woman   person   face

Some symbols are *ideographs:* They represent ideas.

before   after   protection   happy

Still other symbols are *arbitrary.*

a, an   the   this   that

The structure of the system enables the user to expand a small number of basic symbols into a symbol vocabulary of infinite size. Symbol elements are sequenced to create new symbol expressions.

person   and   visit   becomes   visitor

Through the addition or substitution of *indicators*, a symbol may be changed from one part of speech to another.

feeling   becomes   (to) feel   and   (to) sleep   becomes   asleep

A group of symbols designed as *strategies* allows a user to expand his symbol vocabulary. The examples below show the strategies of "opposite meaning" and "part of".

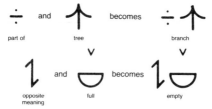

part of   and   tree   becomes   branch

opposite meaning   and   full   becomes   empty

Above all, Blissymbolics provides the user with the capability to communicate in *sentences.*

Father   wrote (a)   letter   Please   read

As an integral part of the system, a word equivalent appears under each symbol. This enables a person unfamiliar with Blissymbols to follow and understand the communications of a symbol user.

Blissymbolics used herein derived from the symbols described in the work, Semantography, original copyright © C.K. Bliss 1949.
BLISSYMBOLICS COMMUNICATION INSTITUTE
Exclusive licenses, 1982.

child may use his hand, a pointer or a light to indicate the message. This type of display is slow and limited but is easy to learn and provides a useful back-up system. There is a range of boards available. The system of symbols most commonly used is Bliss-symbolics.

2. AIDS USING PRINT

This type of aid requires the use of written language to spell out a message. The spelling board is perhaps the most basic and a typewriter the most common aid of this type. There are small portable communicators (some with additional print-out facilities) which fit into a pocket or strap to a wrist and these permit an unlimited number of messages. They take time to learn and use; ideally the child should be able to spell. The advent of micro-computers with memories has helped to increase the speed and selection of a range of frequently-used sentences which can be quickly coded by symbols. Larger computers are an extension of the same principle allowing words and symbols to be displayed either on a screen or printed paper. Such aids also permit children with communication difficulties to study foreign languages.

Fig 2

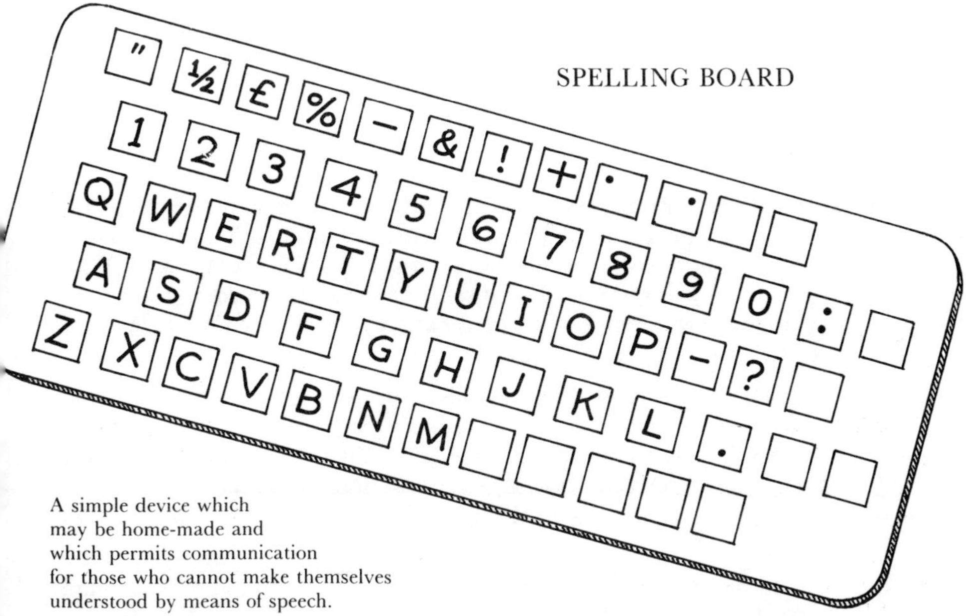

SPELLING BOARD

A simple device which may be home-made and which permits communication for those who cannot make themselves understood by means of speech.

3. SYNTHETIC SPEECH

Modern technology now allows synthetic speech to be produced through computers. Whilst these are currently rare in schools they are likely to be developed and used to a greater extent in the future and will help children with severe communication difficulties to integrate successfully in ordinary schools. The principle, ie. using a keyboard, is similar to the aids using print described above but the message is produced in the form of synthetic speech instead of print. Sometimes synthetic speech is used with visual display boards or aids employing print.

4. NON-VERBAL GESTURE, SIGN LANGUAGE AND SIGN SYSTEMS

These methods of communication include the natural gestures eg. a smile or a shrug, which we all use and structured systems which are formally taught. No one system is better than another; the main consideration is that the system should suit the user and his situation and facilitate his communication with others. As with other forms of communication it takes time to learn and practice using systems. A classroom teacher cannot be expected to learn a complete system (unless he wishes to do so) but it may be helpful it you know a few signs and in particular the sign for initiating contact, ie. "Hello". Peripatetic teachers of the deaf can offer advice about the extent to which signing should be used in individual cases (see also *Hearing Impairment*).

5. AIDS TO WRITTEN WORK

These include adaptations to writing tools, anchoring paper and the positioning of the child's desk; such considerations are particularly important for children with hand/arm disabilities (9) (see also *Loss of Limb*). Paper with extra wide lines may be of help to some children, particularly those with poor hand movement. Typewriters and word processors may sometimes be used in place of pens. When a child has to use a keyboard, keyboard skills need to be learned and speed and accuracy are gained with practice. Initially extra time will be required for written work at school and at home (See chapter 10).

Paper may need to be secured at a particular angle or anchored to the table; some children find it easier to work on a sloping surface. Seating the child in relation to the paper (or aid) may need to be considered to allow him to produce his best work. Some children who can type well need help to insert the paper into the machine although some new models now do this automatically as do many conputers.

Where a child has a visual disability, the choice of pen and paper, in strongly contrasting colours, may make a great difference to the standard of his work. You may find it helpful to seek advice from a peripatetic teacher of the visually impaired.

All technical aids require time for the user (and others) to become familiar with both its potential and limitations. Computers have opened up new and exciting areas for those with communication difficulties and they are gradually becoming established in schools. At the same time, the size of computers is continually decreasing thereby assisting with portability and storage. Computers should be insured either by the LEA or the parents depending upon how they are funded and the terms of the insurance policy will have implications for storage and security.

Often a child will need to learn more than one method of communication so, if his computer breaks down for example, he is still able to communicate by other means.

Further information about communication aids is available from speech therapists and Communication Aids Centres (addresses given in Appendix D). See also sections on Hearing Impairment and Aphasia.

Children with communication difficulties may require extra patience and understanding but they should be included in conversations, group activities and decisions. Try to ensure that they have their chance to "have a say".

CHAPTER 3

SOCIAL ASPECTS OF SCHOOL LIFE

INTRODUCTION

In addition to the benefits of the academic curriculum, children with special needs, like all others, should have the opportunity to develop their social skills whilst at school. This is one of the most important aspects of successful integration and yet, with all the other educational considerations which have to be taken into account, it may be overlooked. Many children with special needs are able to build up their social relationships without any assistance but for some children, particularly those with physical disabilities, special consideration may be required and this section offers suggestions to help encourage social integration at school.

1. ACCESS TO SCHOOL CLUBS AND SOCIETIES

Access to the curriculum is normally considered in detail before a pupil with special needs starts school but similar consideration is often not given to access to school clubs and societies. For example, a child who uses a wheelchair might show an interest in chess. The school chess club meets on Tuesday evening after school and he has to use LEA-provided transport which is inflexible. The problem might be resolved by changing the time of the club meeting or by altering transport arrangements, eg. perhaps one of his parents could pick him up on that evening or the school may be able to make alternative travel arrangements. Realistically, the solution may not be immediate or simple but with ingenuity and co-operation a compromise can often be achieved. It is important that all staff should know, from the time a child with a disability is admitted to the school, what is expected of them in terms of arranging and assisting with any special transport requirements; thus problems can be avoided.

The simple choice of venue for the club meeting may present problems for pupils with disabilites and dissuade them from joining. Wherever possible the room chosen should be accessible to all pupils who may wish to attend. Where there is a special unit attached to an ordinary school it has sometimes been found useful to arrange for clubs to meet in the units thereby encouraging all pupils to use it and helping to dispel a "ghetto" image.

2. UNSUPERVISED TIME

Time between lessons and at breaks allows pupils the opportunity for informal socialising. Where a child has mobility difficulties and has to leave a class early in order to reach the next one on time, this opportunity may be reduced. Similarly if he has regular sessions of physiotherapy or is allowed to stay inside at breaktime

24

in poor weather, these factors also reduce the time he is able to spend with his friends. For each individual pupil, educational and/or medical considerations need to be weighed against social considerations and a satisfactory compromise reached.

3. SCHOOL MEALS

Most children with special needs are able to join their peers in the school dining room and again lunchtime offers an important opportunity for social activity. Some children may have diet restrictions and therefore need different food but they should be encouraged to eat with others.

Where a self-service system is used, it is important that the child learns to manage this independently wherever possible even if it takes him longer than other pupils. This will help him to gain the confidence to use self-service cafes and restaurants when he leaves school.

A few children may have particular problems in eating eg. caused by weakness of facial muscles or poor hand-eye control. You may find it helpful to consult an Occupational Therapist on simple aids such as stabilising mats or special cutlery which will help overcome these problems and allow the pupils to remain part of the group without unnecessary embarrassment.

4. PRIVACY

Privacy is not normally regarded as part of school life but for a few children, particularly those who are incontinent, it is the most important factor in allowing them to become competent in and enjoy the social aspects of school life. Privacy is required for washing and changing if personal care skills are to be encouraged and developed. This helps the child to accept his condition without undue stress caused by curiosity on the part of others. A matter-of-fact routine with the necessary privacy will also encourage good standards of personal hygiene.

Some children may also need privacy while changing for PE.

5. SCHOOL OUTINGS AND HOLIDAYS

Outings and holidays offer extra opportunities for gaining independence and social skills which are of general benefit. They are of particular importance to some children with special needs who may need additional guidance and practice in such skills.

When buying a new school mini-bus it is worth considering the addition of a tail-lift which will assist pupils in electric wheelchairs or heavy pupils in wheelchairs to participate in school outings with the minimum of difficulty. Tail-lifts or ramps can also be fitted to existing mini-buses.

Some children with disabilities may require extra consideration when planning a trip eg. medical supplies, extra clothing or food. In addition, where mobility may be a problem, arrangements may need to be made for a folding chair to be taken

25

or a wheelchair to be available at the destination. This may be particularly important for children who do not normally need assistance with mobility in school but may do so where longer distances are to be undertaken. It is important to discuss this with the child if possible and where there is uncertainty, the parents should also be consulted as they may have worked out ways of meeting their child's needs while on trips and visits and their experience in this respect may be of value to you.

A visit to the destination beforehand, will often pinpoint any problem areas which may not have been considered, eg. access to toilets and unexpected steps. In addition it is often possible to negotiate favourable seating at theatres or concert halls, for children with impaired vision or hearing.

When planning outings it is prudent to check the school's insurance policy to ensure that children with special needs are covered.

6. OTHER SCHOOL ACTIVITIES

Extra-curricular activities such as concerts and plays offer pupils with special needs, not only an opportunity to practise social skills but also the opportunity to display abilities of which perhaps you, and even they, were not aware. The advantages of including children with special needs in such an event could be of enormous value both to the children with special needs, who may be struggling in other areas of school life, and to other pupils. Special arrangements, eg. transport, may be needed to allow a child with special needs to take part in rehearsals but if he knows such arrangements can be made this may encourage him to participate and increase his social skills. Conversely, the child may decide to use practical difficulties as an excuse to avoid practising social skills unless participation is made as easy as possible.

7. SELF ADVOCACY

Many young people with special needs are underconfident in social situations and they may need additional help in learning to express opinions. It is very important that they should know, from an early age, that their views, particularly with regard to decisions affecting them, are valid and will be treated seriously. If this confidence can be gained at school, there is a better chance that they will be able to apply it later in life and be able to take a more positive role in decisions such as where they will live, what job they will do and whether they join social clubs etc.

8. RELATIONSHIPS WITH OTHER PUPILS AND STAFF

Many children with special needs form friendships easily but a few children may need help in this respect. Where social isolation appears to be developing it may be helpful to assign another pupil to sit next to the child with special needs and help him in practical tasks if required. This may help to foster friendships and may only be necessary for a short time until social confidence has developed. The choice of the fellow pupil should be made with care; try to find children who are sympathetic and will allow the child with special needs to contribute to the group without dominating or making excessive demands.

Where a child with special needs has a teacher's aide or welfare assistant working with him, it is important to ensure that the adult does not become an obstacle to relationships with other pupils. If a child is over-dependent, it may be helpful to withdraw the aide/assistant or allocate her to other children from time to time.

Social acceptance of a child with special needs, particularly those who are noticeably physically different, may be enhanced by a brief explanation to the other children before he joins the class. The decision about whether to do this must be made on an individual basis and preferably in consultation with the child's parents as there may be a danger of stigmatising the child. However, when it is considered helpful to give an explanation, the positive attributes of the child should be presented as well as any special difficulties he might have, eg. for secondary pupils you might say:

> "A is joining us next week. He uses a wheelchair because he has weak legs. He may need a bit of help getting around school but he won't be treated differently and I shall expect the same standard of work from him as from you."

It might also be helpful for the child himself to have a simple explanation of his condition to answer curious questions.

All children need the opportunity to practise social skills while they are at school but those with special needs may require more and/or longer opportunities to achieve the same standards as others. Many of the points outlined above are often taken for granted but careful consideration of the social needs of children with special needs can bring enormous benefits. For many children social skills will be as important in determining their future life as any academic qualifications they may achieve.

CHAPTER 4

COUNSELLING AND PASTORAL CARE

INTRODUCTION

Children with special educational needs have the same basic emotional needs as other children but they may require additional support to meet these needs. The approaches and structures adopted by schools for meeting the emotional needs of children vary considerably; likewise the support services for pupils and teachers. Emotional needs of pupils in general may be divided into two broad categories:

(a) learning to manage periods of transition between environments;

(b) learning to adapt to different age-related expectations.

Learning to develop social skills and to accept responsibilities are part of the education of all pupils but are of particular importance to a child who has the additional barrier of a disability to overcome.

1. PROBLEMS OF PUPILS WITH SPECIAL EDUCATIONAL NEEDS DURING TRANSITION PERIODS

There are three main transition periods through which all pupils pass; these and some of their implications are set out below:

Transition Periods for all Pupils	Implications
1) Entering primary school	i) Adapting to new relationships with authority figures eg. teacher not mother
	ii) Adapting to new relationships with peers
	iii) New demands on concentration and attention
	iv) Development of new skills
2) Entering secondary school	i) Adapting to new lines of authority and to a number of teachers
	ii) Adapting to an expanded range of social relations
	iii) Increased and different demands on study skills and organisation of time
	iv) New responsibilities, routines and rules

28

3) Entering Work/Further
   Education and Training
       i) Adapting to new lines of
   administration
       ii) Adapting to different social roles
       iii) Increased and different demands on
   work skills and organisation of time
       iv) Different responsibilities and
   consequences of mistakes

In addition some children with special needs have extra problems which may include:

i) developing independence despite a disability;

ii) facing periods of illness and/or medical restriction on activity;

iii) learning to manage the time demands imposed by the need to acquire additional skills eg. typing or for additional requirements eg. physiotherapy;

iv) overcoming lack of experience in social skills or in using new equipment/materials;

v) learning to assess a situation dispassionately in order to establish the possibilities or accept the restrictions imposed by the disability;

vi) dealing with the expectations of others.

2. PROBLEMS OF PUPILS WITH SPECIAL EDUCATIONAL NEEDS DURING ADOLESCENCE

As they grow older all children are expected to assume more responsibility and develop increased independence. Adolescence brings the new challenge of establishing an adult self-identity which includes an adult self-image; independent responsibility and decision-making; sexual awareness and awareness of mortality.

Children whose special needs may have reduced early experiences or restricted social opportunities may therefore be less well prepared for the changes brought about by adolescence. They also have the specific problem of distinguishing their real abilities and limitations from the stereotype images held by other people.

The need for counselling varies with individual pupils but coming to terms with being a handicapped adult and the consequent adjustments in terms of self-image may cause a great deal of stress which is not necessarily less for a child born with a disability than for one whose disability has been acquired. This realisation may occur suddenly even when a pupil appears to have accepted other implications of his disability. The specialist counselling required in these circumstances is likely to be beyond the resources of an ordinary school and help should be sought from professional counsellors or voluntary organisations with specific knowledge of the disability.

3. EDUCATIONAL COUNSELLING

Children with a disability may require additional information on which to base choices of subject options and career possibilities. The extra time which may have been needed in the early stages of their education to master the use of equipment, or for medical treatment, may affect their choices. Further Education/Training is available in a variety of settings and a knowledge of the possibilities and the way they may meet individual needs is essential for the pupil and his family. Provision of this information may involve obtaining extra material from a Specialist Careers Officer when preparing lessons about options after school (see also chapter 12).

CHAPTER 5
SPECIAL EMOTIONAL AND BEHAVIOURAL NEEDS

INTRODUCTION

All children have emotional needs and ways of meeting these are considered in chapter 4. This chapter is concerned with children who have special emotional needs over and above those of most other children. Whether these emotional needs result in behavioural problems depends partly upon the personal resources of the child, partly upon the nature of the problem and partly upon the type and amount of support provided.

Many emotional problems are transitory and can be resolved without specialist help but there is a small number of children (including those who are hyperactive and/or easily distracted despite their efforts to concentrate) who are particularly vulnerable to emotional stress and who may require specialist help and treatment. Treatment may include medication which can affect attention, memory and vulnerability to accident. Such children may therefore require more protection and supervision.

We all interact with other people and to some extent our behaviour is governed by their response. Hence you may find that a change in your behaviour will produce the desired change in the behaviour of the child. It is particularly important that these children are treated in a consistent manner by adults; parents may be able to work with teachers in seeking to change situations which cause problems for their child. It is therefore especially helpful for schools to develop links, either formally or informally, with parents.

There is a small number of children whose emotional problems are so profound that specialist help is needed (see section 4 below).

1. GENERAL TEACHING TECHNIQUES

It is helpful to look for the positive attributes of the child and strengthen and support these. In terms of curriculum this may mean giving the child alternative ways of expressing himself eg. through a combination of drawing and writing if writing is an area of weakness. It may also be helpful to break tasks down into small stages and give encouragement as each task is completed. Success and praise are important for all children and particularly for those with special emotional needs. In this way a chain of negative behaviour and punishment can be avoided and the child's learning ability can be encouraged.

Some of these children have a limited tolerance to frustration and therefore learn better when they are not under too much pressure. A relaxed manner on the part

31

of adults will help to reduce anxiety in the child and it is sometimes also helpful if he knows that there is a place available to relax.

Counselling may be used to improve the child's awareness of both the source and consequences of his behaviour and is most effective when the child desires help. Without this basic commitment counselling becomes an imposition and is unlikely to achieve the desired result. Counselling must be undertaken with sensitivity under the guidance of the head of pastoral care at the school and other professionals where appropriate.

The overall aim of teaching techniques with regard to children with special emotional needs is to develop a good relationship between adult and child as a foundation for the child to gain success and, in turn, motivation and confidence to explore his environment, both educational and social, and to learn to understand both its potential and its limitations.

2. BEHAVIOUR MANAGEMENT TECHNIQUES

Behaviour management aims to analyse a specific behaviour pattern and where appropriate seeks to alter it in a way which allows for a new pattern to be learned. It is important to be sure of the purpose of such intervention and this should only be undertaken by teachers with the support of a trained professional in this work, eg. a psychologist or psychiatrist.

Children whose behaviour, as a result of their emotional problems, is demanding or aggressive may seem threatening to a teacher but there are many techniques which can be employed to avoid confrontation and develop a more attractive learning environment. The Schools Psychological Service may be able to advise you on such techniques.

Children with special emotional needs often find it helpful if clear limits on their behaviour are set. They may test out those limits but if the restrictions are few and reasonable and the environment is structured and consistent, this will often assist their development.

Some children with special emotional needs also have poor social skills and it may be necessary to develop a conscious programme to improve these skills. A joint approach between teachers, parents and other adults in contact with the child will help to ensure consistency and give him the opportunity to practise social skills with several adults.

3. IMPLICATIONS FOR ORGANISATION AND MANAGEMENT

The atmosphere in the school and the way pastoral care is arranged may affect the behaviour of children with special emotional needs. An emphasis on rewards and praise, opportunity to take responsibility and participate in the running of the school, together with clear leadership and good relationships between staff and pupils, all support children with special emotional needs and will, in turn, help them to develop more acceptable behaviour. It is important to consider classroom routines which enable children to develop their social skills and allow them opportunities for enjoyable social experience which, in turn, encourage a more positive attitude towards school and learning.

Behaviour problems are often associated with emotional difficulties in other parts of children's lives outside school and a supportive school can offer respite for the child. Remedial help where appropriate and setting tasks within the child's ability may assist in building up his self-esteem and a relaxed atmosphere within the classroom may facilitate learning.

4. SOURCES OF HELP AND ADVICE

Where problems are severe, other professionals may be able to assist but before any intervention takes place the problem must be defined in terms of a specific description of behaviour, where and how often it occurs and identification of any precipitating factors. By examining this information a pattern may emerge which, in turn, may indicate ways of intervening. When problems occur in only one type of situation or in one place such as school, a change of environment is usually very effective.

The head of pastoral care will be aware of sources of help and advice outside the school and may also be able to offer support to teachers who wish to explore ways of developing techniques to provide assistance for children with special emotional needs within school. Some LEAs have resources to provide a "breathing space" for children who have severe emotional problems, either in the form of special provision within school or a unit outside the formal school setting. Provision may be made between colleagues on an informal basis or, if necessary, by a formal placement.

Further specialist help is available from the Schools Psychological Service, Child Guidance and Child and Family Psychiatric Clinics.

CHAPTER 6

LIAISON WITH PARENTS AND SUPPORT SERVICES

INTRODUCTION

When a child with a disability starts school, it becomes a focus for many of the professional services surrounding him. Although there may be a large number of professionals involved with the child, the main aim of all of them is to provide support in three basic ways:

1) to enable him to participate fully in school life;
2) to ensure that the social, physical and psychological needs of the child are met;
3) to enable him to use his abilities to the full.

1. LIAISON WITH PARENTS

As those with primary responsibility for meeting the needs of the child, the parents have a very important place in the provision of services. Their personal concern for the child is often increased when he has a disability and this may be shown in different ways depending, to some extent, upon their experiences in attempting to meet the pre-school needs of the child and upon their relationships with other professionals concerned with the child. Most parents, of course, already have several years' experience in meeting the special needs of their child before he starts school and you may find it helpful to draw on this in establishing the best ways to manage the child's needs at school. Good home-school co-operation is particularly important for children with special needs and making an extra effort to get to know parents may be very helpful to both the school and the family.

You are likely to find that parents can supply a great deal of introductory information about the child and his special needs which will be helpful to you. If teachers and parents develop the habit of sharing information at an early stage, this contributes greatly to good relations between them and, even more importantly, to a co-ordinated approach to the child. In this way, parents may be able to help you by reinforcing teaching programmes at home.

Until children with disabilities start school, parents, particularly mothers, are often responsible for 24-hour care which may impose considerable demands upon them. It is worth remembering that school provides a regular routine which enables both children and parents to build up social contacts outside home. A crisis in the child's condition, management problems and learning to accept the

34

Fig 3

MODEL OF MULTI-DISCIPLINARY SUPPORT
FOR A CHILD WITH SPECIAL EDUCATIONAL NEEDS

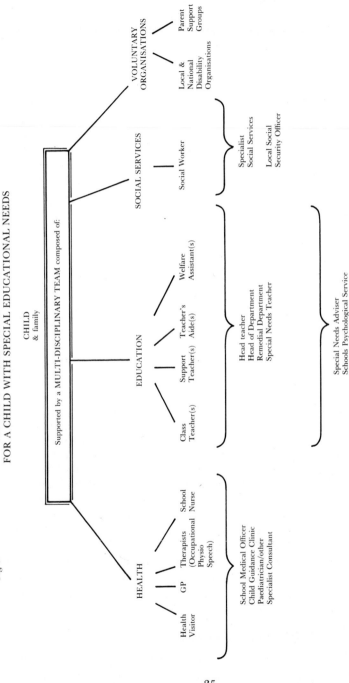

CHILD
& family

Supported by a MULTI-DISCIPLINARY TEAM composed of:

HEALTH

Health
Visitor

GP

Therapists
(Occupational
Physio
Speech)

School
Nurse

School Medical Officer
Child Guidance Clinic
Paediatrician/other
Specialist Consultant

EDUCATION

Class
Teacher(s)

Support
Teacher(s)

Teacher's
Aide(s)

Welfare
Assistant(s)

Head teacher
Head of Department
Remedial Department
Special Needs Teacher

Special Needs Adviser
Schools Psychological Service
Specialist Careers Officer
Educational Welfare Officer
Peripatetic Teaching Service
Teachers Centres
National Professional Associations

SOCIAL SERVICES

Social Worker

Specialist
Social Services

Local Social
Security Officer

VOLUNTARY
ORGANISATIONS

Local &
National
Disability
Organisations

Parent
Support
Groups

* This diagram is intended to give an indication of those who may support a child with special
educational needs and his family at various stages as the child grows up.

35

disability all place additional burdens on the parents and the family may need support from either or both statutory and voluntary services. Whilst it is not to be expected that teachers should take on this responsibility it is important that you are aware of the needs of the whole family in this respect and how these may have a bearing on the child.

2. LIAISON WITH SUPPORT SERVICES

A good communication system is a crucial element in the provision of services for a child with special needs and this may require special consideration within the school; within the Educational Authority; between the Education and Health Services, Social Services and/or Voluntary Agencies. Clearly the parents have a major role in co-ordinating services but the school, and particularly the teacher with responsibility for children with special needs, has a similarly important role in co-ordinating the services, educational or otherwise, available to the child at school.

3. LIAISON WITHIN THE CLASSROOM

Some teachers have the services of a support teacher, teacher's aide or welfare assistant within the classroom; for this additional support to be effective, it is important for those concerned to discuss the way support is to be organised, routines to be established and methods of record-keeping. This enables more flexible use to be made of teaching time and helps to solve difficulties and avoid misunderstanding. Planning and organising classroom support takes time and you may need to take time from your teaching timetable to ensure that adequate preparation and co-ordination takes place.

It is equally necessary to discuss joint concerns and consider strategies with peripatetic teachers and/or Health Authority staff who visit the child. This will help both parties to understand the function of the other. For example, a physiotherapist might want a child to stand for part of the day and it may be possible to arrange this so that he stands in a lesson when a Welfare Assistant is available to assist if necessary. In another instance, a teacher may wish to discuss a child's writing difficulties with an occupational therapist who may be able to suggest a simple and effective way to overcome the problem. The member of staff with overall responsibility for special needs in the school, a peripatetic teacher or school nurse should know how to contact these professionals if they are not already visiting the school.

As stated above, close contact with the child's parents with regard to day-to-day management of learning, health and physical aids is essential to teachers.

4. LIAISON WITHIN THE SCHOOL

Within a school, some methods of communication are formalised (Health and

Safety requirements may be circulated and record-keeping between departments may be collated by a third party) but information about the needs of individual children is often passed from one member of staff to another on an informal basis. It is important to ensure that information is not lost or misinterpreted and therefore, although it may be tedious and time-consuming, it is preferable that such information is written down. Liaison between staff over pupils with special needs may be an extension of existing forms of communication but may also need to be done on a more personal basis. It is important that one member of staff, eg. the teacher with overall responsibility for children with special needs or the class teacher, should be known to everyone as the central point of communication for the special needs of individual pupils.

An effective liaison system is essential where children receive teaching from different sources, eg. a special unit and mainstream classes or a special school and a mainstream school. Areas to be covered might include:

> responsibility for co-ordination of teaching;
>
> provision of special equipment (eg. brailled worksheets);
>
> co-ordination of support staff;
>
> informing those concerned with playground or mealtime supervision of any special needs of pupils (eg. when a child should be allowed to stay inside during bad weather);
>
> arrangement of alternative physical education (eg. swimming with another class instead of field games).

There should be a contact person within each school who is able to advise staff where to seek help regarding any problems which may arise in meeting special educational needs of children. This responsibility is often most usefully designated to a senior member of staff.

5. LIAISON WITH OTHER PROFESSIONALS

Joint professional consultation may take place both formally and informally and a combination of the two approaches is often the most effective. Formal discussion may be of help in the following areas:

> timetable of special requirements (eg. physiotherapy or typing and the consequent implications for time available for other subjects);
>
> provision, maintenance and effectiveness of aids and appliances within the school;
>
> liaison between teachers, parents and medical staff in respect of responsibility for aids, medical appointments, drug treatment, physical care, limits on physical exertion and playground activities;
>
> consideration with regard to school holidays or visits.

6. IN-SERVICE TRAINING

School-based in-service training with regard to children with special needs may be arranged with the help of LEA advisers, parents, professionals and voluntary organisations. Where a member of staff has overall responsibility for special needs within the school, his job description may include arranging in-service training for other members of staff.

The Local Education Authority may arrange in-service training through teachers' centres, summer schools or at local schools. Special school teachers and peripatetic specialist teachers may also be able to help with training.

Consultation and discussion between teachers, parents and professionals from other disciplines is not always easy to arrange but if everyone works together and understands the purpose and role of others this will lead to an improvement in the way a child's special needs are met at school.

CHAPTER 7

MEDICAL AND PERSONAL NEEDS

INTRODUCTION

Each school has its own system for dealing with the medical needs of its pupils which might include, for example, a sick-bay, first aid kit, accident book and visits by medical staff on a routine basis. Any additional medical or personal requirements of children with special needs can usually be accommodated within the existing system or be made an extension of it. Many children with special needs have no additional medical and/or personal needs which require special consideration at school but some may have such needs in the following areas:

1. incontinence
2. administration of drugs
3. personal health care equipment – eg. inhalers, syringes
4. diet/fluid restrictions.

Parents can supply information and advice on their child's medical/personal needs. It is essential to keep a record of any routine health care needs of individual pupils and also to have two emergency telephone numbers of parents or other relatives together with the appropriate medical contact.

WELFARE ASSISTANCE

Welfare assistance, ie. an adult helper, is provided where a child needs extra personal help in order to attend school. This help is often in the form of physical assistance; in ensuring that the child (with any necessary equipment) is in the right place at the right time; assisting with toileting and sometimes also assisting where practical help is needed in lessons. The roles of the teacher's aide (see page 17) and the welfare assistant may be indistinct in some education authorities but in general terms a welfare assistant is primarily concerned with the physical needs of the child whereas the function of a teacher's aide is primarily to supply support in learning. In practice the two coincide in many areas; both forms of assistance are designed to allow the child, whether at primary or secondary level, to gain maximum benefit from his education.

At secondary level, although the purpose of welfare assistance may be the same as for primary children, methods of carrying it out should be adapted in line with both the increasing maturity of the child and the increased complexity of the secondary school environment. Children at secondary school have, not only to work out new solutions to old problems, but also to tackle new problems posed by increasing independence and responsibility. Children are often unaware of, or unwilling to ask for, additional help and support and may all too readily accept the idea that their difficulties are their own responsibility rather than the result of environmental factors.

The four areas listed in the introduction above are discussed in more detail below:

1. INCONTINENCE

Only a small proportion of children, mostly those with spinal damage, are incontinent yet this is often the factor which causes most concern among teachers. Of those who are incontinent most children currently being placed in ordinary schools have developed a method of managing their incontinence with the minimum inconvenience. Many older pupils are able to manage independently and younger children are normally allocated a welfare assistant to help with these needs. A routine can usually be developed and this lessens the risk of "accidents". If an "accident" does occur in the classroom, allow the child to be excus. immediately without causing him embarrassment. If this starts to happen frequently, it is advisable to consult the child's parents and, if necessary, see medical advice. It might be useful to keep a record of any "accidents" and if you find they occur regularly on, for example, Wednesday afternoons at the beginning of a particular lesson, start asking questions!

The basic requirements for successful management of incontinence are the provision of appropriate facilities, eg. a flat surface to lie on and mirrors in the changing room, privacy and an established routine. Physical arrangements and appropriate assistance may have resource implications which should be carefully considered in advance to prevent discomfort or embarrassment for pupils and overburdening of staff. It is also important to remember that some pupils, eg. those with progressive diseases such as Muscular Dystrophy, are likely to need an increasing amount of help. In each instance the child should know what he needs to do and who to ask for help if it is required.

2. ADMINISTRATION OF DRUGS

Some conditions require the use of drugs on a regular basis and a few children may need to take them during school time. Depending upon the age and maturity of the child, it may be possible for him to take responsibility for any drugs he needs himself. For younger children it is usually preferable for a simple procedure to be devised and for one person to take responsibility for the drugs being taken; for example, as described in the following instructions:

> "J's tablets are kept in the locked cupboard in the school secretary's office.* He must have two each lunch-time and will come and ask for them at the end of morning lessons. In emergencies, his mother may be contacted at . . . . . . or telephone Dr. Smith . . . . ."

The routine makes it easier for all concerned to remember that the drugs must be taken and should be rigidly kept even on sports days etc.

*Any drugs kept in school must be kept in a locked cupboard designated for that purpose in a room which is not normally accessible to children and is itself lockable.

When school outings are being planned, consideration must be given to essential drugs for any pupil. When outings last longer than the normal school day, it may sometimes be necessary for children who do not normally need drugs in school time to take them. It is essential for one person to have responsibility to ensure that the child takes any necessary drugs during the outing. Some conditions, eg. epilepsy, may be controlled by regular dosage of drugs and missing a dose may have serious consequences later on.

Some drug treatments have side effects which may need consideration. A few children may have treatments which physically alter their appearance and the psychological effects of this may need to be taken into account, eg. the child may need protection from teasing from others. Some drugs may cause drowsiness which in turn affects the child's performance in school. This may happen temporarily whilst doctors are establishing the correct dosage to control the condition but if it becomes a regular occurrence you should discuss this with the child's parents and the school doctor.

3. PERSONAL HEALTH CARE EQUIPMENT

A few children may need to use personal medical equipment such as inhalers (for children with asthma) and syringes (for children with diabetes and haemophilia). It is important that staff understand their function and therefore when they should be used, eg. inhalers may be used before exercise although there is no apparent reason for a child to use them at such a time. Written instructions concerning the use of such equipment should be available to staff. As with drugs, a simple routine is usually the best way for both the child and staff to manage these needs.

4. DIET/FLUID RESTRICTIONS

A few children have diet requirements which must be strictly observed. Such requirements should be discussed with the child's parents and medical advisers before he starts school. Once the diet is established it is essential that all staff including dinner ladies are kept informed of any special arrangements.

Some children, particularly those in wheelchairs, may become overweight and are advised to diet by their doctors. The parents may seek the co-operation of the school in keeping to the diet and again, it is important, even though it may seem harsh, to maintain the diet. A dinner lady who feels sorry for an overweight child in a wheelchair and offers him an extra portion of chips can, in seconds, ruin the efforts of everyone else.

If medical and personal needs are recognised and ways to manage them planned in advance, they should not present undue difficulties for the classroom teacher. Simple routines usually suffice but it is important that all staff in contact with the child are aware of the appropriate action to take. Communication is perhaps the greatest problem in a large school; it is useful for all staff (including supply teachers and non-teaching staff where appropriate) to know where to obtain advice concerning the medical needs of individual children.

41

CHAPTER 8

DESIGN AND ENVIRONMENTAL NEEDS

INTRODUCTION

Among children with special needs those with physical and sensory disabilities may require additional consideration in terms of design and the physical environment of the school. Such disabled pupils need to be able to use the school premises with the maximum degree of independence and on the same terms as other pupils if their placement within an ordinary school is to be successful. The term "access" covers not only the ability to get into a building but, more widely, the avoidance of barriers and the provision of features to enable disabled people to make maximum use of the facilities. Within a school, access for disabled pupils needs to be considered with regard not only to classrooms but also other areas such as sports facilities and social areas.

1. SCHOOL BUILDINGS

The Department of Education and Science has issued guidance[1] outlining the basic features of a school which are necessary for unhindered use by disabled pupils; these include parking arrangements, entrances, maximum ramp gradients, widths of doors and doorways, internal changes of level and adaptations to toilet facilities. The Department has also issued guidance[2] covering room lay-out, both general and for particular subjects, storage and other space requirements and on the specific design requirements of children with sensory disabilities[3].

Although new school buildings should now be designed with the needs of disabled pupils in mind, many existing buildings are not so designed. In many instances it is possible to carry out adaptations to improve access for disabled pupils and often alterations are only of a minor nature and can be made within existing school resources. DES guidance must inevitably be based upon general requirements and even in an "accessible" school adjustments may be needed for individual pupils. Equally, a school which does not meet the standards of the guidance may still be able to cater successfully for disabled pupils.

2. PUPILS WITH MOBILITY PROBLEMS

If your school is considering taking pupils with mobility problems, a valuable practical exercise is to borrow a wheelchair (from a local special school, social services department or hospital) sit in it and find your way around the school. Apart from the practical use of such an experiment, it will also give you a much clearer insight into the difficulties a child in a wheelchair might have in the school building. This knowledge can then be used both to support the case for any building work and also to anticipate any problems. It will also be of value in discussing the requirements of individual pupils. It should be remembered that such requirements may vary significantly as the child grows up.

It is often not recognised that children who use walking aids, calipers, sticks and crutches, may have greater difficulty in getting around a school building than those who are more severely disabled and use wheelchairs. They are likely to be more vulnerable to accidents through crowding in corridors and playgrounds and may take much longer to travel from one classroom to another than a child in a wheelchair. For long distances it may be more convenient for the child to use a wheelchair instead of struggling with walking aids; the advantages and disadvantages should be carefully weighed in each case. It is important to establish the level of mobility of such children before they enter school as you may find, for example, that a child can manage on a flat surface but cannot cope with stairs. Children using crutches and walking aids often need almost as much space to manoeuvre as those in wheelchairs and this should be taken into account when arranging classroom furniture etc.

3. EASY ADAPTATIONS

Frequently, the alterations needed to make a building accessible can be carried out easily. At the simplest level, such alterations may only involve changing the height of a coat hook, moving a door-stop so that the door opens more widely, or rearranging furniture. It may be appropriate to use temporary ramps, whether they be portable ones which are put in place only when required or those which can be left in position on a longer term basis. Handrails and half steps (See illustration) may be helpful to some children particularly those with poor mobility. Marking steps and other ground-level hazards (with a contrasting coloured paint – usually white) is a safety precaution of general value but will also be of particular help to children with poor sight.

While permanent solutions to problems in the use of buildings are desirable, realistically it may be acceptable to employ temporary solutions to meet immediate needs. For example, tap turners can be used in laboratories and kitchens prior to permanent adaptations to make taps easier to use. (See illustration). Desks, tables and other furniture can be raised by the use of blocks under the legs and a wide range of devices are available to assist pupils in the use of controls and objects that would otherwise be out of reach or difficult to manipulate. An occupational therapist can advise on such adaptations. Aids and adaptations of this nature can be bought but many secondary schools take pride in making them within woodwork or metalwork classes. Primary schools may be able to ask their local secondary school for assistance. Sometimes caretakers are able to help with this type of work.

Fig 4   HALF-STEP

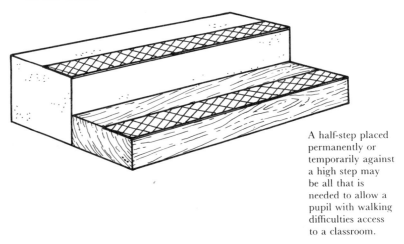

A half-step placed
permanently or
temporarily against
a high step may
be all that is
needed to allow a
pupil with walking
difficulties access
to a classroom.

Fig 5   TAP TURNERS

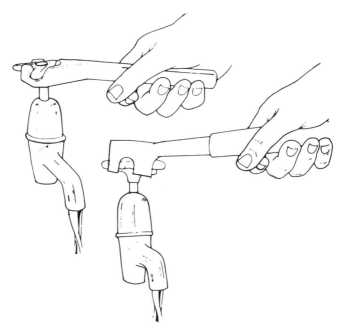

Long-handled tap turners

4. TIMETABLING

Where buildings cause severe problems you may be able to consider adjustments to the timetable and arrangements within lessons. In some instances it may be possible to move a lesson from an inaccessible to an accessible part of the building. Clearly, it is preferable to take such points into account when planning the timetable but there may be occasions, eg. when a pupil has to use a wheelchair while recovering from an accident, when relocation of lessons is an option to consider on a short-term basis. The storage of material may also be arranged so that objects needed by a disabled pupil are within his reach. It may be helpful for him to use a particular part of the classroom where all the materials he requires are easily available. Additional time for travel between classes may be required particularly if long distances have to be covered or special equipment such as scissor lifts or mobile stair-climbers have to be used. (See also chaper 1).

5. SCHOOL VISITS

When school visits are arranged the needs of disabled pupils in terms of accessibility of places to be visited should be taken into consideration. This is covered in more detail in chapters 3 and 9.

In some instances, help from other people, whether welfare assistants, teaching staff or fellow pupils, may be unavoidable. However this should be kept to a minimum to avoid both overdependence on the part of the pupil and unnecessary work for other people. In the short term it may be expedient for a child in a wheelchair to have assistance in managing a doorstep but this should not be used as an excuse for not providing a ramp. Design may either promote or obstruct personal independence and can play an important part in the shaping of attitudes of disabled children.

1. *Access for Disabled People to Education Buildings*   Design Note 18
   Department of Education and Science   Architects and Building Group (1984)
2. *Design for Children with Special Educational Needs – Ordinary Schools*
   Building Bulletin 61   Department of Education and Science (1984)
3. *Lighting and Acoustic Criteria for the Visually Handicapped and Hearing Impaired in Schools*
   Design Note 25   Department of Education and Science (1981)

(See also reading list in Appendix C)

CHAPTER 9

SAFETY

INTRODUCTION

When first considering the possible placement of a child with special needs in an ordinary school, teachers are often very concerned about safety issues. Safety is undoubtedly important but it must be placed within the wider context of the child's individual needs and the facilities of the school. Realistically, you cannot guarantee that a child with special needs will not have an accident while at school; neither can this be guaranteed for any other child. However, there are a number of precautions which can be taken to minimise the risk of accidents and this chapter offers a few general points which you may like to consider and adapt as appropriate for your own situation.

Teachers are sometimes worried about being held responsible in the case of an accident. You may therefore find it helpful to know that the legal requirement of teachers is that they should exercise a standard of care equivalent to that of a reasonably careful parent. Neither a headteacher nor a teacher is automatically legally liable for any injury sustained by pupils in their care. In order to maintain legal liability it is necessary to establish that there has been negligence or carelessness which has directly resulted in injury to a pupil. This applies equally to all children, including those with special needs. Safety issues should be discussed before the child starts school but if you are concerned about specific aspects of safety you may find it helpful to discuss these with a senior member of staff.

Many children with special needs present no additional safety problems for ordinary schools. Therefore, to have a child with special needs in your class does not automatically imply the need for any additional safety precautions. Each child will need individual consideration. However, there are six groups of children with special needs who may require additional consideration:

1.   those with poor co-ordination
2.   those with sensory disabilities
3.   those prone to fractures and/or bruising
4.   those in wheelchairs
5.   those who walk slowly and/or have balancing difficulties
6.   those with epilepsy.

The following general guidelines may be of help to you in ensuring the safety of children with special needs:

(a) obtain as much information as possible about the child's needs;

(b) talk to the child's parents about safety (they may be able to give you a great deal of help in anticipating any difficulties which could arise);

(c) make emergency plans in advance so that you know what to do if an accident should occur and ensure that all the staff (including non-teaching staff) are aware of the appropriate procedures to take in the event of an accident;

(d) as far as possible, ensure that all pupils are aware of (and understand the reason for) any special safety precautions which need to be made to protect a child with special needs.

1. SAFETY AT SCHOOL

With certain areas of schooling, some children with special needs may require additional consideration over and above that which would apply to all pupils. In order to help identify safety considerations you may like to draw up a check list or grid similar to the one illustrated below:

	Movement of pupils	Supervision	Organisation of materials	Equipment	Tidiness
Classrooms					
Labs/Kitchens/Workshops					
Physical Education					
Playgrounds/Corridors					
Outings/Holidays					

Some of these considerations are discussed in more detail below:

(a) In the Classroom

Clearly, less general movement in the classroom helps to prevent accidents occurring. With older children movement is easily reduced by pupils raising their hands for attention but in infant and primary classes where children need to move about to collect equipment or materials it may be helpful to establish a simple route around the classroom which everyone is required to follow.

For children with poor co-ordination and/or spatial problems additional care may need to be taken with sharp objects, eg. scissors, compasses. It may also help to instruct some children not to lift or carry certain objects, eg. things which are breakable (bottles, equipment etc).

For hearing impaired children who may not respond to oral instructions of warning, you may find it useful to develop a recognised sign for "Careful" which can then be used consistently with the child (see *Hearing Impairment*). Children with poor sight may have a reduced field of vision or may not be able to see things clearly. It is helpful to give them time to familiarise themselves with the lay-out of their classroom and other parts of the school. Tidiness of equipment (so that they know where to find things they need without asking) and obstacles kept to a minimum will also assist them (see *Visual Impairment*).

(b)   In the Science Laboratory/Kitchen/Workshop

Many teachers are anxious about accidents occurring in science laboratories and other areas where practical work takes place. There are a number of ways in which precautions may be taken to reduce the risk of accidents.

Pupils are often encouraged to work in small groups and in this way you can delegate certain tasks, eg. mixing two chemicals, to one member of the group while a pupil who has poor co-ordination, for example, could do other tasks. This may involve a little more organisation but if you allow each pupil a task within the overall lesson this can enable a child with special needs to make a useful contribution without being exposed to any unnecessary risk.

There are many ways of making simple adaptations to science/practical equipment (see chapter 1.) and of stabilising equipment which will help to make the science laboratory safer whilst at the same time allowing children with special needs access to practical aspects of the school curriculum. In addition, a lowered bench will allow a child in a wheelchair to take part in lessons without unnecessary reaching which may also contribute to accidents.

(c)   In Physical Education

Most children with special needs benefit from forms of exercise and wherever possible they should be included in ordinary PE lessons. However, for children with physical disabilities in particular, you should seek advice from a PE Adviser, a physiotherapist and the parents about the extent to which the child should be included in PE. This is especially important for children who have conditions which vary from day to day. Extra safety equipment, eg. mats may be needed by some children.

With a little ingenuity and imagination many exercises can be adapted to allow a child with a disability to participate. If full participation in team games is not possible you may like to consider whether the child could take part in a form of a scorer or by other means.

Swimming is generally considered one of the best forms of exercise for many children with disabilities and is often used as part of their physiotherapy. Properly supervised, it is also one of the safest forms of exercise. It is important to check with the child's parents and medical staff that swimming is a suitable exercise. A routine check should be made for all children with disabilities including those for whom there is no apparent reason to check, eg. those with sensory impairments. Deafness, for example, may be associated with a perforated eardrum and swimming could cause further damage to the child. Sports staff should be made aware of all children with disabilities particularly those with "hidden disabilities". Where children with epilepsy are swimming a member of staff or adult helper should be designated to pay specific attention to such children. They will then be able to take immediate action to remove a child from the pool if he appears inert or in difficulty in the water.

(d) *In the Playground and School Corridors*

Most children with disabilities are able to participate in the normal social activities of free time during breaks. All children need the chance to relax with their peers and safety considerations should only interfere with social integration when absolutely necessary. The need for safety precautions must be carefully weighed against the disadvantages of social isolation in each instance.

Children prone to bruising or bone injury may be nervous of crowded corridors and busy playgrounds. You may find it helpful to talk to their parents about the best line to adopt. Sometimes it is necessary to reserve a "quiet area" where running about and physical games are prohibited. This need not be reserved exclusively for children with disabilities but may be a useful means of building up their confidence. From this area, they may then be encouraged to join in with groups of pupils in less boisterous games. The needs of each child are individual and may relate more to his personality than any disability but wherever possible full social integration in the playground should be encouraged.

Staff supervising break periods should be aware of children with special needs and therefore be able to anticipate accidents. They should also be fully aware of what to do if an accident does occur.

Children in wheelchairs and others with poor mobility plus those with progressive diseases and poor general health may need additional protection in cold or damp weather. This should be discussed with the parents before the child starts school.

It may also be helpful to allow children who use wheelchairs/crutches etc., or who are easily injured to leave classrooms earlier/later than the mass of pupils so they can move to their next class without difficulty. Again safety considerations need to be weighed against social considerations. Some children may prefer to join in the general exodus rather than be picked out for special attention.

2. SAFETY DURING OUTINGS AND HOLIDAYS

It is important to check that any outings or holidays in which children with special needs are included are covered by the school's insurance policy. It may also be necessary to seek the advice of the child's parents about any requirements he might have whilst on a school visit. Many of the same considerations which apply to school also apply to places you visit. Unfamiliarity and crowds may cause difficulties for some children and from safety, and other points of view, it is often helpful to visit the destination yourself beforehand, so problems can be anticipated and avoided. Whilst safety is an important factor for all children, try not to put too many restraints on a child with special needs while on a school outing.

3. EMERGENCY PROCEDURES AND FIRE REGULATIONS

Like all public buildings, schools are subject to fire regulations which lay down certain standards of safety. As a general rule, one-storey buildings should present no problem but where a school has more than one storey some children with special needs, particularly those in wheelchairs or using other mobility aids, may at first sight present difficulties for those concerned with the enforcement of fire regulations. However with a little ingenuity and determination it is often possible to find methods to satisfy fire regulations. This should be discussed within the school in conjunction with the child's parents and the Health and Safety Officer. Further advice, if required, may be obtained from RADAR.

Emergency procedures need to be worked out in advance before the child enters school and all those working with him should know what to do in the event of an emergency. In evacuation procedures, a child in a wheelchair or one who has difficulty in walking should not be permitted to block the exit of other pupils and it may be necessary to hold him back until last. Sometimes an adult can be designated to escort particular children out of the school in an emergency but if this is not possible a fellow pupil may be chosen for the task. Children with a hearing loss who cannot hear the fire bells may be helped by a system of flashing lights or simply a familiar sign from the teacher. With a little thought and planning it should not be too difficult to incorporate children with special needs into the emergency procedures of the school.

4. HANDLING WHEELCHAIRS AND LIFTING CHILDREN

It is important that a child who depends upon a wheelchair for mobility should be able to control it and make fine adjustments to his position. The Royal Association for the Prevention of Accidents (ROSPA) has devised a "Wheelchair Proficiency Scheme" (along similar lines to the Cycling Proficiency Scheme) to encourage pupils to care for and use their wheelchairs safely. Details of the Scheme may be obtained from ROSPA (see appendix D for address). It is also important that the wheelchair should be kept in good condition and in particular that the brakes function properly. Often parents take responsibility for this but as the child grows older he should be encouraged to take as much responsibility as possible for himself.

Most children who use wheelchairs are very safety-conscious but children who have poor spatial perception and/or mental handicap may not be totally reliable or may need additional reminders/supervision to ensure that they are safe and not likely to cause an accident.

Methods of transferring from a wheelchair should be discussed with the child's parents and medical staff before he starts school but it is not advisable to lift a child from a wheelchair unless absolutely necessary. If you have to do so, take care to lift bending your legs so that they, not your back, take the strain. Seek the advice of a physiotherapist to avoid hurting either the child or yourself.

5. FIRSTAID

All schools have a first-aid kit. If you are in charge of a child with special needs it is prudent to ensure that the kit contains any special first-aid equipment that he might need. Make sure you know where the kit is kept and what it contains or if a designated person is responsible for it, check that he knows what sort of first-aid equipment the child might need.

CHAPTER 10

ADDITIONAL AIDS AND EQUIPMENT

INTRODUCTION

Some children with special needs require additional aids and equipment to enable them to take a full part in school life. There are three main points to consider with regard to all aids:

(a) the purpose of any aid needs to be understood by the child (and those working with him) in order to use it both safely and to the best advantage;

(b) using aids requires time and practice to achieve their best effects;

(c) every aid must be considered in the light of how much it facilitates a task against the effort required to use it.

For children at school, aids may be considered in the following broad categories:

i. Education Aids

ii. Mobility Aids

iii. Seating Aids

iv. Communication Aids

v. Personal Care Aids

vi. Daily Living Aids

Although the remainder of this chapter will consider aids in each category, in practice the areas of overlap may be substantial eg. a computer can be both an education and communication aid.

1. EDUCATION AIDS

The range of aids covered by this category is enormous, embracing everything from a rubber handle on a lead pencil to the latest computer equipment. The purpose of all these aids is to supply easier access to learning for the child. They are tools to be used. The following are examples which you may come across in a classroom with children with special needs:

Aids to Writing Equipment

Children with poor co-ordination, perception or hand control may have difficulty in gripping pens and pencils. Adjustments to the shaft of the pencil, eg. a foam

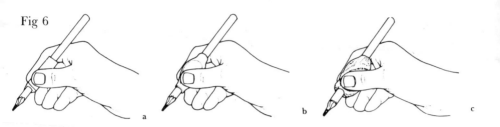
Fig 6

Enlarged handgrips: *a*. Taskmaster pencil grip; *b*. Homecraft penholder; *c*. Gripkit individually moulded grip

covering or a small foam ball may assist grip or a splint may be fixed to the child's hand to stabilise it. Sometimes it helps to anchor the paper, eg. by using sellotape, a clipboard or weights. If a child has to write with the hand he does not normally use, it may be helpful to turn the paper around and use stabilising methods.

Typewriters

Where a child is unable to use pens a typewriter may be helpful. Typewriters can be supplied in the normal form or with modified keyboards (eg. an expanded keyboard to help children with poor co-ordination). Typing, of course, requires practice and it may take some time before a child is sufficiently proficient in typing to produce written work. It may be helpful for him to use a tape recorder instead of trying to take notes on a typewriter. A few children type using one hand only or, very exceptionally, a head pointer (a long stick attached to a head band used by children with poor hand movement); it will obviously take them longer to complete work using such methods. The noise of typewriters may be distracting to other children at first but they usually accept it fairly quickly. There are models which function quietly. If a typewriter has to be moved around with the child, a trolley is of great help.

Personal Computers

Computers offer many new opportunities to children with special needs and have opened up areas of the curriculum to which they previously have not had access. It takes time for a child to master such equipment but once this is achieved, communication and the speed of work can be greatly increased. Specialist instruction on the use of computers is available through Special Education Micro-Electronic Resource Centres (SEMERCs addresses given in Appendix D) and from most manufacturers. The latest models are becoming smaller and more easily transportable. As with typewriters, a trolley may be a great boon to a child using such equipment. Personal computers should be insured by the parents and information about insurance is available from RADAR.

Calculators

Similarly, calculators with specially adapted keyboards where necessary, may help some children with special needs to study mathematics.

Music

Some musical instruments may also be adapted to allow children with special needs to use them. The use of electronics in music has opened up this area of the curriculum to more children with special needs. Further advice is available from the Disabled Living Foundation. (See Appendix D).

2. MOBILITY AIDS

Aids to mobility include wheelchairs, crutches, walking frames and special boots and/or splints. Many of these are obtained from hospitals or social services departments. For children who need wheelchairs on a long-term basis, these are supplied by the DHSS through Artificial Limb and Appliance Centres (ALACs). They are provided on the recommendation of the child's GP or hospital and the parents are also supplied with details of firms which repair them as necessary. As the child grows older, he should gradually take over full responsibility for the care and maintenance of the aid and know who to notify when repairs are needed. The ROSPA Wheelchair Proficiency Scheme (see chapter 9) encourages children to learn to maintain their wheelchairs.

Using a Wheelchair in an Ordinary School

Wheelchairs are either manually-operated (self-propelled or pushed) or battery-powered. Battery-powered chairs need to be recharged regularly but their range is normally sufficient to cover a school day. Their advantage is that they offer increased mobility, and therefore independence, to children who cannot physically manage a manual chair but they are normally heavier than manually-operated chairs and more difficult to transport.

Manoeuvring a wheelchair requires space and, in particular, additional space may be needed in aisles, around doorways and shelving to allow access to someone in a seated position; space should also be allowed beside and in front of shelves, sinks and desks. (This is covered in more detail in chapter 8).

Where a wheelchair is being pushed, the feet of the child in the chair are likely to be vulnerable to knocks and getting caught in furniture and doors particularly when changing level. Ramps facilitate access for wheelchair-users and single low steps may be managed (see chapter 8). The mechanics of using a wheelchair and methods of transferring from the chair (to the toilet seat for example) should be considered before the child starts school and discussed with the child himself, the parents and an occupational therapist.

Using Other Mobility Aids in the Ordinary School

Other mobility aids also require additional space for the child to manoeuvre; a child using double elbow-crutches needs almost as much space as one in a wheelchair. As with a wheelchair, additional room to manoeuvre is often needed in aisles, doorways and near shelves. Children whose balance is not good may be particularly vulnerable near swing doors and additional time and effort may be required. For some children, additional time may also be needed for changing for

PE. Calipers and surgical boots need to fit the child closely in order to be of benefit; they may be difficult to get on and off and this is sometimes a problem for young children. Parents and an occupational therapist should be able to advise you on this if necessary.

3. SEATING

Comfortable seating at the correct height is essential for successful use of the shoulders and arms, which in turn affects all writing tasks. It is particularly important that children should be able to place their feet flat on the floor where their disability permits this. An occupational therapist can advise on any special seating arrangements and these will obviously need to be reviewed as the child grows.

Work surfaces may be adapted in many ways to make learning easier. The height of such surfaces (including kitchen tables and science benches as well as desks) will particularly affect the amount of work a child in a wheelchair can complete unaided. Desks/tables of different heights may be needed for different skills, eg. writing and typing; an adjustable trolley may be useful for typing. A tilt-top table or book-rest can assist reading by positioning the book at a convenient height and angle.

4. COMMUNICATION AIDS

Many aids used by children with special needs are both communication and education aids. Those used for communication purposes are discussed in chapter 2.

5. PERSONAL CARE AIDS

Some children with special needs require additional aids for personal care, eg. incontinence pads. Arrangements for managing personal care needs should be discussed with the parents before the child starts school (see chapter 7).

6. DAILY LIVING AIDS

There is a wide range of aids to assist children with special needs in managing day-today tasks which are normally taken for granted. Some are very sophisticated but most are surprisingly simple. If a child has difficulty in eating, for example, an occupational therapist will be able to advise on ways in which this can be overcome by adapting handles or using non-slip plastic mats to stabilise plates. The occupational therapist can also supply such aids.

If a child is having practical difficulties in school, aids may be one way in which they can be alleviated. Many are simple and can be easily devised and provided. You may be able to supply the aid yourself from school resources but advice and support is also available from occupational therapists, physiotherapists and the child's parents. If a commercially supplied aid cannot be found to meet the child's needs, REMAP (Rehabilitation Engineering Movement Advisory Panels) can provide one-off aids (see Appendix D for address).

CHAPTER 11
EXAMINATION NEEDS

INTRODUCTION

Many children with special needs are able to follow the same academic curriculum as their peers and are therefore likely to sit examinations and tests. The artificial conditions created by examinations can pose additional difficulties for children with special needs and in recognition of this Examination Boards are often able to make special arrangements for individual pupils. These arrangements are not "allowances" or "concessions" which might give a child with special needs an advantage over his peers but are made in order to compensate for any special difficulties the child might have so he is able as far as possible to compete on an equal basis with others. In order to achieve this, special arrangements may be made for both internal and external examinations. The policies of individual Examination Boards vary and it is wise to check what arrangements they might consider well in advance (even before a child starts an examination syllabus).

Many children with special needs do not need any special consideration with regard to taking examinations but there are a number for whom this may be necessary. Such children are likely to include those who have difficulties with vision or hearing, those with communication difficulties (eg. children with speech problems; those who handwriting is poor/slow and those using typewriters or other aids). In addition, pupils who have difficulty in organising information (eg. children with Dyslexia) may also need special consideration as will pupils with conditions which are unpredictable on a day-to-day basis (eg. those with Leukaemia or kidney failure) and those whose condition may be aggravated by the additional stress of examinations (eg. children with epilepsy and severe forms of skin disorder).

For some children with special needs other forms of assessment may be preferable to examinations. Examinations devised by teachers with the aptitudes of particular pupils in mind are often helpful for pupils with special needs and certain forms of assessment, graded tests and profiling, for example, allow schools greater flexibility to test the abilities of pupils and may be considered a more accurate way of assessing their achievement. The form of assessment used is a matter for school policy but wherever possible a child with special needs should be tested by the same method as his peers.

1. ARRANGEMENTS BEFORE EXAMINATIONS TAKE PLACE

Most Examination Boards are able to make special arrangements for pupils with special needs if they are given sufficient notice. To make sure that no difficulties will arise at a later stage, it is often helpful to send a letter to the Board formally notifying them that the child is about to start, for example, a Geography 'O' level course.

Many schools have a designated Examination Officer and it should be decided who will approach the Board about special arrangements for individual pupils. This may require liaison between a number of staff.

The Board should be notified approximately six months in advance of the pupil sitting the examination so there is enough time to plan any special arrangements which may be necessary. Boards require an accurate account of the pupils needs together with suggestions from the school of special arrangements which might be made. A medical and/or psychological report is normally needed to support the evidence of the school. The Board will make the final decision and inform the school of the special arrangements to be permitted.

When the examination timetable is published it is prudent to check that pupils with special needs will be able to meet the requirements of the timetable and if not what arrangements can be made to enable them to sit the paper. For example, a pupil who requires time extensions may not be able to sit two examinations in the same day and may need overnight supervision.

2. ARRANGEMENTS DURING EXAMINATIONS

Wherever possible a pupil with special needs should be able to sit examinations alongside his peers. Any special arrangements he might need should be planned in advance and carried out as unobtrusively as possible. In some instances it may be helpful to place an invigilator close to the pupil where he is able to observe the needs of the child (eg. a diabetic pupil may need a biscuit during a long examination) but often this is not necessary. Where pupils are using an amanuensis or technical aids they normally require a separate room and individual invigilation.

Special Arrangements Available

Careful consideration should be given to the type of arrangements required and the ways in which they will assist the pupil. Some Examination Boards require that the pupil writes as much as he can, even if this is only a few sentences and will then allow other arrangements. Many Boards will make one, or a combination of, the following arrangements:

(a) Additional Time

Additional time may be granted for pupils who have difficulty in writing (eg. some children with Cerebral Palsy, and those with hand/arm disabilities), those with sensory disabilities and those who, for medical reasons, become unduly fatigued. Some Boards allow additional time for pupils with Dyslexia. The amount of additional time allowed varies but, for example, an extra ten minutes may be given for every hour. It is important that the extra time used, as distinct from that allowed, is recorded.

(b) Amanuensis

Many Boards allow pupils with visual problems or writing difficulties to dictate answers to an amanuensis. There may be restrictions on the choice of person acting in this capacity; most Boards will not permit the subject teacher to do this and an invigilator may be required.

Where it is known in advance that a pupil will be allowed to dictate his answers, he should be given every opportunity to practice using this technique. Special consideration may be required where drawing diagrams or maps is an integral part of the examination and advice should be sought from the Examination Board.

(c) Alternative Forms or Presentation

Some Boards are able to present examination papers in an alternative way. Many Boards are able to offer papers translated into Braille, for example, and sometimes it is possible to present an alternative wording of questions which may be of help to deaf pupils in particular and others whose vocabulary may not be as highly developed as normal because of their disability.

(d) Consideration in the Event of Illness during an Examination

Where a pupil is taken ill during an examination this will normally be taken into account by the Board if notified immediately. A note from the invigilator, explaining what happened, should accompany the pupil's paper.

Where a pupil has completed a reasonable proportion (the precise amount varies according to individual policies) of the examination, some Boards will mark the paper on the basis of what has been received.

3. RESITTING EXAMINATIONS

If a pupil is not able to take an examination because of illness he may be able to re-sit it at the following session, eg. in the Autumn after Summer examinations. It should not be assumed that special arrangements made for the original examination will automatically apply for the re-sit and the Board should be notified again.

CHAPTER 12

SCHOOL LEAVERS WITH SPECIAL NEEDS

INTRODUCTION

All pupils, including those with special needs, have a legal right to receive education either in school or at college up to the age of 19. Whilst all education may ultimately be seen in terms of preparation for adult life, specific preparation for school leavers usually begins with subject choices and careers guidance at about the age of 14. Many people argue, that for those with special needs, planning should begin even earlier. Under the Education Act 1981, pupils who have statements must be reassessed between the ages of 13½ and 14½ if this has not already been done during the previous 12 months. This formal reassessment procedure aims to ensure that all the professionals working with the child are aware of his needs when planning for what the pupil will do on reaching statutory school-leaving age. The Act encourages the involvement of parents and pupils themselves and it is particularly important that pupils should be given the opportunity to contribute to their reassessment and decisions based upon it. There are, of course, many pupils with special needs who do not have the formal protection of a statement but who would also benefit from a review of their needs at this point in their school lives.

Your observations of both academic performance and social skills will form a major contribution to the reassessment; therefore it is particularly important to ensure that you are familiar with the needs of the child, his abilities and disabilities, at this time. You may find it helpful to consult a checklist of points produced by the DES (printed on page 160).

1. WHO CAN HELP?

Effective liaison between the various services supporting children with special needs, both those with statements and especially those who do not have statements, is essential. Sometimes the needs of a child may only be known to one service and it is important to establish a system based upon a key person who is able to co-ordinate input from education, health, social services and perhaps voluntary organisations as well. Often an educational psychologist is designated for this task and the local authority special needs advisers are also able to help. (See also chapter 6).

Most schools receive regular visits from careers officers to advise and guide pupils towards suitable placement after school. In addition to these careers officers, there are also specialist careers officers (SCOs) whose work, in the past, has been mainly in special schools. Arrangements vary in different Education Authorities but they all have someone who has specialist knowledge and who can be called upon to assist pupils with special needs.

Where pupils are successfully placed in an ordinary school on an individual basis they may become "lost in the system" and their need for specialist help at this point should not be overlooked. Most careers officers will refer a pupil with special needs to their specialist colleagues automatically if they recognise that the young person needs extra help but, if you think that a pupil in your care would benefit from the assistance of a specialist careers officer, please ask that this should be arranged.

Pupils with special needs may also be in contact with a disablement resettlement officer (DRO) at the local Jobcentre. It is usual for a SCO to arrange the first placement for young people with special needs and for a DRO to provide any subsequent help needed. In many instances the two work closely together but as a general principle the school will usually find the SCO the main source of reference.

2. PUPILS WITH SPECIAL NEEDS

On leaving school many pupils with special needs are able to follow the same course as their peers and often the preparation they require is identical. However, some young people with special needs may require extra time, extra support and extra help in the period of transition. Many of these young people may be immature and lacking in confidence as they have had limited experience of everyday activities like shopping and have not therefore had the opportunity to learn appropriate social skills (see also chapter 3).

In addition, administrative arrangements of many of the services supporting the child and his family change as he is officially recognised as an adult. This may have implications for the supply of aids and equipment, and benefits and allowances may also need to be reviewed. For example, young people can begin to claim benefits in their own right from the age of 16 and some may be claimed while they are still at school. Whilst teachers cannot be expected to advise pupils in such matters, it is important that staff are aware of administrative changes which are likely to occur in other services and that pupils may need additional help at this time. Social workers and local disability organisations should be able to advise the family about these matters.

3. PREPARATION AT SCHOOL

(a) School-Leavers' Programmes

Active consideration of the special needs of pupils with regard to post-school placement should be an integral part of all stages of education. Some young people with special needs have the additional problem of immaturity which may also need to be taken into account. Many schools have a concentrated programme for school-leavers during their last two years at school and such programmes are of particular help to pupils with special needs who often lack

60

confidence and social skills. It may be useful to build elements into the leavers' programme which will specifically help young people with special needs, eg. how to explain their health care requirements to a stranger, as well as making a conscious effort to ensure that the general school-leavers programme is relevant to their needs. This type of training is equally important for young people with special needs following academic courses as for others.

(b) Link Courses

In many areas schools and colleges of FE arrange link courses whereby pupils with special needs attend college for part of the week during their final year at school. Whilst an open day may be sufficient for most pupils, some young people with special needs may require longer to adjust to FE and this has proved a very successful method of introduction.

(c) Work Experience

Pupils in their final year at school may be encouraged to gain an insight into the world of work by taking part in work experience schemes. Arrangements vary according to local and individual circumstances but it is important that participation by pupils with special needs should not be overlooked since they too will frequently gain particular benefit.

(d) Other Schemes and Courses

There is a multitude of schemes and courses used by schools to help their pupils prepare for adult life. A grounding in vocational skills is often supplied through the Technical and Vocational Education Initiative (TVEI) and the Certificate of Pre-Vocational Education (CPVE). Pupils with special needs may benefit from such courses and may be seriously disadvantaged later on if they are excluded. A disability of some kind may present a challenge to those running these courses but it should not be used as an excuse for preventing a pupil from taking part.

4. OPTIONS AFTER SCHOOL

Many young people with special needs are able to follow the same post-school course as their peers. Sometimes modifications are needed to the job/training or physical environment and these should be arranged in advance. In addition, there is a range of special provision for those who require it. Whatever choice the pupil makes, the SCO will be able to offer help and support. The various options for school-leavers with special needs are briefly described below:

(a) Special Arrangements within Ordinary Provision

    i. *Further Education*
    Many young people with special needs now spend a year or more in further education. They may join mainstream classes or may be placed in special classes catering specifically for their needs. Some colleges of FE offer "bridging courses" for young people with special needs which

aim to fill any gaps in education, increase independence and encourage confidence. Some also have a vocational element. Students often progress from bridging courses to other courses offered by the college.

ii. *Higher Education*
Facilities for students with special needs at polytechnics, colleges of higher education and universities have been greatly improved during the last few years. Details of any special needs should be given to the Universities Central Council on Admissions (UCCA) well in advance and information about facilities at specific institutions may be obtained from the National Bureau for Handicapped Students (address given in Appendix D). The Open University has developed many services for people with special needs and also offers a wide range of courses both for degree study and for interest.

iii. *Adult Education and Correspondence Colleges*
If a full-time course is not possible, a young person with special needs may wish to consider evening classes or other forms of education provided by Adult Education Institutes. A wide variety of courses is available, including literacy, and some courses are offered specifically for those with special needs.

Similarly, a range of courses may be studied by correspondence and this has been found to be a particularly helpful method of education for those with mobility problems who are not able to use the local education services although a high degree of personal motivation is usually required. The Council for the Accreditation of Correspondence Colleges (address given in Appendix D) can supply a list of approved colleges.

iv. *The Youth Training Scheme*
Amongst the range of training available through the Manpower Services Commission (MSC) is the Youth Training Scheme which offers a period (up to 2 years) of training which is usually employer-based but may also be supplied within the voluntary sector or colleges of FE. Young people with special needs may be able to join mainstream schemes or may be placed on a special scheme with others of their ability. The eligibility criteria for young people with disabilities are slightly more flexible than for others and, in addition, they may be allowed extra time on courses.

v. *Employment**
Despite the current unemployment situation, some young people with special needs are able to obtain work immediately on leaving school and many prove themselves good employees. The MSC operates several

*RADAR has published a similar guide to disabilities for employers. Details are to be found in Appendix C.

schemes to assist disabled young people in obtaining work. Under the *Job Introduction Scheme*, the MSC is able to contribute towards the wages of a disabled person during an initial trial period. The *Fares to Work Scheme* assists with the payment of transport costs for disabled people who are unable to use public transport. The MSC will also loan equipment to allow disabled people to obtain or keep a job and will pay for adaptations to premises and equipment where needed. Many of the MSC schemes apply also to people with disabilities serving apprenticeships.

Within open industry, employers may provide sheltered placement schemes whereby a disabled young person could be employed within an ordinary factory or office but would be expected to produce only a proportion of the normal level of production and would be paid appropriately.

Details about all the schemes outlined above are available from SCOs and DROs. They are also able to advise individual young people on the advantages and disadvantages of registering as disabled for employment purposes. Registration takes place through DROs.

(b) Special Provision

i. *Employment Rehabilitation Centres (ERCs)*
The MSC administers a number of ERCs where young people with disabilities can attend courses of varying lengths to try different types of work. They are assessed by the staff at the centre who produce a report with recommendations for each young person. Such courses are arranged in conjunction with the SCO or DRO.

ii. *Residential FE/Training*
There are a number of specialist residential colleges which offer a range of further education and training for young people with disabilities. Many of these colleges help their students to increase their social skills and some of them also offer vocational training. Details about these colleges can be obtained from SCOs or the National Bureau for Handicapped Students (address given in Appendix D).

iii. *Sheltered Workshops*
Sheltered Workshops, such as those operated by REMPLOY, carry out a variety of skilled, semi-skilled and unskilled work at a reduced level of productivity taking into account the effects of disability. As a general rule, employees are expected to produce approximately one third of normal production but productivity should not be so high that the young person could compete in ordinary employment.

iv. *Day Centres and Adult Training Centres*
For disabled people who are not able to work, or undertake training or further education, day centres and adult training centres (run by Social

Services Departments/Health Authorities) offer social activities and sometimes education. Day centres cater principally for those with physical disabilities while Adult Training Centres are for those with mental disabilities. The quality of provision they offer varies and parents and young people should be encouraged to visit the centre before deciding to attend.

PART TWO

APHASIA/DYSPHASIA

1. DESCRIPTION

The terms "aphasia" and "dysphasia" have been in use since the 1960s to describe both acquired and developmental impairment of spoken language. Aphasia describes severe impairment and dysphasia describes slight to moderate impairment.

The most common causes of failure of speech to develop are profound deafness and severe mental handicap but as assessment techniques improved it was found that, in some children, failure to develop speech and language was not associated with deafness, mental handicap, apparent brain injury or disease. In other words, there was found to be in some children, from birth, a specific failure of the normal growth of language functions (developmental aphasia/dysphasia). Aphasia/dysphasia may also occur following brain damage caused by illness or injury and may occur in isolation or as a facet of another disability (acquired aphasia/dysphasia).

There is usually nothing in the appearance of these children to suggest that they are anything other than "normal", but it cannot be assumed that they will grow out of their "disability". Some will, but not all.

Some children have near normal understanding of speech but a disability in speaking (expressive aphasia/dysphasia). Depending on the severity of the disorder, a child may have difficulty with word and sentence formation and limited vocabulary, while another may produce strings of unintelligible sounds, and another may hear and repeat spoken language correctly without knowing the meaning of what he is saying. They have difficulty in remembering the written or spoken word and they are likely to have reading difficulties, including a right-left confusion. They *can* perceive order and *can* retain speech-like sounds but often need much longer to acquire proficiency than their peers.

Others may have a disability in both understanding and expression of speech and, in extreme cases, there may be no understanding at all (receptive aphasia/dysphasia). Some suffer from high frequency deafness which means that, as most consonant sounds are carried in the higher frequencies, words such as bat, cat, sack, and sad will sound identical (see also *Hearing Impairment*).

In addition some children may have particular difficulty with rhythmic activities and may also display clumsiness, restlessness, distractibility and some confusion perceiving directions and relationship of objects in space.

2. EDUCATIONAL IMPLICATIONS

(i) Learning Difficulties

Children with specific speech and language disorders, such as those with aphasia/dysphasia, need specialist help, often beginning at 18 months–2 years, and children may need to attend a language unit attached to an ordinary school or sometimes a special school so this can be given as early as possible. You may therefore find it helpful to talk to the parents of the child and to other professionals (particularly the speech therapist) who have been working with the child before he started school. It is likely that children with aphasia/ dysphasia will need help in the following areas:

Sequencing and structure

Where a child has difficulty in learning the order of a task, it helps to structure the sequence of skills and simplify each step. This is particularly useful to children who do not identify relevant clues successfully in an informal situation and greater attention to structure and order may be needed to assist them in gaining salient points. Unstructured learning using a variety of experiences and materials may be confusing for these children. Initially, teaching should concentrate on methods of establishing communication which are helpful to the child and later learning can then be based upon this. With carefully structured teaching methods, written language and silent reading may far exceed performance in spoken language.

Additional means of communication

Additional means of communication which aid understanding may be used to develop meaning. Some schools and units for children with language difficulties use sign language as an aid to communication. Good communication may be achieved in written language even where spoken language is delayed.

Extra support

Extra support may be needed by children with aphasia/dysphasia in the following areas to assist their learning.

(a) *Attention Training* – as these children gain most of their information about events from visual clues, extra concentration on the spoken word or the task in hand may be needed.

(b) *Following Procedures* – as a result of gaps in early learning and difficulty in learning from incidental experiences, these children may require specific direction and/or instructions in their school work. A clear structure to work also assists their learning.

(c) *Individual Checks on Progress* – a few minutes spent with a child at the beginning of an exercise to ensure that he has understood instructions may be helpful. Group work/discussion may be confusing for these children.

(d) *Writing/diagrams*
Writing provides a static pattern which may be considered at the child's individual pace and is helpful to children with sequencing problems.

Written back-up to learning is therefore particularly useful to these children and diagrams and illustrations may also be helpful.

(e) *Motivation and Success*

Motivation is important for all children with learning difficulties and using a child's own interests as the basis of classwork may be especially valuable. Like all children they benefit from success and encouragement and appreciation of effort are likely to increase motivation and persistence. Careful consideration of the goals to be attained can also provide success and further motivation.

(ii) Considerations for Classroom Management

Behaviour

Communication problems often cause frustration which may be manifested in aggressive or defensive behaviour. Children with aphasia/dysphasia may need additional practice in social skills and in learning the order of turn-taking and sequencing responses. Classroom routines which reduce the need for requests and lead to predictable sequences may be of help.

Direction

Many children with aphasia/dysphasia find it difficult to manage free time effectively and it may be helpful to set specific tasks eg. reading library books or using personal workbooks which are stored where the child can find them easily. In this way a settled occupation can be provided and difficulties arising from the child not knowing what is expected can be avoided.

Social Skills

In primary schools assistance may be needed in learning the skills of working with other children. The interaction between pupils may need to be monitored to ensure that opportunities for co-operation and communication occur.

Co-ordination Between Staff

Where several teachers are in contact with a pupil known to have aphasia/ dysphasia, everyone needs to be aware of the child's means of communication or communication problems and be willing to allow additional time to understand. If a child has difficulty in carrying messages, for example, all teachers should be aware of this and a note supplied where necessary.

3.   ADDITIONAL POINTS

Speech Therapy

Speech therapy is essential to children with aphasia/dysphasia and you will find it helpful to liaise with the child's Speech Therapist to develop a co-ordinated approach.

Maturity and Independence

Children with aphasia/dysphasia may be more immature and dependent than other children but as their confidence and their ability to understand grows, so their level of maturity and independence increases. It is important to remember that their inability to understand or be understood may cause frustration and it may be helpful if this is explained to other children (with the permission of the child's parents).

Clumsiness

Some children, especially those with other related disabilities, may be clumsy in movement and this is most apparent in PE and in awkwardness in handling pencils, scissors and cutlery. An occupational therapist and/or physiotherapist may be able to help.

ARTHRITIS

1. DESCRIPTION

Juvenile Chronic Arthritis (JCA) is a progressive disease which causes inflammation of the lining membrane of joints in children. There are several forms of the disease. Pain and stiffness associated with JCA vary considerably from day to day. In general, it is most severe in the early morning.

The condition is treated with drugs and physiotherapy and in many instances it can be arrested. Treatment is long-term but many children with JCA reach adulthood with only residual stiffness and no functional loss.

Inflammation of the eye is sometimes associated with JCA and this may lead to difficulties with vision (see *Visual Impairment*).

2. EDUCATIONAL IMPLICATIONS

(i) Learning Difficulties

There are no learning difficulties specifically associated with this condition. However, children with JCA may need to spend periods of time in hospital. They may still be able to learn during these times and it may be possible for you (with the co-operation of hospital teachers and/or the parents) to arrange a continuous plan of work for the child to carry out. Accurate record-keeping will assist all those involved with the child.

As many children with JCA make a full recovery and are able to live a normal adult life, it is particularly important that they should have access to the full academic curriculum to enable them to make appropriate career choices, whether or not their disability persists.

(ii) Considerations for Classroom Management

Stiffness in the Hands

Many children with JCA have stiffness in their hands and this is likely to cause all handwork to become slow and/or painful. It may be necessary to consider other methods to compensate, eg. use of tape-recorders, electric typewriters, sewing machines etc.

Mobility

Because of stiffness and pain involved in movement it may take some children longer to walk from one classroom to another. Children using elbow crutches are somewhat vulnerable in busy corridors and may have difficulty managing swing doors. Where distances are long, younger children may need to use a mobility aid, eg. a tricycle or wheelchair. For all these reasons it may be necessary to allow extra time for the child to get to the next lesson. You may find that this is a particular worry for parents and it might be helpful to discuss it with them.

Physical Education

You should discuss physical education with the child's physiotherapist who will be able to advise on suitable activities. Wherever possible allow the child to join in with the rest of the class but make certain that the exercise is suitable for him. Physiotherapy can often be incorporated into PE lessons but if this proves impossible it may be practical for him to receive physiotherapy whilst the rest of the class has PE.

3. ADDITIONAL POINTS

Pastoral Care/Counselling

This condition can be extremely painful but the children do not always complain or admit to the pain which they suffer. Pain, combined with a sense of frustration through not being able to join in all physical activities, may result in tiredness, withdrawal or bad behaviour. You may find it helpful to look out for these signs and, if necessary, talk to the child and his parents about any problems which may arise.

Administration of Drugs

Drugs may occasionally be needed at school and older pupils may carry an emergency supply with them. For younger children, it is preferable for the school to keep the drugs and supply them as necessary. You should consult with parents about giving drugs.

ASTHMA

1. DESCRIPTION

Asthma is a condition which narrows the breathing tubes or airways of the lungs. This occurs in three ways:

(a) the muscles in the airways contract (causing a spasm);

(b) the lining of the airway becomes swollen and irritated;

(c) too much mucus is produced in the lungs.

The most noticeable symptom of asthma is breathlessness with wheezing which occurs as air is forced through the narrowed airways. A child may hunch his shoulders or lean forward in an effort to gain more air. Frequently there is also an irritating, but non-infectious, cough. The severity of attacks varies greatly. Mild attacks may need no treatment at all but very severe attacks, though rare, require prompt medical assistance.

Asthma attacks may be provoked by a number of factors (often in combination) including:

virus infection (coughs, colds etc.)
excessive exercise (especially where this involved sudden changes in temperature)
allergic reactions
emotion (excitement or upset).

Asthma is treated by drugs which widen the airways of the lungs and allow the child to breathe more easily. Treatment is of two types: preventative and relief. Preventative treatment must be given regularly and relief treatment given when an attack is imminent or has started to occur. Inhalers, which give immediate relief, are called bronchodilators and both forms of treatment are best supplied by means of inhalers. Some children may have tablets or syrup as an alternative. In addition, many children are taught to do simple breathing exercises to help them relax during an attack.

2. EDUCATIONAL IMPLICATIONS

(i) Learning Difficulties

There are no learning difficulties specifically associated with this condition but breathing difficulties may sometimes indirectly lead to learning problems as the child's reduced physical condition may in turn reduce his ability to learn. Only a few children with very severe asthma require any restrictions which prevent them taking a full part in school activities.

HOW TO USE AN INHALER

The following procedure has now been accepted as standard, whatever the drug and whatever the manufacturer. In most instances pupils are able to use an inhaler without assistance.

Fig. 7

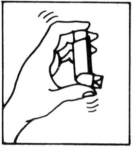  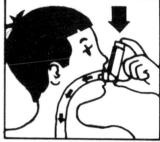

1 The pupil should remove the cover from the mouthpiece and shake the inhaler vigorously.

2 The inhaler should be held as shown while the pupil breathes out gently (but not fully) and then immediately . . .

3 . . . places the mouthpiece in his mouth and closes his lips around it. After starting to breathe in slowly and deeply through his mouth he should press the inhaler firmly as shown above to release the medication and continue to breath in.

4 He should then hold his breath for 10 seconds, or as long as is comfortable, before breathing out slowly.

5 If a second inhalation is taken the pupil should wait at least one minute before repeating steps 2, 3 and 4.

6 After use the cover should be replaced on the inhaler.

(ii) Considerations for Classroom Management

Management of an Asthma Attack

Minor asthma attacks will probably not disturb the pupil sufficiently to interrupt his concentration on school work and may well pass unnoticed. If a child with asthma has difficulty in breathing, there are three basic rules to follow:

(a) stay calm (anxiety always aggravates an attack);

(b) use the correct medication (usually an inhaler as described below);

(c) if this does not bring relief call medical help.

The child may have a preferred position whilst waiting for medical help.

Inhalers

There are various types of inhalers which work in different ways but the basic operation of the inhaler is described on page 74.

Young children may need a little assistance but older children should be able to use the inhaler quickly and unobtrusively without supervision. The pupil should preferably be responsible for his inhalers but if this is not practical he should at least know where they are kept and have easy access to them. Preventative inhalers must be used regularly at the times recommended by the doctor. Bronchodilator inhalers should only be used when needed but you may find some pupils are over-anxious about their breathing and perhaps tend to over-use their inhaler. Although this should not be encouraged it is not dangerous and it is preferable for the child to use it too much rather than be prohibited from using it, which may precipitate an attack. Children can normally accurately anticipate an attack and know when to use their inhaler. If the child does not respond to the inhaler treatment (the effects of the inhalation should work almost immediately), this indicates that the attack is severe and medical assistance should be sought.

Allergies

Asthma attacks are often triggered by allergic reactions; some of the most common substances to which a child with asthma may react are:

(a) Pollen – such an allergy may increase asthma attacks in the pollen season (May–July). Newly-mown grass should be avoided;

(b) Animals – unfortunately the fur of pets (eg. rabbits and guinea pigs) kept in classrooms may precipitate an asthma attack;

(c) Certain foods – some children have food allergies which provoke asthma attacks. While such allergies are being identified, children may have to avoid certain foods.

In addition, certain irritants in the atmosphere, such as cigarette smoke or paint fumes, may trigger attacks.

75

Physical Education

Asthma attacks are most frequently provoked in school by exercise particularly on cold, dry days. Attacks can normally be prevented by the child using a bronchodilator inhaler or sometimes taking a tablet about 20 minutes before the PE lesson. The use of such drugs will usually allow the child to participate normally in PE.

Swimming is usually a good form of exercise for children with asthma if a heated pool is available.

Children should not be allowed to use their asthma as an excuse to avoid PE. It may be helpful to discuss any reluctance to participate in sport with the parents to establish how far this may be related to genuine anxiety about their condition. Success in PE often gives children with asthma greater confidence in themselves and it is worth remembering that a number of well-known athletes have overcome this disability.

3. ADDITIONAL POINTS

After School Placement

The use of drugs and inhalants has revolutionised the management of asthma but school leavers with more severe forms of asthma may need to seek work in areas where they can control their physical activity and avoid substances to which they are allergic.

BRITTLE BONES
(Osteogenesis Imperfecta)

1. DESCRIPTION

The term Brittle Bones refers to a variety of conditions resulting from an abnormality in the protein structure of the bones. This causes the bones to break more easily than normal and, in addition, the ligaments (tissues which join the bones) may be lax and the joints more mobile than normal. Brittle bones is usually an inherited condition. It is not a calcium deficiency and there is no cure for it. Children should be monitored by their doctor to prevent deformity and may need therapy and aids.

2. EDUCATIONAL IMPLICATIONS

(i) Learning Difficulties

There are no learning difficulties specifically associated with this condition. After fractures have occurred, surgery is sometimes needed to prevent deformity and this may interrupt the child's education. If a child has to be kept away from school for some time it may be helpful to set work for him to do at home.

Some of these children have very restricted mobility in their early years which leads to frustration and may affect their attitude to learning. You may find it helpful to talk to the child's parents if this appears to be a problem and an educational psychologist may also be able to help.

(ii) Considerations for Classroom Management

Fractures

There is no general indicator of how easily a child with brittle bones may fracture. Some are much more vulnerable to breaks than others. It often happens that children have a bad spell of fractures and may then go for a number of years without one. Some children fracture less easily as they grow older. Children rarely fracture at school and are just as likely to experience a break when turning over in bed. You will therefore not be held responsible if a break occurs at school. If this worries you, you may like to discuss it with the child's parents and a senior member of staff.

Handwriting

Some children with brittle bones have joints in their hands which are more mobile than is usual and their hand and arm structure may also be impaired by the effect of previous fractures. Hence, writing may present some difficulties. Approximately 80% of very severely affected children are either left-handed or hold their pens in an unusual manner. It may be necessary to experiment with different types of pen, the width of lines on paper and perhaps a plastic pencil holder or triangular pencil. Fibre-tip pens are often found to be most suitable. To some extent, increased muscle tone compensates for ligament laxity but many of

77

these children experience fatigue when they are required to write for long periods. Practice and extra exercises may help. Slowness in writing may necessitate extra time and may lead to difficulties in note-taking at secondary level. Hand-outs or copies of other pupil's notes may therefore be helpful. Some children prefer to use a typewriter but they should be encouraged to use their handwriting as much as possible.

Children with brittle bones sometimes have short and/or bent arms and younger children may have difficulty in reaching the top of the page; this is easily solved by halving the paper horizontally. Children who are small (see *Short Stature*) or have restricted arm movement may need special consideration with regard to seating arrangements.

Mobility

Children who are very susceptible to fracturing are often confined to a wheelchair for safety as well as support. A child who breaks a limb may temporarily need to use a wheelchair or the limb may simply be protected by splints and the child allowed to return to school.

Children who are less severely affected may use other mobility aids, eg. sticks and crutches, and in some ways they are more vulnerable to the knocks and bumps of everyday school life than those who use wheelchairs.

Physical Education

Many forms of exercise are not suitable for children with brittle bones but swimming is an ideal sport and non-weight bearing and non-restricted exercises may also be suitable.

Hearing

Sometimes the bones within the ear may be affected by this condition and it is useful to watch out for any signs of hearing problems (see *Hearing Impairment*).

3. ADDITIONAL POINTS

Playgrounds and Corridors

Children protected by their wheelchairs will normally be able to join their peers in the playground, especially if there is a quiet area. A child with other mobility aids may be more at risk and may need to be restricted to a quiet area, preferably on grass or a carpet. To reduce social isolation, a few friends might be asked to join him. It may be necessary to keep this group under supervision to a greater or lesser extent.

In order to avoid accidental knocking as the children rush out for break it may be wise to tell the child to wait until the rush is over or alternatively allow him out a few minutes early. The same principle applies when children are changing lessons.

Toilet Needs

Some children may need assistance in using toilet facilities and special arrangements may need to be made. It is essential that these needs are checked before the child starts school so provision can be made in advance.

Examinations

Where children have difficulty in writing, you may need to consider making an application to the Examination Board for special arrangements to compensate for this. Applications should be made well in advance (see Chapter 11).

After School Placement

Because of their restricted mobility, children with brittle bones often become avid readers and do well at school. Their disability will necessarily affect their choice of career and they will need careful careers guidance.

CEREBRAL PALSY
(Commonly known as Spasticity)

1. DESCRIPTION

Cerebral Palsy (literally paralysis of part of the brain) takes many forms and no two children with this condition are affected in the same way. It is a disorder of movement and posture which appears at or soon after birth and is caused by damage to, or lack of normal development of, the part of the brain controlling movement. Sometimes the damage extends to nearby parts of the brain as well causing deafness and other difficulties in perception.

There are three main forms of Cerebral Palsy. Most children who have Cerebral Palsy have disordered control of movement, muscle weakness and often disturbance of growth and development (Spasticity). The second form is manifested in involuntary movements of the body (Athetosis). There are now ways of preventing this form of Cerebral Palsy and it is less common in babies born today. The third type (known as Ataxia) is manifested in the form of balancing problems and an unsteady gait.

It is important to emphasise the widely varying effects of Cerebral Palsy. Some children are only slightly handicapped (eg. by a poor gait) but others have very severe multiple disabilities which may include communication problems, mental handicap, hearing and visual impairment and epilepsy (please refer to appropriate sections in Part 2). Many people mistakenly believe that all children with Cerebral Palsy are automatically mentally handicapped. Whilst this may be true for some children, it is not an inevitable feature of this disabilty. First appearances can be deceptive; a child who cannot control his limbs and has a speech impediment is not necessarily mentally handicapped as well.

Cerebral Palsy is not curable but, with therapy and stimulation, most children maintain a stable condition and do not normally deteriorate. They are no more or less likely than able-bodied children to suffer the normal childhood illnesses. Some children may need to enter hospital occasionally for corrective surgery.

It is currently unlikely that children with severe forms of Cerebral Palsy will attend ordinary classes except where very specialised provision is available for them.

2. EDUCATIONAL IMPLICATIONS

(i) Learning Difficulties

Not all children with Cerebral Palsy need extra assistance in learning but, if classroom performance causes you concern, it is useful to know that spatial and/or perceptual difficulties are common. Children with limited mobility, particularly those in wheelchairs, may lack tactile experience and therefore have limited sensory experience which in turn may affect their learning.

Reading, Writing and Number Work

Many children have specific learning difficulties in perceptual and spatial judgements which affect hand-eye co-ordination. Perceptual problems may cause delays in learning to read while motor and spatial problems may cause difficulties with number work and handwriting. These problems may be overcome by careful teaching techniques, repetition and perseverance.

Eye defects and poor concentration may also cause some children difficulty in reading and number work. Each factor will need individual consideration.

Co-ordination

Some children have poor motor organisation which may particularly affect handwriting, number work and physical education. For example, ball-handling skills may prove difficult for these children. Teaching which emphasizes the 'feel' of correct sequencing has proved most effective in such instances.

Distractability

If a child is easily distractible it helps to insist on concentration and limit talk to the job in hand.

(ii) Considerations for Classroom Management

Involuntary Movement and Spatial Problems

Many children with Cerebral Palsy are unable to control their muscles in the usual way and therefore have difficulty with fine movement and this may often be made worse by the child's efforts to improve his movements. This may be combined with spatial problems and lead to apparent clumsiness or untidiness in school work. These involuntary movements are part of the condition and cannot be controlled by the child although they may be improved by relaxation and other techniques. An occupational therapist will be able to advise you on simple and effective ways of stabilising equipment or the child's hands which may help to alleviate these difficulties.

Handwriting

Poor fine movement inevitably has implications for the quality of handwriting a child with Cerebral Palsy is able to produce. Considerable improvements in handwriting may be achieved if the paper is weighted or "sellotaped" to keep it firmly anchored. Sometimes a child may have difficulty in grasping a pen or pencil and this may be remedied by use of a "fat" pen or slipping a piece of sponge rubber tubing over the pen to give the child additional grip. Again, an occupational therapist can advise you. Even with aids it may still be necessary to make allowances for untidy work. If handwriting proves too difficult or timeconsuming, you may need to consider other alternatives such as a typewriter or other equipment which serves a similar function and is more portable. A wide range of electronic equipment is now available to assist children with poor fine movement (see chapter 2).

81

Communication

Some children with Cerebral Palsy have difficulty in speaking because they cannot control the muscles of their mouth and this may lead to some form of speech impediment. You may have to take extra time to ensure that you understand what a child is saying. Speech often improves when a child is relaxed and knows that he will not be placed under pressure by another person in conversation. Conversely, in unfamiliar situations, or where he feels under pressure, eg. in an interview, his speech may deteriorate. Your understanding of his speech will improve as you get to know the child but if you are worried seek the advice of a speech therapist (see also chapter 2).

Tiredness

Children with an appreciable disability may tire more easily than their able-bodied peers as they need to use more energy to achieve the same results. Tiredness causes fine movement to deteriorate and hence may lead to poor work. This point may have a bearing on the way you timetable lessons; a balanced timetable will, of course, be of benefit to all children but particularly to those with disabilities which cause tiredness.

3. ADDITIONAL POINTS

Self Care

Because of their poor fine movement some children with Cerebral Palsy may need extra time to complete dressing and changing tasks. Some may need help but many will be able to complete these tasks unassisted. They should all be encouraged to do as much as possible for themselves. Generally, children with Cerebral Palsy should not need to use the lavatory any more than able-bodied children but some of them may need help in transferring from a wheelchair to the lavatory. It may take them longer than normal to use the lavatory, so do not penalise them for this. You may find it helpful to discuss aspects of self-care with the child's parents before he starts school.

As children with Cerebral Palsy grow they may become more ungainly and problems with posture may become more apparent. Additional physiotherapy and occupational therapy may be needed for adolescents to maintain and enhance their personal independence.

Pastoral Care/Counselling

The limiting effects of a severe disability may cause frustration and emotional problems for children with Cerebral Palsy. They may appear immature in comparison with their peers and may react to situations in ways which differ from normal. Careful counselling, from both within and outside school, may be needed.

School Meals

Children with Cerebral Palsy do not normally have any diet problems and school meals are generally suitable for them. School meals offer one of the most important opportunities for social integration and wherever possible children with Cerebral Palsy should be encouraged to eat with their peers. Some children, particularly those in wheelchairs, may need to keep a check on their diet to ensure that they do not become overweight. A few may have difficulty in chewing and swallowing food and these may need special consideration.

Balancing Difficulties

Some children with Cerebral Palsy have balancing problems and may be more prone to falling than normal. This may be overcome by the use of sticks or perhaps a wheelchair for outside use only. Many manage with no special equipment. As a general principle, wherever possible try to provide the equipment needed to allow the child to join in the full range of activities rather than curtail the activities in which he is able to participate. A physiotherapist or occupational therapist will be able to supply advice. Every child needs individual consideration but talk to the parents and try not to over-protect the child so much that he is unable to take the normal risks that all children take in playing together.

COELIAC CONDITION

1. DESCRIPTION

The Coeliac Condition is caused by a sensitivity to gluten, a protein found in wheat and rye. Similar proteins are also found in barley and oats. Sensitivity to gluten may cause one or both of the following types of reaction:

(a) damage to the lining of the small intestine which reduces its ability to absorb nutrients from food, leading to wasting and a severe illness resembling malnutrition;

(b) a skin condition of small irritating blisters (known medically as Dermatitis Herpetiformis).

Both reactions are treated in the same way by means of a strict diet which entirely obviates the need for drugs. It is several months before the full benefit of the diet is achieved and small lapses reduce its effectiveness.

The initial onset of the condition does not necessarily occur in infancy and it may develop at any age.

2. EDUCATIONAL IMPLICATIONS

(i) Learning Difficulties

There are no learning difficulties specifically associated with this condition.

(ii) Considerations for Classroom Management

No special considerations are needed for children with Coeliac Condition.

3. ADDITIONAL POINTS

School Meals

Diet is the only aspect of this condition which may affect a child at school. Absolute compliance with the diet is essential because even small lapses may cause difficulties. Gluten is present in most bread, biscuits and many snacks, so these must be avoided but it is often possible to arrange gluten-free school meals or parents may prefer to supply food from home. Children who maintain their diet are normally healthy and require no other special consideration.

2. EDUCATIONAL IMPLICATIONS

(i) Learning Difficulties

Structured Learning

Children with mental handicap respond very well to regular routines and structured learning experiences which help them to learn cognitive and social skills. They often have difficulty in anticipating the consequences of an action or selecting the correct cues to help them make a decision. This problem of identifying relevant information also means that they are often unable to generalise a well-established pattern into a new situation. Children with learning difficulties will, therefore, need to be taught not only specific skills but also when and how to apply them.

Sequencing Learning

It is important to give children with mental handicap a sense of achievement at each stage. Clearly defined goals which enable the pupil to recognise when he has reached the goal are very important. The child should be able to recognise the finished task so when a learning sequence is devised, the last sequential stage should be taught first thus maintaining the child's interest and enabling him to feel that he always finishes.

Concentration

Many children with mental handicap have limited concentration and therefore many short teaching sessions are preferable to one long one. Varying work will also be helpful in maintaining interest.

(ii) Considerations for Classroom Management

Play

For young children play is very important regardless of their level of intellectual ability. As children get older their type of play changes but children with mental handicap may still need a level of play appropriate to their intellectual level, yet socially inappropriate for their chronological age.

Behaviour

For children with mental handicap, behaviour within the class may need to be consciously taught. Often inappropriate behaviour is unconsciously encouraged by the reactions of other children or even the teacher. A consistency of approach is essential and, as a general rule, inappropriate behaviour should be ignored or handled with the minimum of fuss. Conversely, praise and attention for appropriate behaviour is extremely important. Whenever possible children with mental handicap should mix with a wide range of other children and it may be helpful to encourage more able members of the class to assist them in becoming more confident in both social and educational skills.

3. ADDITIONAL POINTS

Expectations

The social and emotional needs of all children are similar and immaturity in intellectual skills should not be equated with dependence and becoming a "child-like" adult. Many children with mild or moderate mental handicap are reliable and efficient in carrying out well-learned tasks and many, with appropriate support, can become independent in the community and later in the workplace.

After School Placement

Many people with mental handicap are capable of work. Sometimes this may be provided within a sheltered environment where a lower output of work is expected. Social Services Departments run Adult Training Centres or Social Education Centres for mentally handicapped people who are unable to work. The specialist careers officer will be able to offer further advice.

MIGRAINE

1. DESCRIPTION

Migraine in children does not differ in any essential way from Migraine in adults but the symptoms associated with the headache may be more pronounced. These symptoms may include: nausea and vomiting, abdominal discomfort, irritability, loss of appetite and sleeplessness. It is not always easy to distinguish the symptoms of Migraine from other complaints, particularly as the headache itself may not necessarily be severe.

The cause of Migraine is not known but understanding of the factors which cause it has been developed and if these factors can be identified and avoided this will help considerably in the control of the Migraine. Examples of such factors are: missed meals, elements in the diet, anxiety and irregular or insufficient sleep. Anxiety may be due to concern about school performance, relationships or even fear of the headaches themselves.

2. EDUCATIONAL IMPLICATIONS

(i) Learning Difficulties

There are no learning difficulties specifically associated with this condition but children who suffer severe or frequent attacks may have their education interrupted.

(ii) Considerations for Classroom Management

Management of a Migraine Attack

If a child is known to be susceptible to Migraine attacks before he begins school it is helpful to both parents and teachers to work out a procedure of action in the event of the child having an attack at school. Each child has individual needs and the parents will be able to advise you on individual requirements. It is important that a Migraine attack is treated as early as possible and if the child appears pale or irritable this may be an indication that an attack is imminent. Allow him to rest, or sleep if possible, and contact his parents.

Administration of Drugs

It is very unusual for children to be on continuous medication to prevent attacks but they may be advised to carry an emergency supply of a few tablets. For young children, emergency tablets should be kept in the school medical cupboard and given as appropriate. It is important to reach an agreement about administration of drugs with the child's parents in advance (see also chapter 7).

3. ADDITIONAL POINTS

There are no additional points.

MUSCULAR DYSTROPHY

1. DESCRIPTION

There are several kinds of Muscular Dystrophy all of which are progressive, hereditary diseases. The cause is unknown but the essential characteristic of Muscular Dystrophy is the progressive breakdown and death of muscle fibre resulting in gradually increasing weakness. Some forms affect both sexes but the most common form is Duchenne Muscular Dystrophy which is carried through the female line and affects only boys. The boys appear normal at birth. Sometimes walking may be delayed and at some time between 2 and 5 difficulties in movement become noticeable.

The muscle weakness progresses slowly. There are times of remission and times when deterioration is rapid. Bedrest, for any reason, tends to increase the disability and as the muscles deteriorate, posture and movement become more limited. Although children with Muscular Dystrophy are actively encouraged to use all the mobility they have for as long as possible, a wheelchair finally becomes inevitable. Children can normally retain independent mobility provided a suitable electric wheelchair is supplied. Intellectual functioning is not affected.

Despite continued research, the life expectancy of young people with Muscular Dystrophy is limited and some of them die in their late teens or twenties.

2. EDUCATIONAL IMPLICATIONS

The progressive nature of the disease means that all educational considerations must include anticipation of lowered mobility levels.

(i) Learning Difficulties

There are no learning difficulties specifically associated with this condition. Education may occasionally be interrupted for treatment in hospital. Children may tire more easily than normal.

(ii) Considerations for Classroom Management

Access to the Curriculum – Special Equipment

As the child becomes weaker and muscles in the arms and hands are affected, it may be necessary to provide special equipment, eg. an electric typewriter or a calculator, to compensate for his lack of hand control. It may be a good idea to introduce typing before the child needs it to give him a better chance of mastering the typewriter before his muscles become very weak.

CONGENITAL HEART DISEASE

1. DESCRIPTION

Heart disease is the term used to describe an abnormality in the functioning of the heart. In children the most common form is Congenital Heart Disease which indicates that the defect has been present since birth. It is estimated that eight out of every 1000 children may have a defect in their heart, of which about one-third are very mild and need no treatment. The most common defect, often called "hole-in-the-heart", occurs where there is a hole between two of the chambers of the heart. In many children the hole closes or becomes insignificantly small without treatment before they start school and they will be able to join in all aspects of the curriculum.

Some children born with a heart defect require surgery and, where possible, this is usually carried out before they start school and many of them will also be able to lead normal lives. A few children, eg. those awaiting surgery and those whose condition cannot be completely cured, need special consideration at school.

2. EDUCATIONAL IMPLICATIONS

(i) Learning Difficulties

Where heart disease causes circulatory problems and therefore reduced oxygen supply this may cause tiredness, which can occur quite suddenly, and reduce the child's ability to learn but there are no learning difficulties specifically associated with this condition. Education may also be disrupted for medical treatment as, although many children have corrective surgery before they start school, some corrections may be left until the child is older. Following an operation a period of convalescence, usually about half a term, is often necessary. Some children have to undergo a series of operations and the implications for disrupted school work may need particular consideration. It may be helpful to set work for the child to do at home and an effective liaison system with hospital teachers and the child's parents should be established.

(ii) Considerations for Classroom Management

Physical Education

Most children with heart disease can lead normal lives and should be allowed to participate in PE. However pressure should not be placed on children who, on medical grounds, have been advised not to take part in PE and special consideration should be given to swimming. Parents are usually aware of any physical restrictions placed on their child and it is also advisable to check with the child's doctor that the level of activity expected of him is within his ability.

3. ADDITIONAL POINTS

Health

Children with certain heart diseases, particularly valvular abnormalities, may be liable to a special type of infection of the heart (called endocarditis). The most common source of infection is from the teeth or gums and dental care is most important for these children. Milk teeth are not usually a source of infection but antibiotics should be given with all dental treatment as a precaution for children at risk of this infection. Other sources of infection may be the ears and skin and again antibiotics may be needed.

The normal immunisation programme is also of particular importance to children with heart disease. Some children may be more prone to coughs and colds but many have normal health.

CYSTIC FIBROSIS

1. DESCRIPTION

Cystic Fibrosis is one of the most common genetically-determined disorders affecting children in Britain. It causes a thickening of the mucus secreted by the body which leads to two main problems:

(a) the lungs, which are normally lined with a thin layer of mucus are lined with a much thicker layer and this tends to block the air passages which then causes difficulty in breathing. Children with Cystic Fibrosis are prone to lung infections, eg. bronchitis and pneumonia. If these infections are not controlled the lungs may become permanently damaged;

(b) the pancreas normally produces digestive enzymes which filter into the small intestine, but where Cystic Fibrosis occurs this is prevented by thickened mucus. Without treatment, children are not able to digest protein and fat and may become severely malnourished. Sometimes surgery is needed to clear the intestine.

Modern treatment has improved the survival and lifestyle of children with Cystic Fibrosis. Regular respiratory education and physiotherapy programmes together with enzyme supplements to the diet are started immediately the condition is diagnosed and are a permanent feature of the child's life.

2. EDUCATIONAL IMPLICATIONS

(i) Learning Difficulties

There are no learning difficulties specifically associated with this condition but, because of the possibility of frequent and sometimes lengthy periods in hospital or in bed at home, education is likely to be interrupted. Children may be able to learn during these periods and it is helpful to arrange a programme of work in conjunction with hospital teachers and the parents. Accurate record-keeping will assist all those involved with the child.

Regular physiotherapy is usually essential for children with Cystic Fibrosis and wherever possible this should be arranged so as to cause minimum disruption to the child's education. Physiotherapy is essential for these children and may sometimes cause distress which in turn may have a bearing on their ability to learn. (See *Physiotherapy* below.)

(ii) Considerations for Classroom Management

Coughing

Coughing helps to clear the lungs; it is non-infectious. It is very necessary to the child's health and it may be helpful to explain this tactfully to other teachers and classmates who may find it annoying.

87

Some children are prescribed special inhalants, normally used at home through a facemask. You may find it useful to know if a child uses such inhalants.

Physiotherapy

Depending upon the severity of the condition, physiotherapy may be needed 2–3 times a day. The privacy of a medical room is essential for this. Physiotherapy treatment may be unpleasant for the child and the effects of this may be seen in both his learning ability and his behaviour (see *Pastoral Care/Counselling* below).

Infection

As infections are potentially very serious for children with Cystic Fibrosis, sensible precautions should be taken in order to minimise the chance of infection. This may include immunisation and protection against cold and dampness, eg. a child may be allowed to stay inside during breaktimes on wet days. You will probably find that this is a cause of some anxiety to parents and it may be useful for teachers and parents to work out a management system so the child is treated consistently and neither under or over protected at school.

Physical Activity

The amount of restriction on the child's physical activity should be determined by a doctor in consultation with the parents. The school, and in particular the class teacher, should be informed of restrictions and of any changes to these restrictions. Children with Cystic Fibrosis often benefit from physical activity which helps clear the lungs.

3. ADDITIONAL POINTS

Pastoral Care/Counselling

Some children with Cystic Fibrosis do not understand their condition and may develop false ideas about the implications of it. Like all young people, pupils with Cystic Fibrosis tend to rebel during their teenage years and may reject their treatment at this time. It may be useful for you to know and be able to explain the need for the rigid physiotherapy programme and special diet. You may also be able to suggest ways in which the child might relax if he is anxious or weary of the treatment. Despite medical advances the life expectancy of some children with Cystic Fibrosis may be poor and they may need counselling from both within and outside school.

School Meals

Children with Cystic Fibrosis can eat school meals but parents may like to see menus in advance, if this is possible, to enable them to make the most suitable choice. Fatty foods should be avoided but special oils and margarines are now available. A dietary supplement must be taken with meals. Sometimes snacks between meals are also needed and this may be arranged to coincide with breaks.

Teachers supervising the child at this time should be made aware that this is part of the dietary management of the child.

In very hot weather children may need drinks containing extra salt (of the type given to athletes) to replace salt lost through perspiration.

Bowels

Children with Cystic Fibrosis do not generally have incontinence problems but because of their digestive difficulties there is sometimes a particularly offensive smell when the child's bowels are opened. This cannot be helped.

DIABETES

1. DESCRIPTION

Diabetes is a condition in which the body lacks the hormone, Insulin. Without Insulin, tissues (especially the muscles) are unable to absorb glucose and thereby produce energy. As it is not absorbed, the level of glucose in the blood rises causing thirst, frequent passing of urine and weight loss. Although diabetes occurs only rarely in school children, the onset is usually rapid and the symptoms (as described above) severe.

Diabetes is treated by insulin injections and a controlled diet. The aim is to achieve a balance whereby sufficient insulin is given to ensure effective use of glucose. Such a balance is needed in order to avoid later complications, eg. blindness and heart disease. Once this balance is achieved a pupil with diabetes should be able to participate in all school activities. Insulin is usually self-administered, or administered by an adult, early in the morning and injections are not normally needed during the school day.

2. EDUCATIONAL IMPLICATIONS

(i) Learning Difficulties

There are no learning difficulties specifically associated with this condition.

(ii) Considerations for Classroom Management

Management of an Insulin Reaction (Hypoglycaemia)

If a diabetic child has not had sufficient food, is late for a meal or unusually energetic, this may cause the level of glucose in the blood to drop resulting in an insulin reaction (also called Hypoglycaemia). The symptoms of this may include:

* ★ lack of concentration, drowsiness

* ★ pallor, sweating, shakiness

* ★ difficulty in reading or answering questions

* ★ untypical behaviour (eg. tearfulness or stubbornness)

* ★ vomiting

* ★ stomach ache.

In young children it is not always easy to distinguish these symptoms from naughtiness but if they occur before a meal or after active exercise it is likely that they result from an insulin reaction.

The simple treatment is to give the child sugar immediately. Many diabetic children carry glucose tablets or sugar and are able to recognise for themselves the symptoms of insulin reaction. They can therefore take sugar before the reaction becomes serious. You may wish to keep an emergency supply on hand, especially for young children who may not yet have learned the importance of regular intake of sugar. The simple rule is:

"IF IN DOUBT, GIVE SUGAR"

Children will normally make a rapid recovery and be back to normal within minutes. However, if a diabetic child lapses into unconsciousness, do not try to give sugar by mouth but seek medical attention immediately, calling an ambulance if necessary.

Physical Education

Children who have diabetes can normally take part in most forms of PE. To avoid an insulin reaction, they may need a snack, eg. biscuits, milk or chocolate, before exercise and occasionally afterwards or at half-time in a team game. Strenuous activities like cross country running should be supervised by an informed person who has supplies of sugar available if needed.

3. ADDITIONAL POINTS

School Meals

You may find it helpful to discuss any special dietary requirements with the child's parents. In order to maintain the glucose levels in the blood, snacks may be required at breaktimes and this may need to be explained to staff who do not have regular contact with the child. Most school meals are suitable for diabetic children but they may need extra sugar or carbohydrate, eg. in the form of an extra potato. It is important that the child eats regularly and does not miss meals.

School Trips

There should be no difficulty in including a pupil with diabetes on day trips as long as food is available for him. For longer periods, you may find it helpful to discuss any special arrangements with the child's parents to ensure that insulin injections can be given at the correct times and that the diet is maintained.

Pastoral Care/Counselling

Because diabetes is fairly rare among children, a pupil with this condition may feel rather isolated. Encouragement may be needed to help him come to terms with the condition and the restraints it imposes. Many older children become independent in their own management of diabetes. Because it is not apparent to other people, adolescents in particular may be tempted to conceal or ignore their condition and may need help to learn to accept the restraints involved.

Bruising

Some diabetic children are susceptible to bruising which does not heal easily. If a pupil appears bruised you should discuss this with parents and medical advisers and it may be necessary to limit contact sports.

After School Placement

Diabetic pupils will be able to follow most careers except those with the Armed Forces, Police Force or work requiring a HGV or PSV licence. Work involving heavy machinery is discouraged. A specialist careers officer will be able to advise the pupil if required.

DYSLEXIA

1. DESCRIPTION

Dyslexia describes individually varied difficulties which interfere with the acquisition of literacy and allied symbolic skills. The principal alerting sign is a noticeable discrepancy in those skills requiring sequential or spatial ordering of letters or numbers. Dyslexia is independent of intelligence as defined by traditional psychological tests and may therefore occur over a wide range of measured I.Q. Hence some children who are orally very competent may need special assistance in one or all of the following: reading, writing, spelling or arithmetic skills.

2. EDUCATIONAL IMPLICATIONS

(i) Learning Difficulties

Most children with dyslexia benefit from well established teaching methods based on a multi-sensory approach and overlearning of correct responses. Multi-sensory learning ensures that every possible channel is utilised, viz: sight, hearing, speech, touch and muscle movement, providing the child with mutually supporting ways of retaining the meaning of symbols. Approaches to learning which emphasise the meaning and association of the symbol are also helpful. The following guidelines have been found useful to children with dyslexia:

(a) arrange work to permit success in areas of strength. Encourage participation in discussion, oral and project work;

(b) reward correct responses, and mark what is right;

(c) use very small steps and a variety of ways of presenting material in areas which cause difficulty;

(d) do not overload short-term memory. Allow markers to keep the place while reading or copying, and establish logical ways of problem-solving in mathematics and spelling. Read blackboard copying work aloud;

(e) use memory aids, eg. mnemonics and association techniques, to help strengthen sequencing;

(f) use concrete methods to establish sequence patterns, and always use aids to help in sequencing (eg. mathematical table cards);

(g) teach each spelling rule specifically (there are no "easy" words);

(h) where handwriting is poor, use wide lined paper to reduce difficulties (perceptual problems and/or poor fine hand control are sometimes associated with dyslexia). Some children find typing a morale booster.

The overall plan should be to maintain the pupil's progress in acquiring information while at the same time improving his ability to acquire and express this knowledge. Many of the educational computer programmes are helpful to children with dyslexia.

(ii) Considerations for Classroom Management

Behaviour

Children with dyslexia often become worried and frustrated by their lack of progress and they may feel their difficulties are aggravated by lack of understandng from the teacher and/or their peers. This in turn may lead to retiring or clownish behaviour or other behaviour problems. Early identification will help to avoid such difficulties.

One of the more puzzling aspects of dyslexia is the variability in the child's performance. To prevent misunderstanding, it is important to know that this variability does not corrolate with the amount of effort on the child's part.

3. ADDITIONAL POINTS

Examinations

Despite the progress made in teaching children with dyslexia, many pupils still experience difficulties in taking examinations. The most common problems are:

(a) lack of speed in reading comprehension;

(b) lack of written fluency;

(c) residual spelling difficulties;

(d) lack of speed in mathematics (as distinct from the intellectual ability to solve mathematical problems).

If Examination Boards are informed of these difficulties well in advance, appropriate special arrangements may be made.

After School Placement

Specialist careers officers will be able to advise young people with dyslexia and, in particular, supply information about further and higher education where the effects of dyslexia can be further alleviated.

EPILEPSY

1. DESCRIPTION

Epilepsy is not a disease but a symptom of a disorder of the central nervous system characterised by sudden disorganised discharges of energy in the brain, manifested in the form of an epileptic seizure (also called a fit or attack). Such seizures vary widely and may occur after brain damage (see *Head Injury*) or occasionally in young children in association with a fever. However, most people with epilepsy simply have a lowered resistance to these discharges. There is sometimes a familial tendency to epilepsy but this does not mean that it is inherited.

There is no cure for epilepsy but, with the aid of the right drug, it can usually be completely controlled (in about 70% of cases) thus allowing most children with epilepsy to lead near normal lives.

A wide range of brain function may be disturbed during an epileptic seizure and this may be manifested in different forms as described below.

Generalised Tonic-Clonic Seizure (previously called Grand Mal)
This is the most well-known form of epilepsy and is usually easy to recognise. The child becomes unconscious and usually falls to the floor. Muscles stiffen and relax in convulsive movements which may last for several minutes before the child regains consciousness. He may be dazed or confused and need to sleep after such a seizure. Incontinence and/or dribbling sometimes occur during the seizure. This type of seizure most frequently occurs early in the morning and, where the epilepsy is well-controlled by drugs, rarely happens at school. It should be remembered that some children who merely faint may have mild jerking movement before they recover.

Generalised Absences (previously called Petit Mal)
Absences are very brief interruptions of consciousness without jerking movements and may be difficult to detect. They may make a child appear dreamy or inattentive and may pass unnoticed by both the child and the teacher.

Complex Partial Epilepsy (previously called Temporal Lobe)
Focal or partial seizures describe a period of clouded consciousness in which there may be fidgety, repetitive movements unlike normal behaviour which can be mistaken· for silliness or psychological disturbance. The repetitive nature of the movements and confusion as the child regains full consciousness are indications of this form of epilepsy.

A child who has epilepsy usually develops a pattern of recurrent seizures, not always of the same kind, over a period of time. The seizures are spontaneous, occurring usually without apparent cause. They are also usually of short duration and stop without intervention except in the case of status epilepticus which requires medical intervention in order to terminate a very prolonged seizure or series of seizures.

95

EDUCATIONAL IMPLICATIONS

(i) Learning Difficulties

Epileps, affects children across the whole range of ability. The major learning difficulty generally associated with this condition is the disruptive effect it may have on a child's education. Other factors associated with epilepsy, both neurological and social, may influence a child's learning ability and in some severe cases there may be brain damage.

Most epileptic seizures interrupt concentration and may also affect memory. Absences may not be noticeable as they happen so quickly and often have no outward manifestation but they may cause a child to lose concentration and therefore interrupt his learning. The accumulated effect of several absences can cause severe difficulties in learning and it is helpful to check more frequently than usual that the child understands the work. A review of classwork in the form of homework notes and study notes may also be valuable.

Children who have Generalised Tonic-Clonic seizures are likely to suffer substantial interruption of their education as they may need sleep following a seizure.

The effects of drugs which control epilepsy vary considerably and in some children they may cause drowsiness and affect concentration and their ability to learn particularly during the initial period of treatment.

(ii) Considerations for Classroom Management

Management of a Generalised Tonic-Clonic Seizure

Once a Generalised Tonic-Clonic seizure has started it must be allowed to run its course. It will stop spontaneously and there is nothing you can do to arrest it. As the child loses consciousness he does not feel pain during the seizure but the convulsive movements may look frightening to other members of the class. Perhaps the most helpful thing you can do is to remain calm and offer reassurance to the rest of the class. For the child himself you should:

(a) ensure he is not in any danger. He should only be moved if he is likely to hurt himself against hot or sharp objects or is in a dangerous position, eg. by a road or swimming pool;

(b) allow the seizure to run its course and do not restrain the convulsive movements in any way;

(c) do not try to put anything in the child's mouth;

(d) after the jerking movements have stopped, roll the child on his side in the recovery position and wipe his face if necessary;

(e) offer reassurance if required in the confused period after the seizure. One or two of the child's friends might be allowed to do this if appropriate. Sometimes a child may be incontinent during a seizure and the embarrassment this may cause should be taken into account;

(f) record in detail the events before, during and after the seizure which may be helpful to the child's doctor;

(g) call a doctor if the seizure is very long (over 15 minutes);

(h) allow the child to sleep after a seizure if he wishes to do so. If a medical room is available the child should be encouraged to remain at school and resume normal activities as soon as possible;

(i) make sure the parents are notified of the seizure.

Safety

Safety issues should be considered on an individual basis in conjunction with the child's parents and medical advisers. However, with suitable supervision pupils with epilepsy are normally able to join in all school activities including PE. It is recommended that 1:1 supervision should be provided for swimming. Working with a partner in science laboratories, kitchens and workshops provides a useful safeguard. Some children have a "premonition" in advance of a seizure and this allows them to alert someone else and/or ensure that they are in a safe position.

Flickering Lights

Most children with epilepsy are not photosensitive but a minority may have a seizure, usually a Tonic-Clonic, when exposed to certain types of flashing or flickering light. Girls are more susceptible than boys and it is most likely to develop around the age of puberty. Photosensitive children with epilepsy need not be restricted from watching television provided they sit about 2 metres from the screen and do not approach it to adjust the set, or from using most computer screens provided they are properly adjusted. Sometimes fluorescent lighting may be a source of photosensitivity but this is rare. Flashing lights of the type used in discotheques may induce a seizure and should be avoided by children who are photosensitive.

3. ADDITIONAL POINTS

Administration of Drugs

The timing and dosage of drugs is very important for children with this condition. If a child does not take his drugs at the appropriate time this may precipitate a seizure. Many children do not need drugs during a normal school day but where they do a regular routine should be established with the aid of the parents. This should also be taken into account when planning school trips.

After epilepsy is first diagnosed it may take a while to establish the correct balance of drugs and during this time the drugs may affect the behaviour of the child; he might, for example, become aggressive or excessively passive. The drugs may therefore affect the performance of the child in the classroom.

Pastoral Care/Counselling

Responsibility for the restraints involved in successful management of epilepsy, eg. regular sleep, regular drugs and avoidance of situations known to trigger seizures, should gradually be taken over by the child himself as he grows up. Adolescents may need counselling over matters of self-management and in improving their social skills and building self-confidence.

Family

Parents have considerable experience of managing epileptic seizures and are also very knowledgeable about the factors which may trigger a seizure. Regular contact with them about the day-to-day condition of the child will be very valuable to the school. Ironically, some parents may deny the existence of epilepsy or be very anxious about disclosing it to the school for fear of stigmatising their child. It is important that parents are treated sensitively and their attitudes towards the condition established.

Examinations

Seizures can be triggered by fatigue or stress and may therefore occur at examination time. It is wise to inform Examination Boards in advance of any candidates known to have epilepsy. If a pupil has a seizure during or just prior to an examination the appropriate Board should be notified immediately and account will be taken of this. Absences are particularly difficult to identify and it may be helpful to place a child who is prone to absences close to an invigilator so there is a better chance of such a seizure being noticed. It may also help to have an invigilator who knows the child well and is likely to recognise any symptoms of a seizure.

After School Placement

There are some jobs which are not open to people with epilepsy on safety grounds. Early discussion about careers and advice from a specialist careers officer will be helpful to the pupil.

FRIEDREICH'S ATAXIA

1. DESCRIPTION

Friedreich's Ataxia is a fairly rare inherited disease of the central nervous system which causes progressive deterioration of co-ordination and muscle control. It is genetic in origin.

It usually becomes apparent between the ages of 4 and 16 and the onset is insidious as the child appears "just clumsy". First the muscles of the legs are affected, then arms and hands and finally vision and/or hearing but it does not affect intellectual functioning. Associated problems which may also occur are:

poor circulation;

slight weakness of the heart causing occasional palpitations;

diabetes (see *Diabetes*).

2. EDUCATIONAL IMPLICATIONS

(i) Learning Difficulties

There are no learning difficulties specifically associated with this condition. Education may occasionally be interrupted for treatment in hospital.

(ii) Considerations for Classroom Management

Access to the Curriculum – Special Equipment

As the child becomes weaker and muscles in the arms and hands are affected, it may be necessary to provide special equipment, eg. electric typewriter, a calculator or electronic music-maker, to compensate for the child's lack of strength/grip. An occupational therapist will be able to advise on the most appropriate equipment. (See also chapter 2.)

Mobility and Exercise

Most children with Friedreich's Ataxia are able to complete their junior schooling without mobility aids. However regular exercise is needed to keep the child in the best physical condition and an exercise programme is normally initiated as early as possible with the assistance of a physiotherapist. Physiotherapy is also used to teach stability in movement and to maintain mobility for as long as possible. This programme is part of the daily routine of the child. Eventually, when the use of a wheelchair becomes essential, exercise is needed to keep correct posture and avoid pressure sores (see also paragraph on *Using a Wheelchair in an Ordinary School* in chapter 10).

Mouth Muscles and Speech

If the child's mouth muscles are affected whilst he is at school, speech may become blurred and it may be advisable to contact a speech therapist for assessment and advice. In addition to speech, the child's ability to eat and drink may also be impaired by weak muscles. The parents and perhaps a dietician will be able to help with this problem.

3. ADDITIONAL POINTS

Pastoral Care/Counselling

Most children with this disease start their schooling at an ordinary school and wish to stay as long as possible. As the disease progresses it becomes increasingly important to find interests which can be pursued in spite of the gradual loss of mobility. The limitations imposed by the condition may also have a bearing on the school subjects chosen by the child. Extra consideration may be needed to allow the child to participate in after-school clubs. In addition, remember that the child may be embarrassed by his increasing dependence on others at a time when peers are becoming more independent. It is therefore important to allow the pupil as much independence as possible and this may involve special efforts to ensure that he is included in social events and class activities. Counselling, from both within and outside school, about the nature of the child's disability may be needed and carefully considered careers guidance is essential.

The Family

By the time the first child has been diagnosed as having Friedreich's Ataxia he may have younger brothers and sisters who may also develop the disease. The emotional implications for the parents with one or more children with this condition are very considerable. Close and regular contact with the family may be helpful.

HAEMOPHILIA

1. DESCRIPTION

The term Haemophilia is used to describe a group of inherited diseases in which there is a permanent defect in a blood clotting factor. The three most common forms of Haemophilia are:

Haemophilia A (also called *Classical Haemophilia*) – affects boys

Haemophilia B (also called *Christmas Disease*) – affects boys

Van Willebrand's Disease – affects both sexes.

Children with Haemophilia may bleed for much longer than normal after injury and/or accidental bruising. Those with severe forms of Haemophilia may also bleed apparently spontaneously into joints, muscles and other parts of the body. Children usually learn to recognise the "feel" of internal bleeding before the external signs of swelling and bruising become apparent but they may suffer frequent pain due to stiffness in their joints caused by internal bleeding.

There is no general indicator of how frequently bleeding may occur but it is known that stress may be a contributing factor.

2. EDUCATIONAL IMPLICATIONS

(i) Learning Difficulties

There are no learning difficulties specifically associated with this condition. However, education may be interrupted by the need for rest following bleeds and visits to a Haemophilia Centre which may be some distance away. It is helpful to try to maintain a continuous education programme to cover short absences.

(ii) Considerations for Classroom Management

Management of Haemophilia

In the past bleeding had to be treated at Haemophilia Centres but now there is an increasing emphasis on home management. The missing clotting factor is supplied in the form of an injection. Older children may learn to manage their own bleeding and carry a personal medical kit. Arrangements for managing bleeds should be discussed with the parents in advance of the child starting school and an individual procedure established. Teachers are not to be expected to give any injections but you should check whether normal first aid is appropriate for small cuts or whether these should be subject to the individual procedure mentioned above.

Protection in the Classroom

You may like to consider arrangement of desks and equipment within the classroom to allow maximum access and ways of managing pupils to reduce jostling and accidental bruising but there is normally no need to create a special

101

environment for a pupil with Haemophilia and he should be encouraged to be as independent as possible. Occasionally a child may need to use splints or a wheelchair (temporarily) in order to rest limbs and may then require extra consideration in moving about the school.

Physical Education

Most children with Haemophilia can participate to some extent in PE and restrictions should be kept to a minimum but contact sports including rugby and football should be avoided. You should check with the child's parents about the extent to which he may participate in PE. The likelihood of damage to the tissues is reduced by general fitness and swimming usually provides excellent exercise.

Practical Lessons

Many pupils with Haemophilia are able to participate in practical lessons such as woodwork, metal work and science. As with PE, it is advisable to discuss any restrictions and/or precautions to be taken with the child's parents in advance.

Playground and Corridors

In order to avoid accidental knocking as children rush out at break time it may be wise to tell a child with Haemophilia to wait until the rush is over or excuse him from the lesson a few minutes early. The same principle applies when children are changing lessons. You may find it useful to discuss this with parents as well. Only rarely is it necessary to have extra playground supervision but children who have severe forms of Haemophilia may have to be restricted to a quiet area of play.

3. ADDITIONAL POINTS

Pastoral Care/Counselling

Many pupils with Haemophilia find it difficult to accept the restrictions imposed upon them by their disability particularly as they appear and want to be considered "normal". Teenagers in particular are prone to react against treatment and may need counselling from both within and outside school. It should also be remembered, particularly as this is a hereditary condition, that the parents may need counselling too.

Treatment Prior to Exams and School Trips

Medical treatment may be given to prevent bleeds during examination time and may also be worth considering to cover school trips lasting longer than one day and involving absence from home. When planning a school trip which will include a pupil with Haemophilia it is a useful precaution to find out where the nearest Haemophilia Centre is so the information is available if needed. A list of Haemophilia Centres in the UK may be obtained from the DHSS (details under *Haemophilia* in Appendix B).

After School Placement

As the treatment of Haemophilia is becoming easier to manage and more successful there are now fewer restrictions on the options available to pupils with Haemophilia after school. Advice is available from the specialist careers officer.

HEAD INJURY

1. DESCRIPTION

Head injuries are often caused by road accidents and are most commonly found among young men. The effects of such injuries vary from very severe, involving gross and sometimes specific handicaps, to slight and transitory reduction of concentration, speed of thought and memory. The spectrum of effects is so wide that the label "Head Injury" in itself cannot give any indication of the pupil's likely performance in class as no two children with such injuries will be affected in the same way.

Following the accident when the head injury occurs, there is usually a period of unconsciousness and it is likely that a child injured in this way will have no recollection of the event. Memory loss (Post Traumatic Amnesia – PTA) often occurs after the accident and may last for some time. It is therefore possible that a child could return to school during the period of PTA. It is important to remember that, although the child is recovering from a physical illness, the experience is one of disorientation and bewilderment.

In many instances it is almost impossible to know whether the effects of the injury will be permanent or transitory.

Problems associated with head injuries include impairment of vision and hearing and sometimes epilepsy (see separate sections on each of these).

2. EDUCATIONAL IMPLICATIONS

(i) Learning Difficulties

Language

Head injuries may affect a child's ability to use and understand language.

If the central control of the muscles involved in speech is affected by the injury the child may have articulation problems (see *Speech Disorders*). Injuries may also cause difficulties with the concepts of language which in turn may lead to a child becoming less fluent in speech or, for example, having problems in naming objects. The child may also respond less well to verbal instructions through a lack of understanding. You may therefore find it necessary to repeat phrases, re-word sentences or add demonstration to help the pupil. Sometimes children experience difficulty in producing the correct volume of speech and, where language difficulties are conceptual, it is likely that written work will also be affected (see *Dyslexia*). Whilst reading/writing may be impaired by conceptual or articulation problems, this could also be the result of visual difficulties. Therefore it is important to establish the causes of language difficulties with the aid of other professionals, particularly a speech therapist, in order to help the child overcome these problems.

Memory

Memory difficulties are likely in the early stages after the accident. Many children recover the use of their memory but for some, difficulties may persist. In association with this, children may find it hard to sustain attention for extended periods. If large areas are forgotten the child's sequencing skills may be affected. In addition, the child's memory may be confused; for example, he may muddle events which occurred before the accident and those which occurred afterwards and be unable to recall immediate past events, eg. the instructions you have just given.

Hand Control

As a result of damage to their central nervous system, some children may experience poor co-ordination in general and poor hand control in particular. This difficulty will be different to that caused by bone injury which may also have occurred. The preferred hand may be affected but some may, even though seemingly recovered, use only one hand for bimanual tasks. They should be encouraged to use the impaired or neglected hand as much as possible. Where the child is unable to use the non-preferred hand fully, anchoring writing materials may help. It is important that the child continues to express himself through writing and it will be worthwhile experimenting with a variety of pens and pencils. Some children may find it easier to use a typewriter, possibly with an expanded keyboard. You should seek advice from an occupational therapist and consider whether a computer or other types of new technology may help the child.

(ii) Considerations for Classroom Management

Children with head injuries differ from most other pupils with disabilities in that they return to school while active change and recovery is still taking place. The early period after receiving head injury is of crucial importance in determining how the pupil will adjust and live in the future. There are two main forms of adjustment to consider: educational and social.

Educational Adjustment

There are many pressures on a head-injured child returning to school; he will have missed a period of education while recovering from the accident, his parents may be anxious to see him back at school as a sign of returning normality and for older pupils there is also the pressure exerted by examination schedules. It is clearly important that very careful assessment is made of the pupil when he first returns to school. Initially he may find it very difficult to cope with academic learning and, although the child will naturally want to return to his former class, it may be in his best interests to be moved to another class and it may also be necessary to reconsider the curriculum he is following and his examination prospects. It is very important that the pupil experiences success, however small, to build up confidence.

A head-injured child may be very much in need of individual help but may reject this to avoid being singled out from the class. This leads to a danger that the child may become silent when he needs help and may resort to lying about class and home work in order to cover up. It is very important that these children are kept under constant appraisal so that their needs can be met as quickly as possible.

A child may be able to cope adequately in a one-to-one situation but may find it more difficult to take part in a group activity where conversation is moving in several directions.

Social Adjustment

It is very difficult for a child who has previously been an "ordinary" member of a class to accept that he may now need special help. He will return to school after the accident needing renewed acceptance from teachers and peers, particularly if he has been obviously damaged or scarred. It can be a very demanding and confusing time for such a pupil and extra patience and care may be required.

It is particularly difficult for a child who was previously good at physical education, for example, to come to terms with increased clumsiness or slowness in movement and it is almost inevitable that frustration will occur from time to time. Academic progress may initially be very slow despite great efforts by the pupil and this too may cause frustration.

Other children may find it difficult to understand what has happened to a head-injured child especially if his responsiveness has changed. You may find it necessary to explain to the class what has happened but this must be done with great care to avoid embarrassing the child or causing him distress. It is important to gain the consent of the child and family before doing this.

In order to gain acceptance from his peers the child may resort to becoming a "joker" or behave in an unco-operative manner with adults. The reasons for this behaviour need to be recognised and it should not be taken to indicate a sudden, sinister and permanent change of character. Stress may be manifested in terms of unacceptable behaviour and/or rejection of school. If the pupil has changed classes, teachers may find it helpful to discuss together any such difficulties and try to establish realistic expectations based upon past experience of the pupil.

3. ADDITIONAL POINTS

Pastoral Care/Counselling

It seems a characteristic of head-injured children to resist mixing with other children whom they consider disabled even when the physical consequences of their injury are obvious and severe. In the short term, at least, it is unlikely that the child will recognise the full extent of his difficulties and counselling, from both within and outside school, may be needed to help the child come to terms with his injury.

Tiredness

Many children who have had head injuries become easily tired as a result of the additional effort required of them. In addition some children take a considerable time to restore the normal patterns of sleep and wakefulness following the accident.

Family

In addition to the effects of his injuries, the pupil may also have to come to terms with parental protection. This is a particularly difficult problem for teenagers and some pupils may reject their parents' concern in an attempt to assert their own independence. The family situation may be further complicated where a younger brother or sister is seen to be given more freedom and responsibility, or is seen to be more capable than the head-injured child. Occasionally a parent or close relative may have been killed in the same accident in which the child was injured and the presence of Post Traumatic Amnesia with a consequent lack of direct perception of this loss may further complicate an already difficult situation; the child's apparent lack of concern may be distressing for others.

Damages

The parents may be involved in litigation to seek damages. This can, to some extent, influence the way in which difficulties are viewed and, rarely, lead to conflict where recovery implies a reduction in the likely compensation. In addition to the normal follow-up appointments the child will be required to undergo a number of examinations by experts who will provide evidence. This may be distressing for the child and disrupt schooling long after recovery is complete. The school may also be required to give evidence of past and present education and therefore adequate records are particularly important.

Administering Drugs

Some head-injured children may need to take drugs which may affect their performance at school. If the child has had an epileptic fit following the accident he may be given drugs to prevent this recurring. Sometimes anti-epileptic drugs are prescribed even when a fit has not occurred (see *Epilepsy*).

Physiotherapy

Physiotherapy may be required by some children in order to improve their movement skills.

Noise

Head injury often makes children particularly sensitive to noise and this may cause distress. It may be useful to bear this in mind in classes where noisy machinery or loud recordings are used.

HEARING IMPAIRMENT

Fig 8

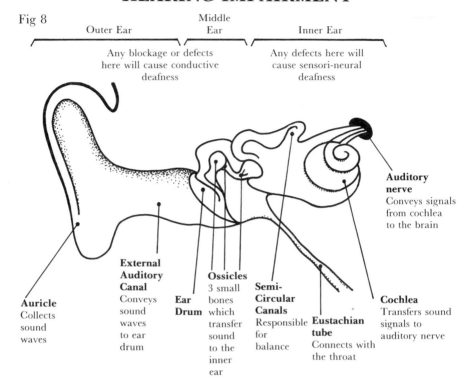

CROSS SECTION REPRESENTATION OF THE EAR

1. DESCRIPTION

The ear has three functional divisions: the outer, middle and inner ear. Sound enters the outer ear and is conducted through a stretched membrane (the eardrum) to the middle ear where it is transferred through three small bones to the inner ear. In the inner ear, within the cochlea, the sounds are transformed into electrical impulses which travel up the auditory nerve to the brain (see diagram). Damage to the ear results in hearing loss of one of the following types:

Conductive Deafness
Conductive deafness results from obstruction or malformation of any part of the outer or middle ear. Most common, however, is the occurrence of middle ear infection, which causes temporary or partial deafness in 20% of children at any one time. Such infections may be persistent or intermittent and treatment can bring improvement in hearing.

Sensori-Neural Deafness
Sensori-neural deafness results from a malfunction in the inner ear or auditory

108

nerve and prevents perception of certain sounds. Hearing loss may be permanent and severe, but may also be alleviated by the use of hearing aids.

Mixed Conductive and Sensori-Neural Deafness
Some children have a mixed conductive and sensori-neural loss.

2. EDUCATIONAL IMPLICATIONS

(i) Learning Difficulties

The educational implications of teaching children with hearing loss depend on two major factors: the degree and type of hearing loss and the time of onset. Deafness has many causes and occurs in various degrees of severity. Hearing loss is measured in two ways: by loudness (in decibels (dBs)) and pitch (frequency). The most useful classroom indicators are:

its effects on the way language is understood and expressed;

its effects on the way the child believes speech is acquired and used.

The personality of the child will clearly also have a major bearing on the way in which he copes with his hearing loss.

Degree and Types of Hearing Loss

(a) *Mild Hearing Loss*
Even a mild hearing loss can have serious educational implications and a child with such a loss will often have difficulty in hearing speech in the normal way. A loss as slight as 25 dBs (similar to that sometimes experienced with a heavy cold) may require a hearing aid, though hearing aids are not normally prescribed to children with a loss of less than 40 dBs. Using hearing aids in ordinary classrooms can be difficult, especially in open-plan primary schools where distinguishing what is relevant out of the cacophony of sounds is difficult even with the most appropriate hearing aid (see section on hearing aids below).

Hearing loss is such that sounds are distorted depending upon frequency of each sound and, for example, sounds like "S" and "F" may not be perceived at all. Thus some words may be unintelligible out of context and further explanation will be needed.

A loss which is ·mild, intermittent or affects specific frequencies may go undetected during the early school years or until language difficulty begins to cause concern. Such hearing losses may be the cause of inattention, learning difficulties and sometimes of consequent behaviour problems. It is therefore important that thorough hearing tests are carried out on children with such difficulties. Once treated or given the appropriate hearing aid many children are able to make full use of the opportunities in an ordinary classroom.

If you think that a child in your class may have a hearing problem, speak to the school doctor who will arrange for a hearing assessment. You may like to use the following checklist as a guide.

1. Does he have poor speech?

2. Does he daydream?

3. Does he often mishear words or phrases?

4. Does he check to make sure he knows what to do?

5. Does he hear some days and not others?

6. Does he lip-read?

7. Does he have a language delay with poor sentence construction?

8. Is he unusually noisy or quiet?

9. Does he depend on visual clues?

10. Does he seem inattentive?

11. Does he have difficulty grasping abstract concepts?

12. Does he appear tense or over-anxious?

Children with a mild hearing loss are those most likely to be found in an ordinary classroom.

(b) *Moderate Hearing Loss*

Children with moderate hearing loss may need additional assistance in following the normal curriculum. They may rely on lip-reading (see below) as well as any auditory clues they can obtain. Monitoring their own voices may be difficult for some children. Most will need special help with language and speech (see *Peripatetic Teachers of the Deaf* and *Speech Therapists* below). They often receive support in their school work from either a peripatetic teacher of the deaf or a support teacher in the school.

(c) *Severe and Profound Hearing Loss*

Where there is severe or profound hearing loss the acquisition and development of spoken language may be affected especially if the loss occurs before spoken language has developed (see *Onset of Hearing Loss* below). Such a loss will also severely limit the warning use of sound which most people take for granted. Children will rely a great deal on visual and other non-auditory clues both to understand their environment and to communicate and may need sign language to supplement speech, in order both to understand and express themselves. The specialist help of a teacher of the deaf and a speech therapist is essential for these children.

Onset of Hearing Loss

(a) *Children with Prelingual Deafness*

Where deafness occurs before spoken language has developed there is severe interference with the normal acquisition of language and speech skills. The crucial importance of early detection is widely recognised and specialist help from a teacher of the deaf is arranged for the parents and child immediately after diagnosis which is usually before school age. The importance of early learning cannot be over-emphasised. Concept formation and language acquisition are

110

fundamental to cognitive development. Severe and profoundly deaf children are encouraged to use their residual hearing to the limit and non-verbal forms of communication may also be used to encourage the acquisition of concepts and grammatical rules. Typical difficulties encountered in such children include: understanding concepts; mastering the basic rules of language such as word order, plurals, pronouns, verbs and tenses; new vocabulary. Speech is likely to be delayed and even if the child acquires some mastery of language, speech is likely to be affected because of his inability to monitor the sound of his own voice. A speech therapist will be able to provide assessment and help for the child working closely with a teacher of the deaf.

(b) *Children with Later Onset of Deafness*
Later onset of deafness generally causes less educational difficulty as language skills have either been acquired or partially acquired so that there is a good basis for subsequent learning. However, children will still need additional help and/or experience and time to learn and use new concepts, linguistic rules and vocabulary. It is important to ensure that the child's speech does not deteriorate because he cannot hear his own speech so well. He should be seen by a speech therapist at regular intervals so his speech can be monitored and help provided as necessary.

(ii) Considerations for Classroom Management

Environment and Lip-reading
Good vision is very important to deaf children. It is helpful for the child to sit near the front of the class so he can see your face clearly. Good lighting, without glare, helps as well. Lip-reading is used by many children with hearing loss and this is easiest when the speaker is:

(a) standing still;

(b) looking directly towards the child (not in profile and not talking while writing on the blackboard);

(c) in good light (not with light directly behind causing a shadow across the face);

(d) not shouting (shouting exaggerates the movements of the mouth and makes lip-reading more difficult);

(e) beardless (beards can obstruct lip-reading);

(f) at the same horizontal level;

(g) using normal rhythm and intonation.

Lip-reading is also more difficult where there is more than one speaker and this should be borne in mind in group work. It is also worth remembering that it is difficult for a child to lip-read and take notes simultaneously.

Teaching Guidelines

Hearing impaired pupils in general have difficulty with new vocabulary and this should be taken into consideration, particularly in specialist subjects. Care should be taken to ensure that the hearing impaired pupil has understood the whole lesson. Follow-up and a link with the peripatetic teacher of the deaf is helpful and summaries (on the blackboard or in the form of a handout) are useful as a supplement to personal notes.

Hearing Aids and Radio Aids

Unless the hearing loss is very mild (see *Mild Hearing Loss* above) it is normal practice for a hearing impaired child to wear a hearing aid which amplifies sound. The purpose of amplification is to make the most of the child's residual hearing so that sounds become a meaningful source of information and can assist the child to acquire spoken language naturally where possible. Although the hearing aid is a helpful tool it does not compensate for hearing loss in the way that glasses compensate for defective sight and children have to learn to listen very carefully to what they hear. Unfortunately, hearing aids amplify background noise so do not always make speech clearer. For this reason, a quiet acoustically-treated room is particularly helpful to a child who uses a hearing aid.

A hearing aid consists of a battery-powered amplifier connected to an ear mould. The hearing aid may be worn on a strap on the body or behind the ear. Earmoulds are individually fitted and should lie snugly in the ear. If too much sound leaks around a loose mould the microphone will pick it up and this results in a squeal which is unhelpful to the deaf child and irritating to hearing people near him. If the aid whistles in this way, make sure it is properly inserted and correctly adjusted; the parents or a teacher of the deaf will be able to tell you the correct setting. It may be turned up too loud but if it whistles persistently you should inform the teacher of the deaf or the support teacher as the child may need a new ear mould.

To minimise the problem of background noise, radio aids are often used in classrooms. The teacher wears a small microphone which transmits sound into the child's hearing aid so that the teacher's voice is directly received and background noise is reduced.

3. ADDITIONAL POINTS

Professional Resources

(a) *Peripatetic Teachers of the Deaf*
Teachers of the deaf are specially trained to work with deaf children; peripatetic teachers of the deaf are concerned largely with children in mainstream schools and also give guidance to parents of pre-school children with hearing impairments. They offer support to teachers in the management of hearing-impaired children and from their own experience or links with other professionals can advise on the following:

★ school work;

★ management of hearing aids and supply of batteries;

- ★ optimum listening conditions;

- ★ social management including counselling;

- ★ language and speech development in conjunction with class teachers and speech therapists;

- ★ additional support methods for better communication (eg. sign language, gestures);

- ★ special arrangements for sitting school and public examinations;

- ★ special arrangements for implementing safety procedures (eg. fire drills);

- ★ teaching techniques to help hearing impaired children;

- ★ links with colleges of further education;

- ★ choice and advice on careers.

Peripatetic teachers are therefore a valuable source of help and information so you should know how to contact the one assigned to your school if difficulties arise.

(b) *Speech Therapists*
Speech therapists are trained in development of all aspects of language and communication skills. Some have specialist knowledge of hearing impaired children and their needs and can play an important part in the communication skills programme of such children. Speech therapy is usually timetabled on a one-to-one basis and may take place in the classroom (in consultation with the teacher) or the child may be withdrawn, particularly if specialist equipment such as visual feed-back devices are used in the therapy.

Communication and Behaviour

Children with more severe forms of hearing loss may need to rely on additional methods of communication. For example, in order to gain your attention a young hearing impaired child may grab you by the hand but as children grow older this is less acceptable and alternative methods of achieving the same end (eg. natural gestures) may need to be worked out. Whatever methods are chosen, it is important that they are used consistently with the child.

Failure of people to understand what you are trying to tell them is a common cause of frustration to everyone and this is a particular problem for hearing impaired children. You may therefore find it helpful to have a "back-up" routine if you fail to understand the first time, eg. "Show me" (for junior pupils) or "Would you mind writing it down/saying it again" (for older pupils).

Sign Language

Many hearing impaired adults use sign language to communicate. A small percentage of hearing impaired children are born to hearing impaired parents and may use sign language at home. In addition, many special schools and units use signing systems to supplement speech. Some children may therefore be used to signing and you may find it helpful to know a few basic signs, eg. sit down, which can be used concurrently with speech.

Safety

When a hearing impaired child is unable to hear normal warning signs (eg. school bells, fire alarms) you will find it helpful to have a warning sign which the child recognises and to which he knows how to respond.

For emergency procedures, eg. fire drills, one person (adult or child) may be designated to ensure the hearing impaired child knows of the warning. The peripatetic teacher of the deaf is able to advise on safety matters.

Examinations

For pupils with appreciable hearing loss it may be necessary to make special arrangements for sitting both school and public examinations. It is important that the pupil understands any spoken instructions and also the examination questions themselves where they contain unfamiliar vocabulary. A list of considerations for hearing impaired candidates has been negotiated by the National Association for the Tertiary Education of the Deaf (see Appendix D).

Pastoral Care/Counselling

Hearing loss is perhaps the most isolating of all disabilities; the more severely handicapped often find support from within the deaf community itself. A few pupils, particularly teenagers, may need counselling and other help to overcome social isolation; peripatetic teachers can advise on the most appropriate forms of help.

Hearing impaired children, expecially those with pre-lingual deafness, may have restricted life experience because of the difficulties caused by their hearing loss and they may need additional opportunities to practise social skills, eg. using public transport and job interview skills.

KIDNEY DISORDERS

1. DESCRIPTION

The kidneys are situated in the lower back, on either side of the spine. Their main function is to filter waste chemical products from the blood which are then excreted in the urine. There are two main types of problem related to kidney function:

Severe Kidney Infection
The fine capillaries of the kidney can normally distinguish between waste products and blood proteins but if they are damaged by infection or high blood pressure they allow the proteins to escape into the urine. Where this happens water seeps into the tissues causing swelling especially of the hands and feet. After treatment in hospital, children with kidney infections usually recover, and although they may have more than one attack, most grow up with both kidneys working normally.

Kidney (Renal) Failure
When the kidneys are irreversibly damaged, artificial methods, ie. dialysis on a kidney machine, are used to replace the function they normally perform. Treatment on a kidney machine does not provide a cure but it enables the condition to be managed until a kidney transplant becomes available. Children with renal failure usually need dialysis three time a week for approximately 5–8 hours each time. The process involves pumping the blood from the child into the machine, where it is "cleaned", and then pumped back again. It is not in itself painful but the treatment may sometimes cause the child to feel unwell and there are likely to be some days when he will not be able to complete school work. Dialysis may be arranged at home but is more often provided in a hospital unit. The treatment is time-consuming and demands strong family support but it allows the child to lead a fairly normal life-style and remain at home.

Anaemia and associated fatigue are common to children with kidney disorders. Where the kidneys do not function properly and waste products are allowed to accumulate in the blood, this may cause the child to become irritable or sometimes confused.

2. EDUCATIONAL IMPLICATIONS

(i) Learning Difficulties

There are no learning difficulties specifically associated with kidney disorders.

Children with severe kidney infections may have their education interrupted while they are receiving hospital treatment. They may not be well enough to receive education in hospital initially and may miss a considerable period of schooling. As their condition improves they may receive education from hospital teachers. Once recovered they should be able to return to school on a normal basis.

Children with renal failure spend an initial period in hospital followed by long-term dialysis and the possibility of surgery. Children are often able to continue their education whilst receiving dialysis treatment and it may be helpful to set work for the child to carry out if he is able to do so. This encourages a sense of normality and may act as a form of occupational therapy. Liaison between school and hospital teachers is particularly important for these children as they may spend every other day on dialysis. A co-ordinated approach will help to achieve a balance of subjects and maintain progress in education.

(ii) Considerations for Classroom Management

Tiredness

Children with kidney problems and particularly those receiving dialysis treatment are likely to tire more easily than normal. This may affect their academic work and also their ability to participate in physical education. If tiredness is a persistent problem you may like to discuss it with the child's parents. It is also advisable to discuss with his doctor the extent to which the child should participate in PE.

3. ADDITIONAL POINTS

School Meals

Although dietary control for children with renal failure is normally strict, school meals are often suitable. Drinks must be limited and most commercial soft drinks are not allowed. In addition, salt should not be used. It is important to know the precise restrictions for each child and the school should discuss meals with the child's parents and perhaps a dietician if necessary. Alternatively parents may prefer to supply food from home. Older children should be encouraged to take responsibility for their dietary management but you may find it necessary to keep an eye on younger children to prevent them eating potentially harmful foods, eg. crisps.

School Trips

Children with renal failure may be able to take part in day trips which are not too physically demanding but, because of the timetable of dialysis treatment, it is unlikely that they would be able to go on longer trips unless provision can be made for them to receive dialysis treatment whilst away.

Family

Parents are often closely involved in the treatment of children with renal failure. Although this may impose a heavy burden on the family it also means that they are able to advise you on day-to-day changes in the child's condition.

After School Placement

Although careers choices are limited while dialysis treatment continues, subject options and careers guidance should take account of the possibility of full-time employment following a successful transplant.

LEUKAEMIA

1. DESCRIPTION

Leukaemia is the term given to a group of diseases in which there is a malignant change in the bone marrow. Although different types of cell may be affected, the consequences for children with acute leukaemia are fairly consistent. Because the leukaemia cells multiply in such profusion, the normal bone marrow is decreased and this leads to a greater or lesser degree of anaemia and problems with infection and bleeding. The most common form in children is acute lymphatic leukaemia; the cure rate for this condition is approximately 60% but over 90% of children achieve a "remission", ie. a return of the bone marrow to normal function. Unfortunately, in some this is not sustained and a relapse occurs.

Treatment is intensive and sometimes debilitating in its early stages. However, most children are discharged from hospital in a couple of weeks and most later treatment is managed on an out-patient basis.

A minority of children develop acute myeloid leukaemia for which the prognosis is far less hopeful than for the lymphatic form.

2. EDUCATIONAL IMPLICATIONS

(i) Learning Difficulties

Some children with leukaemia experience difficulty in concentration and there is a growing body of information to suggest that some forms of therapy can impair some aspects of intellectual function, particularly in mathematics, when treatment begins at a very early age.

Education is likely to be interrupted by hospital treatment and when this occurs regularly it may be helpful to set work to be done while the child is away from school; an effective liaison system with the hospital teachers and the parents should be established.

Some children with leukaemia develop psychological problems which may affect their attitude to learning. You may find it helpful to talk to the child's parents if this appears to be a problem and an educational psychologist may also be able to help (see also 3 below).

(ii) Considerations for Classroom Management

Adjustment of Expectations and Curriculum

Decisions about when/whether the child might return to school will be made by medical staff and the parents in conjunction with the school. Because of disruption to their education and tiredness, children with leukaemia may not be able to keep up with other children in the class and it may be necessary to consider adjustments to their curriculum. It should also be stated that some children are able to manage the normal curriculum without any special arrangements. Educational and social needs must be considered on an individual basis; some children, for example, may benefit more from remaining with their peers even when they find it difficult to keep up with the work than from being moved to a lower class where their educational needs may be more appropriately met.

Tiredness

Leukaemia is likely to cause increased tiredness and individual arrangements may need to be considered to help the child to obtain as much as possible from his education without over-tiring him. Medical advice should be sought and he may need to rest at certain times and physical activities may need to be limited. Sometimes part-time attendance at school may be appropriate. Occasionally a child may need to use a wheelchair on a temporary basis in order to attend school. The child is the best judge of his physical limitations.

3. ADDITIONAL POINTS

Physical Appearance/Psychological Effects and Counselling

During period of remission when the child returns to school, his physical appearance may be deceptively normal and teachers in contact with him should know if he requires any special assistance, eg. a rest period. Children, especially those of primary age, may not be told the full implications of their condition and it is tactful not to use the word "Leukaemia" in front of the child or his classmates.

Although some children may appear normal, for others the treatment they receive may cause changes in their physical appearance; most commonly they may put on weight and therefore look plump or they may lose most or all of their hair. The psychological effects of change in appearance must not be underestimated and you may need to watch out for teasing or unconsciously hurtful remarks from other children. Counselling may be helpful, particularly for older children, and assist in avoiding behaviour problems. Peers may also need help in coming to terms with this condition.

Family

Parents are closely involved in the treatment of children with Leukaemia. Although this may impose a heavy burden on the family it also means that they are able to advise you on day-to-day changes in the child's condition.

LOSS OF LIMB

1. DESCRIPTION

Children may be born without a limb, or part of one, or they may lose all or part of a limb as the result of an accident. Children born with a limb deficiency have sensitivity in the remaining section of the limb and are able to use this to help compensate. This ability often surprises those who do not know them well.

Artificial limbs (prostheses) are usually provided for young children both to encourage development of strength in the muscles and patterns of movement needed to use them effectively. The child is also able to experiment with ways in which they can help him. Learning to use artificial limbs takes time and practice and children may need to be encouraged. Sometimes an artificial limb may be more difficult to use than the child's own preferred method of managing and some children may wish to remove an artificial arm for PE, for example. Parents will be able to advise you about when the limb should be worn or removed.

2. EDUCATIONAL IMPLICATIONS

(i) Learning Difficulties

There are no learning difficulties specifically associated with this condition.

(ii) Considerations for Classroom Management

A child who is fitted with an artificial limb is likely to be in regular contact with an Occupational Therapist who will be able to advise on any problems in using the aid or on new tasks which need to be learned. Older children may have short "courses" in school holidays to develop manipulative skills. A very few children have multiple limb loss; most have one or sometimes two limbs missing. The educational implications of the loss of an arm and the loss of a leg are very different; clearly the loss of an arm is likely to have more serious implications for learning.

Loss of Limb – Arm(s)

Artificial arms
The artificial arms usually supplied to children are made of metal/plastic and have a grasp between the two "fingers" which are normally covered in toning foam to improve the appearance. With practice in using the arm, a child will be able to hold a pencil, cut out with scissors, manage buttons and zips and attend to personal needs without assistance. When a child's shoulders are not strong enough to manage an artificial arm, a power-assisted arm may be used. These are fairly heavy and require some expertise to be effective.

Alternative forms of manipulation
Some children prefer to use their own ways of managing instead of or as well as using an artificial arm. The child's preference is important but it is also advisable to check with the parents and his occupational therapist to ensure a consistent

119

approach. Some children become very adept at using their feet for a variety of tasks and may prefer to do this rather than using an artificial arm. This may require some alteration to seating arrangements. Where a child prefers to use his mouth for pen and paper work or a head pointer for typing, this needs to be arranged at a comfortable working height and paper secured if necessary.

You may find it helpful to talk to the child's parents and perhaps also his occupational therapist before he starts school. The parents will be able to explain how the child operates his arm, what he can and cannot do and how much help he might need.

Loss of Limbs – Leg(s)

Wheelchairs and Balance

Children who have lost one or both legs may be able to use artificial limbs but are still likely to have mobility difficulties. Some may use sticks or crutches and those who are unable to maintain their balance are normally provided with a wheelchair. Children with limb deficiency are likely to have greater stability problems than other wheelchair-users and it may take them longer to learn to manage their wheelchair confidently.

Some wheelchairs may be adjusted in height to allow the child to reach whilst maintaining his balance. These chairs are less manoeuvrable and transportable than other types of chair but may assist the independence and confidence of the child. Mobility difficulties should be taken into account when considering emergency procedures (see chapter 9).

Physical Education

Children who have lost one or part of one leg are likely to be able to join in many PE activities. For those who have no legs, special arrangements may need to be considered but they should be encouraged to take part in PE as far as possible as physical fitness is as important for them as for all other children. A physiotherapist will be able to advise on any special exercises.

3. ADDITIONAL POINTS

Psychological Effects of Losing a Limb

Children who lose a limb following an accident often find it difficult to come to terms with their disability. They can be far more difficult to motivate and discipline than those born with this condition.

Teasing

Sometimes teasing from other children may become a problem for children with a limb deficiency. It may be helpful for the child to have a simple explanation ready to satisfy questions. A matter-of-fact attitude on the part of teachers and parents will help to prevent the child feeling embarrassed about his limb deficiency.

Social Skills and Hygiene

Children who have lost both upper limbs and do not use artificial arms have to learn methods of managing their own personal needs. Initially they may require assistance but with time, perseverance and sometimes an aid, many of them become independent. They may also need to work out a method for storing and gaining easy access to pocket money or a handkerchief. Again parents and an occupational therapist will be able to advise.

MENTAL HANDICAP

1. DESCRIPTION

The phrase "Mental Handicap" covers a wide range of children who vary considerably in their ability. They range from those with profound intellectual impairment to those who are mildly affected and are able to play a full role in the community in which they live.

Mental handicap is not an illness or a disease although sometimes it may be caused by the effects of a severe illness or accident. More commonly it is caused by genetic factors.

A small number of children with mental handicaps have additional physical, sensory, emotional and behavioural disabilities and may need assistance in their daily living throughout their lives. Children with mental handicap fall into three main groups; those with mild, moderate and severe learning difficulties. The three groups are outlined below:

Children with Mild Learning Difficulties
Children whose learning difficulties are classed as mild may need extra assistance in school but are able to work alongside more able children in most lessons. They may have additional disabilities such as hearing loss, poor eye-sight or mild physical limitations. These children are usually educated in ordinary schools.

Children with Moderate Learning Difficulties
Children with moderate learning difficulties learn best when they have a practical integrated curriculum where the teaching material is presented in small, sequential and carefully structured stages. Many are not socially well-adjusted and find it difficult to cope with the problems they encounter in their daily lives. The curriculum should take into account their need to enhance their capacity to communicate and relate to others. Some of these children are placed in ordinary schools; others attend special schools or units.

Children with Severe Learning Difficulties
Children with severe learning difficulties are likely to need a wide range of special provision which is often best provided through a multi-professional approach. Their curriculum includes training in social skills, eg. eating, toilet training and dressing. In addition, some children with severe learning difficulties have physical disabilities as well so they also require training to move and walk as supplied through regular physiotherapy. The development of language and communication is also high on the list of priorities. These children are generally educated in special schools.

Mobility and Exercise

While the child is ambulant he should be encouraged to join in activities at school. Towards his 8th to 10th birthday, or even earlier, his muscle weakness is likely to cause falls in the playground; stairs will become difficult to manage and sports less enjoyable. As for many children with disabilities swimming is encouraged as long as possible and an appropriate exercise programme is needed to maintain the child in the best physical condition. Advice from his consultant will be helpful and the programme should be planned in conjunction with a physiotherapist.

3. ADDITIONAL POINTS

Pastoral Care/Counselling

Many children with this disease start their education at an ordinary school and wish to remain with their friends as long as possible. As the disease progresses it becomes increasingly important to find interests which can be pursued in spite of the gradual loss of mobility. The limitations imposed by the condition may also have a bearing on the school subjects chosen by the child and extra consideration may be needed to allow him to participate in after-school clubs. In addition, remember that the child may be embarrassed by his increasing dependence on others at a time when peers are becoming more independent. It is therefore important to allow the pupil as much independence as possible and this may involve special efforts to ensure that he is included in social events and class activities. Counselling, from both within and outside school, may be needed particularly during adolescence and careful consideration should also be given to the nature of careers guidance.

The Family

By the time the first child has been diagnosed as having Muscular Dystrophy, he may have younger brothers who may also develop the disease. The emotional implications for the parents with one or more children with this condition are very considerable. Close and regular contact with the family may be helpful.

Examinations

Because of their muscle weakness, pupils with Muscular Dystrophy may need special consideration during examinations and extra time or other arrangements should be negotiated with the Examination Board well in advance (see also chapter 11).

SHORT STATURE

1. DESCRIPTION

Short Stature is a consequence of over 100 different medical conditions; it can be divided into proportionate and disproportionate short stature.

Proportionate Short Stature is where the growth of the body as a whole is restricted and includes hormonal disorders, diseases of the heart, kidneys etc. The growth rate can be improved if the underlying problem is successfully treated. It is often in the early school years when growth hormone deficiency is detected, as it is then becoming apparent that the child is growing more slowly than his peers. Obesity is occasionally associated with this type of short stature and if you are worried about this you should mention it to the school doctor. Early diagnosis and treatment gives the child a chance of reaching normal stature.

Disproportionate Short Stature covers a wide range of genetic abnormalities which each affect some aspect of bone and cartilage development. These conditions cannot be treated.

Abnormalities in bone growth may lead to associated orthopaedic problems affecting the child's mobility. Surgery is sometimes necessary to correct deformities, eg. bow legs and club foot. On the whole, these children tend to be fairly robust but may be more prone to tiredness than their peers. Children with growth disorders generally have good health outside the usual childhood ailments.

2. EDUCATIONAL IMPLICATIONS

(i) Learning Difficulties

In general, children of short stature do not experience learning difficulties associated with their condition. However, some girls with Turner's Syndrome may have certain cognitive difficulties including difficulty in grasping abstract concepts, distinguishing left from right and solving mathematical problems. These difficulties, which are not always present, can be overcome with patience and application.

(ii) Considerations for Classroom Management

Positioning within the Class

A comfortable desk and chair are important for a short child, but it may not be necessary or desirable to have a scaled-down version of the classroom furniture specially made. Setting the small child apart from the rest of the class could result in a lack of interaction between them; a foot rest and perhaps a cushion may be all that is required for him to sit happily among the others.

128

It is worth noting that some restricted growth disorders are associated with difficulties of hearing and sight. In any case it makes sense to place a child with restricted growth near the front of the class so he can hear and clearly see the teacher and the blackboard.

Access to Materials and Facilities

Reaching is the most common problem for children with restricted growth. Most reaching problems are fairly easily solved by moving things (eg. coat hook, a toilet door handle) and providing a selection of strategically placed "boxes" (eg. by a toilet).

Writing

Children with small hands often have difficulty grasping a pen and writing clearly. Handwriting improves as they get older but it may be helpful to experiment with a variety of pens. Do not penalise a child for untidy handwriting caused by this problem.

Expectation

It is easy to fall into the trap of treating a small child in a manner appropriate to his size rather than his age. He should be subject to the same expectations as his peers in academic and other respects. This is particularly important as future work is likely to depend on intellectual skills rather than physical strength and stamina.

Physical Education

While children should be encouraged to participate as much as possible in the school sports curriculum, contact sports, eg. rugby, are better avoided and it is not advisable to force a child of short stature to take part in some gymnastics and exhausting team games. As for most children, swimming is usually a good form of exercise. Some children enjoy and do well in physical education but stress may be put on already abnormal joints and the spine and it is wise to seek medical advice if a child is eager to take part in a great deal of physical activity.

Homework

If homework is set it may be helpful to have two sets of text books, one at home and one at school, to avoid carrying heavy bags to and fro. Similarly, to avoid the crush as children change classes it may be worth considering allowing a child of short stature to leave slightly early.

3. ADDITIONAL POINTS

Toilet Needs

The school may find it easier to place a small box or step by one toilet and wash basin rather than lowering these appliances. Children with very short arms may have difficulty with adjusting their clothes when going to the toilet. Most have developed a method of coping and are independent in these needs by the time they start school. As they may have small bladders, children may need to go to the toilet more often than normal.

Teasing and Relationships with other Children

Teasing is often a problem for children with restricted growth. Children learn to cope with words like "dwarf" and "midget" and it is helpful for them to have a simple explanation ready to satisfy questions about why they are small. However, you may need to step in if teasing gets out of hand.

When a small child first joins a school it may be advisable to explain to his class a little about the new pupil, without making him appear too special, to pave the way for the child. If a short child becomes a class "mascot" or indulges in excessive clowning to avoid aggressive encounters, you may find it necessary to curb these tendencies and discuss their underlying cause with the child and parents. Although a sense of humour is a great asset, mascot or clowning behaviour may prevent a child maturing into an adult able to command authority and respect.

School Meals

Children of restricted growth may need to restrict their eating in order to avoid obesity which puts strain on bones and joints. They may therefore need smaller portions of food than normal. Children with Russell-Silver Syndrome are very thin; this is part of the condition and they gain weight after puberty.

SICKLE CELL DISEASE

1. DESCRIPTION

Sickle Cell Disease is not an infection but an inherited disability affecting the haemoglobin (oxygen-carrying) factor in the blood. There are three main types:

Sickle Cell Anaemia (Hb SS)

Sickle Cell Disease (Hb SC)

Sickle Beta Thalassaemia (Hb S Beta Thal)

It is mainly found in the Afro-Caribbean population and also in people originating from the Middle East, Asia and the Mediterranean. As with Haemophilia, people may carry the trait without being aware of it and Sickle Cell Disease only becomes evident in children of two people with the trait.

Children with Sickle Cell Disease first show signs of the condition from about 4–5 months of age as the haemoglobin with which they were born is gradually replaced by sickle haemoglobin. The most common problem is caused by the sickle cells creating blockages in small blood vessels. This causes pain and tenderness and is known as sickling or a sickle cell crisis. There may also be complications which require hospital treatment (see list under *Management of a Sickle Cell Crisis* below).

2. EDUCATIONAL IMPLICATIONS

(i) Learning Difficulties

Most chidren with Sickle Cell Disease are able to attend school regularly but their education is likely to be disrupted by sickle cell crises from time to time. Unfortunately, there is no general indicator of how frequently crises may occur. Some children may go for several months without one but others have them more often. Absences from school may need to be covered by setting work at home. As absences are likely to be irregular in length and timing, particular care is needed to ensure that these children maintain progress in their school work.

(ii) Considerations for Classroom Management

Management of a Sickle Cell Crisis

A sickle cell crisis is usually painful for the child and comfort and reassurance are very important. Children with this condition should know that they must report their pain to the teacher as soon as it begins so appropriate action can be taken immediately. A simple routine will help both the child and the staff in coping with a painful crisis. It is essential to discuss the method of managing a crisis with the parents before the child starts school. As a general rule three simple steps should be followed:

(a) allow the child to rest;

(b) give plenty of fluid immediately;
(Water, squash, milk or fruit juice are recommended but not fizzy drinks. At least one glass of liquid every hour is recommended as a minimum and more if the child will take it. The fluid thins the blood and helps to stop sickling.)

(c) give the recommended painkiller;
(This should be discussed in advance with the child's parents and medical advisers and a supply of the appropriate painkiller kept in the school first-aid kit.)

Prompt action may save the child a great deal of pain. If this routine is followed, in most instances the child will begin to recover within an hour. However, if he is no better after an hour, medical help should be sought. Complications, though rare, may be serious and urgent medical help is needed if the child

★ has a high temperature

★ has severe pain which does not subside after an hour

★ has a bad headache and drowsiness

★ has weakness down one side of the body

★ has diarrhoea or vomiting

★ is short of breath or has difficulty breathing

★ is listless or lacking in energy

★ becomes very pale

★ has a yellow colouring in his eyes

★ has problems with vision

★ has severe pain in his abdomen

Factors which may cause a Sickle Cell Crisis

Sickling may occur for no apparent reason but there are two factors which precipitate sickling and which are of particular relevance to school children:

(a) strenuous exercise – see *Physical Education* below

(b) emotional stress – see *Examinations* below

(a) *Physical Education*
Children with Sickle Cell Disease can usually take part in normal exercise but strenuous and prolonged exercise may cause sickling. PE teachers should be given medical advice about any child who has this condition and the extent to which he should be encouraged to participate in PE. Each child will learn his own limits and children should be allowed to rest if they become breathless.

Sometimes small adaptations to games may be all that is needed to allow them to participate.

(b) *Examinations*
Stress is known to precipitate sickling and this may need to be taken into account when a pupil is taking examinations. Where appropriate, alternative forms of assessment may be considered (see chapter 11).

3. ADDITIONAL POINTS

Pastoral Care/Counselling

Young people with Sickle Cell Disease need to learn to manage their condition and accept any restrictions it may impose on their life-style. Counselling from both within and outside school may be helpful.

Health

Children with Sickle Cell Disease normally have no associated health problems. Doctors and dentists should be aware of the condition and some children may wish to wear a medic-alert bracelet.

After School Placement

Pupils with Sickle Cell Disease can follow most careers but may need to avoid those which involve strenuous activity. Further advice is available from the specialist careers officer.

SKIN CONDITIONS

1. *ECZEMA*

1. DESCRIPTION

Eczema is an itchy, sore and sometimes unsightly skin condition which affects a significant number of people to some degree. It is most common in children but may occur at any age. The cause is unknown but eczema is not infectious and in many instances does not prevent normal activities.

There are several different forms of eczema; the most common form in children is Atopic Eczema. Children with this condition have a sensitive skin which reacts readily to irritants, producing a red, sometimes raw or weeping, rash which is very itchy. In extreme cases the whole body is affected but in most children the rash is more limited and most commonly affects the knee and elbow joints and the hands. Atopic Eczema usually improves as the child grows older and may disappear completely.

Contact Eczema is more common in adults but may also affect children. It is caused by sensitivity to certain substances, eg. straw, metal, detergent, oil. Once the cause has been identified it can usually be well controlled.

2. EDUCATIONAL IMPLICATIONS

(i) Learning Difficulties

There are no learning difficulties specifically associated with this condition but education may be interrupted when the eczema "flares up". When the itching caused by eczema is severe it reduces the child's concentration and may affect school work.

(ii) Considerations for Classroom Management

Avoidance of Irritant Factors

Parents will already be aware of many of the factors which aggravate this condition and you will find it helpful to discuss this with them at an early stage. The following are common irritant factors.

(a) *Temperature*
Skin becomes more sensitive under warm conditions and therefore children with eczema need to keep cool. They should not be seated in direct sunlight or beside radiators.

The skin also needs protection from drying winds and cold air so on cold days it may be wise to keep a child in at breaktime. This must be decided on an individual basis and in conjunction with the parents. For young children, activities such as water play, dough and sand, may not be advisable as they cause the skin to become dry.

(b) *Water*
Some children with eczema are sensitive to chlorinated water and/or seawater and this may need to be considered with regard to swimming. Again, this should be discussed with the parents.

(c) *Animals and Plants*
Animals and sometimes plants, may cause skin irritation. Long-haired animals cause most problems and it may be helpful to remove classroom pets or ensure that a child with eczema is kept away from them.

(d) *Dust*
Dust is another factor which may irritate the skin and chalk dust should be avoided. Please don't ask a child with eczema to clean the blackboard.

(e) *Foods*
Some foods eg. dairy products, may aggravate eczema especially in young children. You may wish to check whether the child is on a special diet and discuss with the parents any necessary arrangements to avoid certain foods in school meals.

Itching and Scratching

There are three main treatments which are used to help relieve the itching caused by eczema:

    (a) emollient creams and moisturisers
         (these have a soothing effect and can be used freely at home and at school);

    (b) steroid creams
         (which are much stronger and should be used sparingly. They are obtained on prescription and are not normally used in school);

    (c) anti-histamine
         (which may be taken in liquid or tablet form and is normally used at night to aid sleep. If used during the day-time, anti-histamine may cause children to become drowsy and lethargic).

Emollient creams and moisturisers may be carried by the child or you may wish to keep them on behalf of young children. They can be used without restriction.

Cooling the skin, eg. with a cold flannel, may also help but some rubbing or scratching is inevitable. To minimise damage, the child should be encouraged to rub rather than scratch the skin.

Stiffness and Soreness

There are natural fluctuations in eczema and when the joints are stiff and sore, movement becomes painful and difficult. Therefore there may be occasions when the child finds PE and handwork, eg. holding a pen or playing a recorder, difficult.

3. ADDITIONAL POINTS

Pastoral Care/Counselling

Scratching and the unsightly appearance of the skin may lead to teasing and become a source of embarrassment to the pupil. Teenagers are particularly sensitive about their appearance and their eczema may cause embarrassment and depression. It may be helpful to allow the pupil extra privacy whilst changing for PE if this is possible without drawing too much attention to the condition. Pupils, especially teenagers, often find the restrictions imposed upon them by their condition a source of frustration and may react against it. Counselling, from both within and outside school, may be needed where the eczema is severe but fortunately many children find that their skin condition improves as they grow up.

Examinations

Eczema may be aggravated by the additional stress caused by examinations and where a pupil has severe eczema the Examination Board should be notified well in advance. If any problems arise on the day of the examination the Board may allow special arrangements for the pupil, eg. extra time or dictating facilities.

Family

Eczema is a condition subject to great fluctuation and it is therefore difficult to lay out precise guidelines. For example, it may be genuinely necessary to excuse a child with eczema from PE on some occasions but not on others. Therefore, you will find regular contact with the parents about the day-to-day condition of the child to be very valuable.

After School Placement

Subject options and careers choices should be considered in the light of the skin condition and where appropriate discussed with a specialist careers officer. Many pupils find their eczema improves as they grow up and have no restrictions on their careers choice on leaving school.

SKIN CONDITIONS
2. EPIDERMOLYSIS BULLOSA

1. DESCRIPTION

Where Epidermolysis Bullosa occurs, the collagen fibres which connect the layers of the skin do not function properly and the layers separate readily, forming blisters. The blisters may occur between any of the layers of the skin and may be deep, blood-tinged and painful. The collagen in the nails may also be affected causing the nails to peel away.

Because of the weakness of the collagen, the blisters tend to enlarge. The treatment is usually to open the blisters and provide a dressing of either vaseline gauze or a non-stick dressing. Adhesive plasters are not suitable for these children.

Blisters may be caused by any sharp contact, eg. the edges of desks and chairs, jumping, clapping, a fall or any rough handling. A child with Epidermolysis Bullosa should refrain from body contact. In addition, lifting should be done very carefully with weight evenly supported.

The health of children with this condition is variable. Creams and gentle exercise help to keep the skin muscles and joints in good condition. Sometimes operations are necessary to free joints.

2. EDUCATIONAL IMPLICATIONS

(i) Learning Difficulties

There are no learning difficulties specifically associated with this condition. Education may occasionally be interrupted for treatment.

(ii) Considerations for Classroom Management

Because of the need to prevent any unnecessary body contact which may result in blistering, a number of simple points should be considered.

Protection of the Skin

Much of the environment around a child with Epidermolysis Bullosa may need to be made safe by the use of padding. This includes the child's chair (padded with sheepskin or foam), the edge of the desk, pencils, paintbrushes, scissors etc. Electric typewriters and calculators may be easier for the child to use than pens. In addition, consideration should be given to padding a toilet seat and the taps of a washbasin.

Playgrounds and Corridors

In order to avoid accidental knocking as children rush out at breaktime it may be advisable to tell the child to wait until the rush is over. The same principle applies when children are changing lessons. You might find it useful to discuss this with the parents.

A child who is more severely affected may have to be restricted to a quiet area of play, preferably on grass or a carpet. To reduce social isolation, a few friends might be asked to join him. It may be necessary to keep this group under supervision to a greater or lesser extent.

Physical Education

Allow children with Epidermolysis Bullosa to join in physical education as far as possible. Many exercises, with the appropriate protection, eg. foam mats, are helpful but demanding team games may not be.

The greatest need is for all joints to be gently stretched and flexed and it may be possible to incorporate these exercises into PE lessons. Such exercises could be arranged in a personal programme if class activity is unsuitable. A physiotherapist will be able to advise you when planning such a programme. Swimming is usually an ideal sport for these children provided medical consent is received and the child dries himself very carefully afterwards.

The child may be embarrassed about the blisters on his body and it may be considerate to provide a certain amount of privacy for him while changing for games.

Tiredness

Because of their diet and need for additional protein, for healing, children with Epidermolysis Bullosa are likely to tire more easily than normal and may be undersized. Medication may also cause drowsiness.

3. ADDITIONAL POINTS

School Meals

If the membranes in the child's mouth and gullet are affected by this condition, eating may prove difficult. A "soft" diet with plenty of liquid may be necessary and the school may need advice from the child's parents and doctor if this is a serious problem. The ability to swallow may vary from day to day and the child's own indications are your best guide.

Infectious Diseases

Infectious Diseases affecting the skin, eg. chicken pox and measles, may be very serious for a child with Epidermolysis Bullosa. If such diseases are known to be in the school the parents of the child should be informed immediately and it may be necessary to consider home tuition on a temporary basis.

SPEECH DISORDERS

1. DESCRIPTION

Disorders of speech include disorders in fluency (stuttering or stammering), articulation and voice. Children with these disorders do not generally require technical aids, although some are available, but they do need additional patience and special consideration. The three main types of disorder affecting speech are described below:

Speech Fluency (Stuttering or Stammering)
Stuttering or stammering is very common in young children and may be a normal stage of speech development. Some children develop speech hesitations in the early stages of language development and reading which disappear as confidence is gained but when difficulties persist and particularly when it is suspected that a child's social development or educational progress may be affected, professional assessment by a speech therapist should be sought without delay.

Articulation
All children struggle with articulation as they first learn to speak and delays in articulation clarity should not cause undue concern in very young children as long as language development continues. If a child does not follow the normal pattern of development, articulation problems may be suspected. Problems in articulation include missing consonants, substitutions eg. "th" for "s" (as in lisping) and poorly contrasted vowels.

Voice
Voice includes elements of pitch, loudness and intonation. For various reasons a few children strain their voices and this may lead to problems in the larynx and a hoarse or breathy voice. Persistent hoarseness which is not of a temporary nature, eg. due to a cold, may indicate problems in the vocal chords. It is advisable to discuss this with the parents and medical treatment may be sought.

Some children may have speech difficulties as a result of a cleft palate and these may also be exacerbated by hearing problems, which are more likely to develop in these children. It is particularly important that such children have hearing tests (see also *Hearing Impairment*).

2. EDUCATIONAL IMPLICATIONS

(i) Learning Difficulties

Speech disorders may sometimes affect a child's ability to learn but with patience and professional assistance, eg. *speech therapy* (see below) such difficulties are usually overcome and most children are able to recover any lost ground very quickly.

(ii) Considerations for Classroom Management

Reading Aloud

Reading difficulties may be associated with lack of confidence and it may take children with speech disorders longer to master reading skills. It is not advisable to ask these children to read aloud in front of others in the early stages of reading until they have gained more confidence. Some children may be happy to join in reading aloud despite their difficulties and they should be gently encouraged. Be patient with delays and help if a child is struggling with particular words or phrases. Often difficulties may be overcome if children are allowed to read in unison so, rather than pass over a child with a speech problem, it may be possible for the class to read in pairs or groups.

Speaking in Front of Others

Some children may become anxious at merely having to say their name aloud in front of a group. If you are asking questions around the class, try not to leave a child with a speech difficulty too long to avoid tension and anxiety building up. If a child is relaxed his speech is likely to improve. Allow plenty of time to answer and do not try to force out a reply. You should also be alert for children who conceal a stammer or other speech difficulties by avoiding speaking in class.

3. ADDITIONAL POINTS

Speech Therapy

Children who are suspected of having a speech disorder may require speech therapy. This should be discussed with the parents and the child may then be referred via the school medical service to a speech therapist for assessment.

If a child needs speech therapy, the therapist will devise a programme and may wish to liaise with both parents and teachers to ensure a consistent approach. Sometimes therapists withdraw children for individual work or they may seek the assistance of the teacher in developing a particular programme. Whatever arrangement is made, the therapist will be happy to discuss ways of overcoming any classroom difficulties with you.

Family

Sometimes speech problems occur only when the child is at school, perhaps because a new environment causes anxiety. Therefore, if you are concerned about the speech development of a particular child, it is especially important to check with the parents to see whether speech problems occur at home as well.

Teasing

Sometimes children with speech difficulties become the victims of teasing and if this occurs you may find it helpful to discuss ways of overcoming it with the child's parents. Often a brief explanation to other pupils will increase their acceptance of the child. Such acceptance will help the child to relax and concentrate on the techniques of speaking normally.

Encouragement

Children with speech disorders may find it helpful to know of adults who have overcome similar problems and now speak fluently in public, eg. Derek Nimmo.

See also *Aphasia/Dysphasia*.

SPINA BIFIDA AND HYDROCEPHALUS

1. DESCRIPTION

Spina Bifida

The spine is an arrangement of reel-like bones through which runs the part of the Central Nervous System known as the Spinal Cord. This bundle of nerve fibres is protected by membranes and fluid.

Where Spina Bifida occurs, the bones of the spine are not closed completely and the nerves and/or their protective sheathing are exposed. The physical consequences depend upon the level of the lesion (or break) and the amount of damage to the spinal cord. This may result in minimal to complete paralysis and partial to complete loss of sensation in the parts of the body below the level of the lesion. In addition there may sometimes be spasticity in the upper limbs caused by brain damage (see *Cerebral Palsy*). Children with Spina Bifida usually have an operation soon after birth and thereafter their condition does not normally deteriorate provided they receive appropriate physiotherapy and exercise.

Fig 9

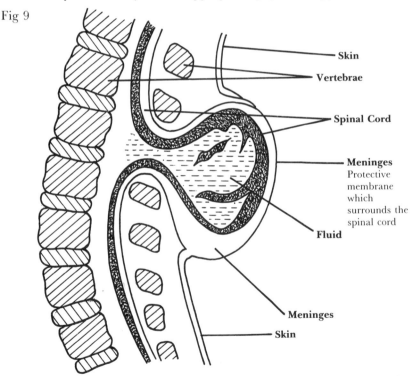

SPINA BIFIDA - Myelomeningocele
(the most common and most serious form)

142

Hydrocephalus

Hydrocephalus is caused by a build up of fluid which may exert pressure on the brain. In some children the fluid drains away on its own but in others, a device known as a "shunt" is implanted to serve this purpose. Shunts usually work very effectively but some children have problems with them from time to time (see the IMPORTANT NOTE on page 145).

These two conditions commonly occur together but may also occur independently. The causes are not known but, once a child with Spina Bifida and/or Hydrocephalus has been born into a family, the risk to further pregnancies is greater than average. Children with these conditions cover the whole range of intellectual functioning but where Hydrocephalus occurs there is an increased likelihood of mental handicap (see *Mental Handicap*). Eye defects, eg. squints, and epilepsy are sometimes associated with Spina Bifida and Hydrocephalus.

2. EDUCATIONAL IMPLICATIONS

(i) Learning Difficulties

Not all children with Spina Bifida and/or Hydrocephalus need extra assistance in learning but if classroom performance causes you concern, it is useful to know that spatial and/or perceptual difficulties are common and there may be considerable disparity between the verbal performance of a child and his intellectual ability.

Reading, Writing and Number Work

Many children have specific learning difficulties in perceptual and spatial judgements which affect hand-eye co-ordination. Perceptual problems may cause delays in learning to read while motor and spatial problems may cause difficulties with number work and handwriting. These problems may be reduced by careful teaching strategies using the child's areas of strength.

Eye defects and poor concentration may cause some children to have difficulty in reading and number work. Both visual acuity and attention span may need to be taken into account when planning lessons.

Co-ordination

Some children have poor motor-organisation which may particularly affect handwriting and physical education. In particular, ball-handling skills may prove difficult for these children. Teaching which emphasizes the "feel" of the correct sequences has proved most effective in such instances.

Comprehension

In language work it is important to check that comprehension matches reading ability as sometimes reading accuracy progresses faster than understanding. Children with Spina Bifida and/or Hydrocephalus are often fluent talkers and may give the impression that they understand without, in fact, doing so!

Organisation Skills

Many children with Hydrocephalus have difficulties in ordering and organising materials, eg. in making lists and establishing priorities. They may need additional help to learn to organise their work.

Distractability

If a child is easily distractable it helps to insist on concentration and limit talk to the job in hand.

(ii) Considerations for Classroom Management

Children in Wheelchairs

Children with the more severe forms of Spina Bifida are usually paralysed in the lower part of their body; this has a number of implications:

(a) *Care of Limbs*
Damage to the spinal cord causes not only paralysis of the lower limbs but also lack of sensation to pain, temperature and touch and means that the child is more susceptible to injury through knocks and burns and even, occasionally, to fractures. As children grow up they need to be able to take responsibility for the care of their limbs and should be encouraged to do this.

(b) *Pressure Sores*
Damage to skin may result in pressure sores. These sores may be prevented by small frequent changes of position to assist circulation and relieve pressure. As part of their self-care skills, pupils should learn of the need to prevent pressure sores. If one does occur, bedrest may be required and this could lead to several weeks off school. A suitably-placed mirror in the room where the pupil changes will enable him to take responsibility for checking his skin for signs of pressure.

(c) *Exercise*
All children using wheelchairs, and especially those who are partially paralysed, should be encouraged to do as much movement as possible to avoid problems related to lack of exercise. Such problems include stiffness of the joints, muscle imbalance, leading to bone displacement and posture difficulties, and weakness of the bones. Also the soft tissues benefit from the use of muscles in posture and weightbearing; exercise helps to improve the functioning of many of the body organs and movement also aids blood circulation.

It is important that these children are reminded to think of the position of their legs to avoid accidental damage. A physiotherapist can advise on the development of a physical education programme which will allow the child to obtain the benefits of exercise, join in with the class activities and gain in movement skills.

Some children are provided with calipers to assist in walking exercise and all have some means of weightbearing or walking short distances. They should be able to spend some part of each day out of their wheelchair to exercise.

Incontinence

The majority of children with the more severe form of Spina Bifida are incontinent of bowels and/or bladder. Some have surgery to bypass the bladder or bowel; others use catheters to drain urine. You should receive advice about any special arrangements before the child begins school. Usually a private area is arranged for changing and management. Many children are, or become, completely independent in the management of their incontinence. Younger children are usually supplied with welfare assistance. Privacy and a careful but matter-of-fact routine will ensure that incontinence is not a problem for either the child or those caring for him. An occupational therapist will be able to advise on the best methods of managing incontinence and establishing a routine which helps to avoid infections. The child may find it reassuring to know that there is one adult who is designated to help if there is any difficulty. A second person should be available to provide back-up help in times of staff absence. Sometimes children who are incontinent need extra care in personal hygiene and it may be advisable to talk both to the pupil and to the parents about this as good hygiene is essential for social acceptance.

Drinking Requirements

Children with Spina Bifida are prone to kidney damage and are often encouraged to drink a lot of fluid to keep the kidneys functioning well. They may therefore need extra drinks particularly during hot weather. Parents and medical advisers will be able to give you details of a child's individual requirements.

Health IMPORTANT NOTE

★ If a child with hydrocephalus develops a severe headache, drowsiness or vomiting this may indicate that the shunt is not working properly and medical attention should be sought immediately. Before he starts school, it is advisable to discuss the parents' preferred method of action if the child needs urgent medical help.

★ If a child with Spina Bifida develops a high temperature this may be indicative of a urinary infection and the parents should be contacted immediately so that the child can receive prompt medical attention.

3. ADDITIONAL POINTS

Behaviour

Because pre-school experience is often limited by medical treatment, poor mobility and perhaps several other factors, many children with Spina Bifida and/or Hydrocephalus show more immature behaviour than their peers. With greater opportunity for regular social contact at school their social skills should improve. The preparation given at school will help the child to cope with the increasing demands of maturity. You can help the child to practise social skills by ensuring that he takes an active part in all class activities. These children may also need a little extra support in making friends, perhaps by seating them with sympathetic classmates.

Adolescence

As with all other young people, adolescents with Spina Bifida need access to information about puberty. They may also need to learn more about their disability and counselling may be advisable. Social isolation can be a problem for many disabled pupils and particularly seems to affect young people with Spina Bifida. You may be able to help by encouraging them to join social clubs and activities.

SPINAL INJURIES

1. DESCRIPTION

The spine is an arrangement of reel-like bones through which runs the part of the Central Nervous System known as the Spinal Cord. This bundle of nerves is protected by membranes and fluid. An injury to the spinal cord, caused by accident or illness results in loss of movement and feeling, ie. paralysis, below the level of the injury or lesion. Some injuries are "incomplete", ie. some movement and feeling remain. The level of the injury determines the extent of functional loss. In general, the higher the point of injury the more severely disabled a child will be.

Damage to the neck results in tetraplegia, sometimes called quadraplegia, ie. it affects all four limbs. Pupils who have a complete tetraplegia have no function below their shoulders, including their hands and arms, and may need assistance in breathing. Such children are only rarely found in ordinary schools.

Damage to the back may cause paraplegia, ie. affects the legs. Most of these children are likely to use a wheelchair but a few may use crutches or calipers.

Paralysis also affects the child's ability to control his bladder and bowels and most of these children need to learn methods of managing incontinence.

Fortunately there are relatively few pupils with spinal injuries. Most of them are teenage boys who have sustained their injury in road or sports accidents.

2. EDUCATIONAL IMPLICATIONS

(i) Learning Difficulties

Children with spinal cord injuries do not usually have any intellectual impairment. Following their accident/illness they may spend several months in a spinal injuries unit and fall behind in their education but, once back at school, they usually make normal progress in learning (see also *Educational Adjustment* and *Classroom Assistance* below).

(ii) Considerations for Classroom Management

Educational Adjustment

Where a child has been absent from school for a long period it is likely that his education will need careful reconsideration. Sometimes it is possible to place the child in his old class but he may need extra help to catch up with the work he has missed and this places additional pressure upon him. Alternatively, it may be preferable to place him in a lower class where he will have to form new friendships with younger children. In either case, the demands upon the child may be great

147

as he learns to come to terms with himself in an old environment with new restrictions.

Classroom Assistance

The degree of assistance required clearly depends upon the extent and complexity of the child's disability. Some children may be able to manage reasonably independently once arrangements have been made to accommodate their wheelchair. Others may have associated disabilities, including mental handicap (see *Mental Handicap*), and may require a greater level of individual support. A welfare assistant (see chapters 3 and 7) is often supplied for these children. Pupils who cannot use their arms, ie. tetraplegics, often need a great deal of assistance in gaining access to the curriculum and their individual needs must be carefully considered. In using books, for example, they may need help in finding the correct page, placing the book where it can be comfortably read and turning pages. Many of these children use a pointer attached to a headband (usually called a headstick) by which they can type. They normally need help in preparing materials, eg. paper, typewriter. Although they are inevitably slower in completing written work than their able-bodied peers, some children develop a good speed using their aids. Occupational therapists are able to advise on the most suitable classroom aids.

Children in Wheelchairs

The loss of movement and feeling in the limbs caused by paralysis has a number of implications:

(a) *Care of the Limbs*
Lack of feeling in the limbs may lead to accidental damage of the skin as children do not feel pain or heat. Pupils need to be aware of the position of their limbs in relation to hazards and should ask for help in moving if appropriate. Advice may be obtained from a physiotherapist.

(b) *Pressure Sores*
Pressure from a cushion or the wheelchair or even creases in clothing, may cause damage to the skin which in turn may result in pressure sores. Such sores may become infected and take a long time to heal. Pressure sores can be prevented by small frequent changes of position to assist circulation and relieve pressure. Children who have arm movement can learn to check and change their position but children without arm movement will need assistance to ensure that this is not overlooked. If a pressure sore does occur, bedrest may be required and this could lead to several weeks off school.

(c) *Exercise*
Anyone confined to a wheelchair, especially if paralysed, is likely to have problems related to lack of exercise. Standing practice helps to reduce future bone and posture deformities and also benefits the soft tissues and internal organs. Children with spinal injuries are taught to stand for part of every day. This may mean using a special type of wheelchair or other support for the standing position

for part of the day, possibly during lessons. Children may need help when changing from a standing to a seated position or vice versa. Whatever standing aid is recommended by the child's medical advisers, everyone in contact with him should understand the importance of exercise and movement programmes which are usually arranged under the guidance of a physiotherapist.

Lack of movement may also cause the child's limbs to be very cold and in winter extra clothing may be necessary and the child may need to sit near a radiator.

Incontinence

Most children with spinal injuries are incontinent of both bowels and bladder. Hence they need to learn methods of managing their incontinence. Pupils may need help in transferring from their wheelchair to the toilet and it is likely that extra time will be required for their toileting needs.

Some children have surgery to bypass the bladder or bowel; others use catheters to drain urine. You should receive advice about any special arrangements before the pupil returns to school. Usually a private area is arranged for changing and management. Children with no use of their arms are often allocated a welfare assistant (see chapter 7) who will assist them with their toileting needs. Those who can use their arms usually learn methods of coping with incontinence. Privacy and a matter-of-fact routine will help to ensure that incontinence is not a problem for either the child or those caring for him. The child may find it reassuring to know that there is one adult who is designated to help if there is any difficulty. Children who are incontinent must take extra care with personal hygiene both to avoid the risk of infection and also for social reasons. It may be advisable to talk to the school medical adviser and the child's parents about this.

3. ADDITIONAL POINTS

Pastoral Care/Counselling

Spinal injury most commonly occurs among teenagers and they find it difficult to come to terms with the restrictions which such an injury imposes on them. They suddenly find themselves in a dependent position at a time when many of their friends are seen to be gaining independence. Therefore counselling, from both within and outside school, may be needed to help the pupil come to terms with his injury and his more restricted lifestyle. It may also be necessary to make special transport arrangements to ensure that the pupil is able to take part in the social activities of the school.

Family

The trauma of an accident which leaves a young person paralysed inevitably has a tremendous impact on the whole family. It is worthwhile bearing in mind that, not only is your pupil learning to adjust his lifestyle and expectations, but his family are also having to come to terms with his condition. They will probably value any support which the school can offer especially during the first few months when the child returns to school.

Professional Resources

In addition to the medical and paramedical professionals normally available to schools, you will find it particularly helpful to consult the staff of the spinal injuries unit where the child received initial treatment after his injury. This helps to ensure that the school routine is consistent with the overall rehabilitation of the child and the unit staff will be able to advise and help you in establishing the best way for him to readjust to school, thereby avoiding difficulties.

Adaptations

For schools to accommodate children with this degree of disability, special adaptations to the buildings need to be made (see also chapter 8).

After School Placement

If spinal injury occurs after initial careers advice has been offered, it is likely, but not inevitable, that the advice may need to be changed to take into account the effects of the injury. Placement after school presents particular difficulties for these pupils especially if they require personal assistance. A specialist careers officer should be able to advise you.

VISUAL IMPAIRMENT

1. DESCRIPTION

The function of the eye is very similar to that of a camera. It controls the input of light and focuses and records the image which is then relayed to the brain to be processed.

Some children, traditionally considered blind in educational terms, are unable to read using enlarged print. They may have some residual vision but need to use other means, eg. braille and tape-recording for learning. They usually require special training in mobility and orientation.

Other less severely visually-impaired children use many of the usual methods of learning but may require adaptations in the presentation of materials and additional time to complete tasks.

Functional loss of vision may be considered in two broad categories:

(a) problems in focus of vision

(b) problems in field of vision

(a) Focussing difficulties may be remedied or assisted by spectacles or other focussing aids but there are some conditions which are not correctable. Sometimes a combination of problems means that glasses may improve the child's vision but not restore it to normal.

(b) Problems in the field of vision may be subdivided into:

1. peripheral problems – peripheral vision is important for mobility and as a warning device eg. of moving objects. It is also used in general scanning of surroundings and for scanning print in particular;

2. problems within the field of vision – we all have a blind spot (a small area of the retina which cannot receive visual images) but sometimes these areas are larger and hence vision may be impaired. Children may have fragmented or fuzzy vision and may also need to use large movements of the head to bring objects into sight.

2. EDUCATIONAL IMPLICATIONS

You will normally be informed of the individual requirements of a child with visual impairment but if these have not yet been recognised and you think a child in your class may have difficulty with his eyesight, suggest that his parents take him for an eye test and/or speak to the school doctor who can arrange a test. You may like to use the following checklist as a guide.

1. Is he apparently clumsy?

2. Does he have poor eye/hand co-ordination?

151

3. Does he hold his head in an unusual manner or use unusually large head movements for reading?

4. Does he frown, grimace or squint more than usual?

5. Does he complain of dizziness or headaches?

6. Does he blink or rub his eyes a great deal?

7. Do his eyes look unusual, eg. red, watering, clouded or inflamed?

8. Does he have untidy or ill-formed handwriting?

9. Does he have difficulty in seeing the blackboard?

It is also essential to know whether a child's eye condition is degenerative as this will have important implications for the planning of his curriculum, eg. sometimes braille can be taught to sighted pupils in the mainstream school as a preparation for the future.

(i) Learning Difficulties

Visual Attention

It is important to remember that most classroom situations require children to be constantly changing their visual attention and visually-impaired children may have difficulty in maintaining their vision in a classroom where visual attention moves constantly from text to blackboard to teacher to exercise books. It may therefore be helpful to plan lessons in a way which reduces any unnecessary movement of visual attention.

Concept Formation

There may be considerable individual differences in the way in which impaired sight appears to affect children's understanding of their environment. They may be able to see large objects but not details, eg. they may see a wall but cannot distinguish individual bricks and this can lead to inadequate or incomplete concepts of the nature and appearance of objects. Therefore, whenever possible, ways of encouraging the child to touch objects and a verbal description should be provided. It is easy to forget the speed which vision confers and it is likely that children with impaired vision will take longer to grasp new concepts (see also *Spectacles and Other Vision Aids* below).

Reading

Impaired vision may affect a child's ability to search and scan along a line of print and to discriminate detail, eg. commas. Thus it may take a child longer to master reading skills. Large print books are not necessarily helpful to children but matt white paper, clearly defined print and good spacing which are helpful to everyone, are especially important to children with poor sight.

Writing

Children with impaired vision may find it difficult to discriminate detail, eg. letter shapes, and may have poor eye/hand co-ordination which affects fine movement including handwriting. Children may require additional help with writing and it is often useful to experiment with different writing materials, positioning of paper (some children can write better if the paper rests on a sloping stand), width of lines on paper and positioning within the classroom. This will allow the child to establish his best method of writing.

(ii) Considerations for Classroom Management

Arrangement of Learning Materials

Children with impaired vision may find it helpful to have duplicated notes of lessons if they are not able to take notes at speed. It is important that such notes should be clearly printed. Diagrams should also be clear and should not be over-detailed. Children may also have difficulty in reading information on the blackboard and will find it helpful if you make a point of reading out whatt you have written.

Some children find it helpful to tape record lessons and recordings may later be transcribed if appropriate. Using hearing as an extensive means of obtaining information takes practice and concentration.

Orderly storage and clear labelling of materials and equipment is particularly helpful to children with poor vision.

Lighting and Positioning

Correct lighting is extremely important for children with impaired vision. The appropriate lighting varies according to the type of eye condition and the particular requirements of individual children should be carefully considered. You will find that a peripatetic teacher of the visually handicapped (see *Professional Resources* below) will be able to advise you on lighting and seating arrangements. Some children need additional lighting but others are badly affected by glare and may need to be seated away from bright light and where the teacher is not silhouetted against a window.

Physical Educations

Children with impaired vision are able to participate in many forms of PE. They may find games which involve the use of small balls difficult especially if they have poor eye/hand co-ordination. Sometimes using a white ball is helpful.

3. ADDITIONAL POINTS

Professional Resources

You will probably find advice on management and adaptation of learning materials valuable in meeting the needs of individual pupils. Most local education authorities now have a peripatetic teacher for children with visual impairment and the adviser for special educational needs should be able to supply details of such help.

Spectacles and Other Vision Aids

Young children using spectacles or other vision aids may need to be reminded to take care of them and wherever possible should have a spare pair. Spectacles should be kept clean and unscratched and should fit comfortably so that the child obtains maximum benefit from them. Scratching of the lens occurs all too readily if the spectacles are placed lens down on a desk or table.

If a child uses a telescopic or other low vision aid this assists him to see but will also reduce the field of vision which in turn is likely to reduce the child's ability to follow the overall meaning of the sentence or phrase. Although low vision aids are very helpful to some children they inevitably increase the time taken to complete tasks such as reading. It is important that all vision aids are comfortable and fit well. An optician will be able to help if the aid needs adjusting.

Keyboard Skills

Most visually-impaired children need to acquire keyboard skills as soon as possible and the typewriter or computer is an essential aid for these children. Some typewriters produce large print and this helps to give good presentation.

Use of Vision

Children with visual impairment need to make maximum use of their residual vision and may need training to achieve this. They cannot strain their eyesight although, like all muscles, those serving the eye can become tired and children who work close to books are helping themselves and should not be discouraged.

Safety

Children with impaired vision often need clear and precise instructions because they cannot use visual clues. It may therefore be useful to spend a little extra time with a child to ensure that he understands what to do in an emergency. In large schools it may be helpful to designate one person, adult or child, to ensure that pupils with impaired vision are assisted to safety during emergency procedures. Regular fire drills are helpful to all pupils.

Corridors and classrooms with unobstructed access will help to prevent children with poor vision falling over and hurting themselves or others.

Examinations

Many examination boards are willing to make special arrangements for pupils with visual impairment provided they are given sufficient warning. Most boards can supply papers in enlarged print or translated into braille. Tape-recorded answers may be permitted where appropriate. It is important to remember that pupils need to practise using such methods in advance of the examinations. If you think a pupil would benefit from special arrangements, consult the examination board as soon as possible (see also chapter 11).

After School Placement

With advances in modern technology, people with impaired vision now have access to an increasing number of jobs. Specialist training is available to those school leavers who need it and the specialist careers officer will be able to give further advice.

APPENDICES

APPENDIX A
SUMMARY OF THE EDUCATION ACT 1981 AND CIRCULAR 1/83

The Education Act 1981 provides a new legal framework for assessment and placement of children with special educational needs. It came into force in April 1983 and covers children under school age and children at school up to the age of 19. Circular 1/83, issued by the Department of Education and Science, offers advice to LEAs on reviewing and revising their procedures to meet the needs of these children.

Sections 1, 2 & 4 of the Act

CHILDREN WITH SPECIAL EDUCATIONAL NEEDS

The old categories based upon medical labels have been abandoned. Instead the Act uses the broad term **Children with Special Educational Needs** (SEN) which the Warnock Committee estimated to be up to 20% of school children at some point during their school lives (this includes approximately 2% currently educated in special schools). According to the Act a child has special educational needs if he has a learning difficulty which requires that special educational provision is made for him. A child has a learning difficulty if:

(a) he has a significantly greater difficulty in learning than the majority of children of his age;

or (b) he has a disability which prevents him from making use of educational facilities of the kind generally provided in schools in the LEA;

or (c) he is under 5 and may fall into either of the above (a) or (b) when over that age.

Children with disabilities may be included in all of these groups.

Section 2

INTEGRATION

Three main conditions need to be met before a child with SEN can be integrated into an ordinary school. These are as follows:

(a) the child must receive the special educational provision he requires;
(b) the education of other children with whom he is educated must not be adversely affected;
(c) it is compatible with "efficient use of resources".

In addition, the LEA must take into account the views of the parents. The Act states that, subject to the conditions (a) – (c) above and wherever reasonably practicable, children with SEN should be educated in ordinary schools alongside other children.

Section 5

ASSESSMENTS

The Act lays out detailed procedures for the assessment of children with SEN. It is essential that the parents should participate fully in these procedures from the earliest stage. The LEA is required to give parents the name of an official from whom they can obtain information about the assessment and, in addition, the circular advises that contact between teachers and parents should be made before formal notice of assessment is given to the parents. It stresses the "crucial importance" of good relations between parents and professionals throughout the period of assessment. In order to make their contribution to the child's assessment, parents need to be able to trust the professionals and work with them. To help create an

159

atmosphere of trust, parents have been given a right both to be present at any examinations of their child during the assessment and to see the reports prepared by professionals, including teachers, involved in their child's assessment.

Teachers will therefore often be required to provide information and support to parents and will also be asked to contribute their views to the assessment procedure. The Department of Education and Science has issued a suggested checklist (to be found in Annex 1 of Circular 1/83) and sections a) and b) may be particularly helpful to teachers in preparing their reports. The checklist is reprinted below:

ADVICE ON SPECIAL EDUCATIONAL NEEDS: SUGGESTED CHECKLIST*

a) DESCRIPTION OF THE CHILD'S FUNCTIONING

1. Description of the child's strengths and weaknesses

Physical State and Functioning
(physical health, developmental function, mobility, hearing, vision)

Emotional State
(link between stress, emotions and physical state)

Cognitive Functioning

Communication Skills
(verbal comprehension, expressive language, speech)

Perceptual and Motor Skills

Adaptive Skills

Social Skills and Interaction

Approaches and Attitudes to Learning

Educational Attainments

Self-image and Interests

Behaviour

2. Factors in the child's environment which lessen or contribute to his needs

In the Home and Family

At School

Elsewhere

* Reproduced by permission of the Department of Education and Science.

160

3. Relevant aspects of the child's history

Personal

Medical

Educational

b) AIMS OF PROVISION

1. General areas of development

Physical Development
(eg to develop self-care skills)

Motor Development
(eg to improve co-ordination of hand and fingers, to achieve hand – eye co-ordination

Cognitive Development
(eg to develop the ability to classify)

Language Development
(eg to improve expressive language skills)

Social Development
(eg to stimulate social contact with peers)

2. Any specific areas of weakness or gaps in skills acquisition which impede the child's progress

Eg short-term memory deficits

3. Suggested methods and approaches

Implications of the Child's Medical Condition
(eg advice on the side-effects of medication for epilepsy)

Teaching and Learning Approaches
(eg teaching methods for the blind or deaf or teaching through other specialised methods)

Emotional Climate and Social Regime
(eg type of regime, size of class or school, need for individual attention)

c) FACILITIES AND RESOURCES

1. Special Equipment
(eg physical aids, auditory aids, visual aids)

2. Specialist Facilities
(eg for incontinence, for medical examinations, treatment and drug administration)

3. Special Educational Resources
(eg specialist equipment for teaching children with physical or sensory disabilities, non-teaching aids)

4. Other Specialist Resources
(eg Nursing, Social Work, Speech Therapy, Occupational Therapy, Physiotherapy, Psychotherapy, Audiology, Orthoptics)

5. Physical Environment
(eg access and facilities for non-ambulant pupils, attention to lighting environment, attention to acoustic environment, attention to thermal environment, health care accommodation)

6. School Organisation and Attendance
(eg day attendance, weekly boarding, termly boarding, relief hostel accommodation)

7. Transport

At the end of the assessment the LEA must decide whether the child has special educational needs which require the formal protection of a statement. Some children may be recognised as having special educational needs which can be met with a little additional help and they may not be given a formal statement.

Section 6   The LEA has the power to assess any child under 19 and at school. In addition children under 5 may also be assessed and the Act lays down special procedures for assessment of children under 2 to assist with early intervention which may prevent difficulties arising later on.

Section 7   STATEMENTS

If, after assessing a child, the LEA decides that he has SEN which require special provision to be made, it must then make an official statement of those needs and the provision to be made to meet them. A statement contains 5 parts plus a number of appendices:

1. Introduction	basic information eg name and age of the child
2. Special Educational Needs	the LEA's description of the child's needs
3. Special Educational Provision	the provision the LEA intends to make to meet the child's needs including any facilities and equipment judged to be necessary and details of proposed staffing and curricular arrangements
4. Appropriate school or other arrangements	details of a particular school or other form of education
5. Additional non-educational provision	any other provision eg physiotherapy which may be required.

Advice and information provided by people concerned in the placement of the child will be added to the statement as appendices:

Appendix A   Parental representations
Appendix B   Parental evidence
Appendix C   Educational Advice
Appendix D   Medical Advice
Appendix E   Psychological advice
Appendix F   Other advice obtained by the LEA
Appendix G   Information from the District Health Authority or Social Services.

The statement should be compiled in close liaison with the child's parents. The Educational Advice given under Appendix C (above) must be obtained from a qualified teacher who is the head of a school which the child has attended in the preceding 18 months. If the head has not taught the child during this period, a teacher who has done so must be consulted.

In the case of a child with a visual or hearing impairment, a teacher with an appropriate special qualification must provide the advice or be consulted by the person doing so. If the child has not attended school during the preceding 18 months the authority must consult someone who has suitable knowledge and experience of the child.

Section 7   The Act lays out detailed procedures for compiling a statement and parents must be consulted at every stage and must see copies of both the draft and final statement prepared by the LEA.

Sections 7 & 8 It is hoped that these procedures will allow the LEA and the parents to reach agreement about the type of provision suitable for the child. However if the parents are not satisfied they have a right to appeal against the placement decided by the LEA. The LEA must give them the name of a person who can provide information and advice about the child's special educational needs. The parents may appeal first to a local appeal committee and then, if necessary, to the Secretary of State. The local appeal committee is able to make recommendations but its decision is not binding upon the LEA. The Secretary of State has the power to reverse or amend a decision or to direct the LEA to cease to maintain a statement.

Section 2   *REVIEW OF SPECIAL EDUCATIONAL NEEDS*

Once a statement has been made, the Act places a duty on LEAs to review the arrangements made under the statement annually. Teachers will be asked to contribute to this review.

Section 7   *RE-ASSESSMENT*

Parents of a child who has a statement may ask for a reassessment of his needs and, provided that this has not been done within the preceding 6 months, the LEA must meet the request. In any case, a child who has a statement must be reassessed between the ages of 13½ and 14½ if this has not already been done since he reached the age of 12½. This arrangement was made in order to assist with planning for the child's future after school.

163

It is useful to remember that the Education Act applies to children up to the age of 19. All children have a right to education up to 19 but their final three years may take place either in school or at a college of further education. The 1981 Act applies only to pupils at school and not to those at college.

MISCELLANEOUS PROVISIONS OF THE ACT

Section 2   *Duty of the School Governors*

The Act places a duty on school governors to "use their best endeavours" to secure appropriate provision for pupils with SEN and to see that teachers are informed of any special needs pupils may have.

Section 3   *Education other than at school*

For a small number of children, school placement may not be appropriate and the Act therefore allows the LEA to make provision otherwise than in a school, eg at home.

Section 10   *The role of Health Authorities (re children under 5)*

If someone working for a Health Authority (eg a paediatrician or district nurse) thinks that a child under 5 might have special educational needs, the Authority must

> a) tell the parents
> b) and then bring the matter to the attention of the LEA.

It is hoped that this will help improve co-ordination between Health and Education Authorities and lead to earlier help for children and their families.

Section 10   *Voluntary Organisations*

If the Authority thinks that a particular voluntary organisation might be able to help the family, it should provide them with details of that organisation.

APPENDIX B

SELECTED FURTHER READING ON SPECIFIC DISABILITIES

This selection of books and leaflets has been prepared with the needs of the mainstream teacher in mind. In some instances there is very little material available and we have therefore indicated the appropriate voluntary organisation as a source of information (addresses of these organisations are given in Appendix D). In other instances a great deal of information has been published and it has been necessary to select a few books which teachers will find helpful. Clearly the list is not exhaustive.

APHASIA/DYSPHASIA   AFASIC can offer further information and advice.

ARTHRITIS (JCA)   *A Guide to Arthritis and other Rheumatic Diseases*
When a Young Person has Arthritis – A Guide for Teachers
both published by the Arthritis and Rheumatism Council.

ASTHMA   *Childhood Asthma – A Guide for Parents and Children*
Understanding Asthma
both available from the Asthma Society.

BRITTLE BONES   *Education for Children with Brittle Bones*
Information sheet from the Brittle Bone Society.

CEREBRAL PALSY   The Spastics Society produce a publications list and a series of information leaflets about Cerebral Palsy.

COELIAC CONDITION   *The Coeliac Handbook* and *The Coeliac Condition* together with dietary advice are available from the Coeliac Society.

CONGENITAL HEART CONDITION   The British Heart Foundation publishes literature.

CYSTIC FIBROSIS   The Cystic Fibrosis Research Trust publishes a series of leaflets of which the following are of particular interest to teachers:

5. School Problems of Children with Cystic Fibrosis
7. Your Cystic Fibrosis Child at School

DIABETES   The British Diabetic Association has a wide range of literature including the following leaflets:

DH126 Childhood and Adolescence
DH127 The Diabetic At School
DH133 Exercise and Sport

They also supply a School Pack for individual children with Diabetes.

DYSLEXIA   The British Dyslexia Association has a series of leaflets, including *Teaching the Dyslexic*. *People with Dyslexia* is a report of a working group commissioned by the British Council for the Rehabilitation of the Disabled and is available from RADAR.

EPILEPSY	The British Epilepsy Association publishes a wide range of information including a leaflet, *Epilepsy: a Guide for Teachers.* The National Society for Epilepsy produces a package of educational material. *The Epilepsy Handbook* by S McGovern, Sheldon Press 1982 *Epilepsy: A Teacher's Handbook* by P J Rogan, Mersey Region Epilepsy Association 1980 *Swimming and Epilepsy* leaflet available from the Sports Council.
FRIEDREICH'S ATAXIA	The Friedreich's Ataxia Group can supply further information.
HAEMOPHILIA	The Haemophilia Society publishes a booklet called *Introduction to Haemophilia – Notes for Teachers.* A list of Haemophilia Centres in the UK may be obtained from the Department of Health and Social Security free of charge. Contact: Health Services Division HSIA, Room 1225, Hannibal House, Elephant and Castle, London SE1 6TE.
HEAD INJURY	There is a dearth of suitable "lay" books on this condition but the following may be helpful to teachers: *Explaining the Brain* by W Richie-Russell with A J Ewar, Oxford University Books 1975 *Shattered Mind: The Person After Brain Damage* by H Gardner, Routledge 1977 *Mechanics of the Mind* by C Blakemore, Cambridge University Press 1977.
HEARING IMPAIRMENT	*Educating Hearing Impaired Children* by M Reed, Open University Press 1984 *The Hearing Impaired Child and the Family* by M Nolan and I Tucker, Souvenir Press Human Horizon Series 1981 *Hearing Impairment* by K Lysons, Woodhead-Faulkner Ltd 1984 *Ways and Means 3: Hearing Impairment* Somerset Education Authority *List of Examination Concessions and Considerations for Hearing Impaired Candidates* prepared by the National Study Group on Further and Higher Education for the Hearing Impaired.
KIDNEY DISORDERS	The British Kidney Association publishes a series of leaflets about kidney problems.
LEUKAEMIA	The Leukaemia Society can provide further information.
LOSS OF LIMB	REACH publishes a series of leaflets. *Rehabilitation of Arm Amputees and Limb Deficient Children* by E Robertson, Balliere Tindall London 1978.
MENTAL HANDICAP	MENCAP publishes a wide range of information. *Learning to Cope* by E Whelan and B Speake, Souvenir Press Human Horizon Series 1980.

MIGRAINE	The Migraine Trust can provide further information.
MUSCULAR DYSTROPHY	The Muscular Dystrophy Group publishes a wide range of literature including a booklet called *Children with Neuro-Muscular Disease*
SHORT STATURE	The Association for Research into Restricted Growth publishes literature.
SICKLE CELL DISEASE	The Sickle Cell Society publishes literature including a *Handbook on Sickle Cell Disease*.
SKIN CONDITIONS 1. ECZEMA	The National Eczema Society publishes information including a leaflet called *Coping with School*.
2. EPIDERMOLYSIS BULLOSA	DEBRA publishes a leaflet called *Dystrophic Epidermolysis Bullosa: A Guide for Schools*.
SPEECH DISORDERS	The Association for Stammerers publishes a leaflet *The Stammering Child at School: Notes for the Teacher*.
SPINA BIFIDA AND HYDROCEPHALUS	ASBAH publishes a wide range of information including a booklet *Children with Spina Bifida At School – A Booklet for Teachers and Students*.
SPINAL INJURIES	The Spinal Injuries Association is able to provide information. *Paraplegia: A Handbook of Practical Care and Advice* M A Rogers, Faber 1978.
VISUAL IMPAIRMENT	The RNIB is able to provide information. *Helping Partially Sighted Children in Ordinary Schools: Guidelines for Teachers* by J Kell, Adviser in Special Education, County Education Offices, Aylesbury, Buckinghamshire. *Visually Handicapped Children and Young People* by E Chapman, Routledge and Kegan Paul 1978.

APPENDIX C

SELECTED FURTHER READING OF A GENERAL NATURE

ANDERSON E M & CLARKE L (1982) *Disability in Adolescence* Methuen

BOOKIS J (1983) *Beyond the School Gate* RADAR

THE BRITISH RED CROSS SOCIETY (1974) *People in Wheelchairs – Hints for Helpers* BRCS*

CHARTERED SOCIETY OF PHYSIOTHERAPISTS (1980) *Handling the Handicapped* Woodhead-Faulkner*

COPE C & ANDERSON E M (1977) *Special Units in Ordinary Schools: an exploratory study of provision for disabled children* University of London Institute of Education

DARNBROUGH A & KINRADE D (1984) *Directory for Disabled People: a handbook of information and opportunities for disabled and handicapped people* Woodhead-Faulkner*

GRIFFITHS D & WYNNE D (1981) *How to Push a Wheelchair* Disabled Motorists Club*

HEGARTY S & POCKLINGTON K (1981) *Educating Pupils with special needs in the ordinary school* NFER/Nelson

HODGSON A, CLUNIES ROSS L & HEGARTY S (1983) *Learning Together* NFER/Nelson

INTERNATIONAL PROJECT FOR COMMUNICATION AIDS FOR THE SPEECH-IMPAIRED (IPCAS) (1984) *Conversations with Non-Speaking People* Canadian Rehabilitation Council for the Disabled*

LILLYSTONE C & SUMMERSON E (1984) *Compendium of Post 16 Education (COPE) in residential training establishments for handicapped young people* National Bureau for Handicapped Students

JAY P (1984) *Coping with Disability* Disabled Living Foundation*

JOWETT S (1982) *Young Disabled People: their further education, training and employment* NFER/Nelson

NATIONAL BUREAU FOR HANDICAPPED STUDENTS (1984) *After 16 What Next?* NBHS

NATIONAL FUND FOR RESEARCH INTO CRIPPLING DISEASES (ACTION RESEARCH) (1974) Does he take sugar in his tea? Action Research

NATIONAL UNION OF TEACHERS (1983) *Pupil Profile – A discussion document* NUT

NATIONAL UNION OF TEACHERS (1984) *Meeting Special Educational Needs in Ordinary Schools – a union guide* NUT

NATIONAL UNION OF TEACHERS (1984) *The Education Act 1981 – a union guide* (revised edition) NUT

NEWELL P (1983) *Special Education Handbook – the new law on children with special needs* Advisory Centre for Education (ACE)

ORTON C (1984) *The Child with a Medical Problem in the Ordinary School* Home and School Council

QUEEN ELIZABETH'S FOUNDATION FOR THE DISABLED (QUEF) (1984) *Directory of Opportunities for School Leavers with Disabilities* QUEF

RADAR (1984) *Guide to the Education Act 1981* RADAR

REDBRIDGE SEMERC *Learning to Cope* (Journal) Redbridge SEMERC

ROWAN P (1980) *What Sort of Life?* NFER

RUSSELL P (1978) *The Wheelchair Child* Souvenir Press

SAUNDERS P (1984) *Micros for Handicapped Users* Helena Press, Orchard Lane, Goathland, Whitby YO22 5JT

THOMPSON N (1979) *The Adaptation of Existing Public Buildings for the Handicapped* Polytechnic of Central London*

GOVERNMENT PUBLICATIONS

The Education Act 1981	HMSO
Circular 8/81 – Education Act 1981	DES/HMSO
Circular 1/83 – Assessments and Statements of Special Educational Needs	DES/HMSO
The Warnock Report – Special Educational Needs: Report of the Committee of Enquiry into the Education of Handicapped Children and Young People (1978)	HMSO
Design Note 18 – Access for Disabled People to Educational Buildings (1984)	HMSO
Design Note 25 – Lighting and Acoustic Criteria for the Visually Handicapped and Hearing Impaired in Schools (1981)	HMSO
Building Bulletin 61 – Designing for Children with Special Educational Needs in Ordinary Schools (1984)	HMSO
Safety at School (Safety Series No 6) 1977	HMSO
Records of Achievement: A Statement of Policy (1984)	HMSO
Children with Special Educational Needs – audio visual training package (1983)	DES Rm 2/11 Information Division

* denotes available from RADAR. A full list of publications carried by RADAR is available on receipt of a SAE.

APPENDIX D

USEFUL NAMES AND ADDRESSES

ACE
18 Victoria Park Square
London E2 9PB (Tel: 01-980 4596)
ACE provides useful information and publications about law in relation to education.

ACE Centre (Aids to Communication in Education)
Ormerod School
Waynflete Road
Headington
Oxford OX3 8DD (Tel: 0865-63508)
For information and advice about communication aids used in school.

Arthritis and Rheumatism Council for Research
41 Eagle Street
London WC1R 4AR (Tel: 01-405 8572)

Arthritis Care (formerly British Rheumatism and Arthritis Association)
6 Grosvenor Crescent
London SW1X 7ER (Tel: 01-235 0902)

Asthma Research Council
St Thomas' Hospital
Lambeth Palace Road
London SE1 7EH (Tel: 01-928 3099)

National **Autistic** Society
276 Willesden Lane
London NW2 5RB (Tel: 01-451 3844) ·

Royal National Institute for the **Blind**
224-228 Great Portland Street
London W1N 6AA (Tel: 01-388 1266)

Brittle Bones Society
112 City Road
Dundee DD2 2PW (Tel: 0382-67603)

Centre for Studies on Integration in Education
The Spastics Society
16 Fitzroy Square
London W1P 5HQ (Tel: 01-387 9571)
Centre set up by the Spastics Society in 1982 to raise public and professional awareness of integration and to promote good practice.

Chest, Heart and Stroke Association
Tavistock House North
Tavistock Square
London WC1H 9JE (Tel: 01-387 3012)

Children's Legal Centre
20 Compton Terrace
London N1 2UN (Tel: 01-359 6251/2)
Provides assistance and advice for parents and others with regard to the law as it affects children.

The **Coeliac** Society
PO Box 181
London NW2 2QY (Tel: 01-459 2440)

Colostomy Welfare Group
38/39 Eccleston Square
London SW1V 1PB (Tel: 01-828 5175)

Council for the Accreditation of Correspondence Colleges
27 Marylebone Road
London NW1 5JS
Supplies a list of recognised correspondence colleges.

Cystic Fibrosis Research Trust
5 Blyth Road
Bromley
Kent BR1 3RS (Tel: 01-464 7211)

The British **Deaf** Association
38 Victoria Place
Carlisle CA1 1HU (Tel: 0228-48844)

National **Deaf** Children's Society
45 Hereford Road
London W2 5AH (01-229 9272)

British Association of Teachers of the **Deaf** (BATOD)
The Rycroft Centre
Royal Schools for the Deaf
Stanley Road
Cheadle Hulme
Cheadle
Cheshire SK8 6RK

170

National Association for Tertiary
Education of the **Deaf**
Contact: Miss R Zannettou
Shirecliffe College
Shirecliffe Road
Sheffield S5 8XZ (Tel: 0742 78301)
*Can offer information and advice to help hearing
impaired young people prepare for college.*

National Study Group on Further and
Higher Education for the **Hearing-
Impaired**
Contact: Mrs J Sutton
Shirecliffe College
Shirecliffe Road
Sheffield S5 8XZ (Tel: 0742 78301)
*Publishes a list of examination concessions and
considerations for hearing-impaired candidates.*

Royal National Institute for the **Deaf**
105 Gower Street
London WC1E 6AH (Tel: 01-387 8033)

The British **Diabetic** Association
10 Queen Anne Street
London W1M 0BD (Tel: 01-323 1531)

Disabled Living Foundation
380/384 Harrow Road
London W9 2HU (Tel: 01-289 6111)
*Maintains an information service and exhibition of
aids and answers telephone and letter enquiries about
aids and equipment.*

Disablement Income Group
Attlee House
28 Commercial Street
London E1 (Tel: 01-247 2128)
Can advise on benefits and allowances.

Down's Children's Association
4 Oxford Street
London W1N 9FL (Tel: 01-580 0511/2)

Disfigurement Guidance Centre
Clydesdale Bank Buildings
High Street
Newburgh
Fife
Scotland

British **Dyslexia** Association
Church Lane
Peppard
Oxfordshire RG9 5JN (Tel: 04917 699)

Dystrophic Epidermolysis Bullosa
Research Association (DEBRA)
7 Sandhurst Lodge
Wokingham Road
Crowthorne
Berkshire RG11 7QD (Tel: 0344-771961)

National **Eczema** Society
Tavistock House North
Tavistock Square
London WC1H 9SR (Tel: 01-388 4097)

British **Epilepsy** Association
Crowthorne House
New Wokingham Road
Wokingham
Berkshire RG11 3AY (Tel: 0344-773122)

National Society for **Epilepsy**
Chalfont Centre for Epilepsy
Chalfont St Peter
Gerrards Cross
Buckinghamshire SL9 0RJ
(Tel: 02407-3991)

Family Fund
PO Box 50
York YO1 1UY (Tel: 0904-21115)
*Provides financial assistance to families caring for a
severely handicapped child.*

Friedreich's Ataxia Group
Burleigh Lodge
Knowle Lane
Cranleigh
Surrey GU6 8RD (Tel: 0483-272741)

Haemophilia Society
PO Box 9
16 Trinity Street
London SE1 1DE (Tel: 01-407 1010)

Headway
National **Head Injuries** Association
200 Mansfield Road
Nottingham NG1 3HX
(Tel: 0602-622382)

British **Heart** Foundation
102 Gloucester Place
London W1H 4DH (Tel: 01-935 0185)

Invalid Children's Aid Association
126 Buckingham Palace Road
London SW1W 9SB (Tel: 01-730 9891)
Runs 4 residential special schools for children with speech and language disorders and supplies information to groups and individuals.

British **Kidney** Patient Association
Bordon
Hants (Tel: 04203 2021/2 & 3430)

Lady Hoare Trust for
Physically Disabled Children
7 North Street
Midhurst
W Sussex GU29 9DJ (Tel: 073 081 3696)
Associated with Arthritis Care.

Leukaemia Research Fund
43 Great Ormond Street
London WC1N 3JJ (Tel: 01-405 0101)

Leukaemia Society
PO Box 82
Exeter
Devon EX2 5DP (Tel: 0392 218514)

Royal Society for **Mentally
Handicapped** Children and Adults
(MENCAP)
123 Golden Lane
London EC1Y 0RT (Tel: 01-253 9433)

Midlands Bureau for Preparatory
Training of the Disabled
14 Barlows Road
Edgbaston
Birmingham B15 2PL
(Tel: 021-454 0122)
Offers information and advice to disabled people in the Midlands. Specifically provides correspondence courses and home tuition to hospital patients and homebound people above school age.

Migraine Trust
45 Great Ormond Street
London WC1N 3HD (Tel: 01-278 2676)

Muscular Dystrophy Group of Great
Britain
Nattrass House
35 Macaulay Road
London SW4 0QP (Tel: 01-720 8055)

National Bureau for Handicapped
Students
336 Brixton Road
London SW9 7AA (Tel: 01-274 0565)
Offers information and advice on further and higher education for disabled people.

National Council for Special Education
1 Wood Street
Stratford-upon-Avon
Warwickshire CV37 6JE
(Tel: 0789 205332)
Professional body of teachers involved in teaching children with special educational needs.

Open University
Adviser on the Education of Students
with Disabilities
Office for Students with Disabilities
Open University
Walton Hall
Milton Keynes
MK7 6AA (Tel: 0908-74066)
Offers home study and courses adapted to meet the needs of students with disabilities.

Partially-Sighted Society
40 Wordsworth Street
Hove
E Sussex BN3 5BH (Tel: 0273-736053)

Physically Handicapped and
Able-Bodied (PHAB)
Tavistock House North
Tavistock Square
London WC1H 9HJ (Tel: 01-388 1963)
Uses social means (clubs and holidays) to bring physically disabled and able-bodied children and young people together.

REACH
85 Newlands Road
Billericay
Essex CM12 0PH (Tel: 02774 4118)
Support group for families with children with limb deficiencies.

Rehabilitation Engineering Movement
Advisory Panels (REMAP)
25 Mortimer Street
London W1N 8AB (Tel: 01-637 5400)
REMAP panels throughout the country give help in designing and making one-off aids (where they are not commercially available) for individual use.

Association for Research into **Restricted Growth**
24 Pinchfield
Maple Cross
Rickmansworth
Hertfordshire WD3 2TP

The Royal Association for Disability and Rehabilitation
25 Mortimer Street
London W1N 8AB (Tel: 01-637 5400)
Supplies publications and information concerning all aspects of physical disability particularly education, access and employment.

Royal Society for the Prevention of Accidents (ROSPA)
Cannon House
Priory Queensway
Birmingham B4 6BS (Tel: 021-233 2461)
Keeps details of the Wheelchair Proficiency Scheme.

Scottish Council on Disability
5 Shandwick Place
Edinburgh EH2 4RG (Tel: 031-229 8632)
Offers advice and information to physically handicapped people in Scotland.

The Shaftesbury Society
2a Amity Grove
Raynes Park
London SW20 0LJ (Tel: 01-946 6634)
Runs schools, hostels and holiday centres for handicapped children and adults.

Organisation for **Sickle Cell Anaemia** Research (OSCAR)
200A High Road
Wood Green
London N22 4HH
(Tel: 01-889 3300/4844)

Sickle Cell Society
c/o Brent Community Health Council
16 High Street
Harlesden
London NW10 4LX (Tel: 01-451 3293)

The **Spastics** Society
(Education Department)
16 Fitzroy Square
London W1P 5HQ (Tel: 01-387 9571)

Association for All **Speech Impaired** Children (AFASIC)
347 Central Markets
Smithfield
London EC1A 9NH (Tel: 01-236 3632/6487)

Association for **Spina Bifida and Hydrocephalus** (ASBAH)
22 Upper Woburn Place
London WC1H 0EP (Tel: 01-388 1382)

Spinal Injuries Association
Yeoman House
76 St James's Lane
London N10 3DF (Tel: 01-444 2121)

British Sports Association for the Disabled
Hayward House
Barnard Crescent
Aylesbury
Buckinghamshire (Tel: 0296-27889)

The Sports Council
16 Upper Woburn Place
London WC1H 0QP (Tel: 01-388 1277)

Association for **Stammerers**
c/o The Finsbury Centre
Pine Street
London EC1R 0JH

Voluntary Council for Handicapped Children
National Children's Bureau
8 Wakley Street
Islington
London EC1V 7QE (Tel: 01-278 9441)
Offers information and support to parents and teachers of children with special needs.

Wales Council for the Disabled
Caerbragdy Industrial Estate
Bedwas Road
Caerphilly
Mid Glamorgan
CF8 3SL (Tel: 0222-887325)
Offers information and advice to physically handicapped people in Wales.

Special Education Microelectronics Resource Centres (SEMERCs)

SEMERCs keep examples of micro-electronic aids for use with children with special needs. Teachers, parents and children are invited to visit the centres (by appointment) to try out various aids. The SEMERCs also arrange travelling exhibitions and can advise on micro-electronic equipment for children with special needs.

Bristol SEMERC
School of Special Education
Faculty of Education and Community
Studies
Bristol Polytechnic
Redland Hill
Bristol BS6 6UZ
(Tel: 0272-733141/741251 ext 31)

Manchester SEMERC
Manchester Polytechnic
Hathersage Road
Manchester M13 0JA
(Tel: 061-225 9054)

Newcastle SEMERC
Newcastle Polytechnic
Coach Lane Campus
Newcastle-upon-Tyne NE7 7XA
(Tel: 0632-665057)

Redbridge SEMERC
Dane Centre
c/o The Teachers' Centre
Melbourne Road
Ilford
Essex IG1 4HT (Tel: 01-478 6363)

Communication Aids Centres

Communication Aids Centres help to find solutions to problems related to speech impairment and can advise on the use of a range of communication aids. Like SEMERCs they have aids on display and parents, teachers and children may visit the centres by appointment.

Bristol CAC
Speech Therapy Department
Frenchay Hospital
Frenchay
Bristol BS16 1LE
(Tel: 0272 565656 ext 204)

Cardiff CAC
Rookwood Hospital
Cardiff
South Wales (Tel: 0222 566281)

Charing Cross CAC (*mainly for adults*)
Charing Cross Hospital
Fulham Palace Road
London W6 (Tel: 01-748 2040)

Wolfson Centre CAC (*mainly for children*)
Mecklenburgh Square
London WC1N 2AP (Tel: 01-837 7618)

Newcastle CAC
Dene Centre
Castles Farm Road
Newcastle-upon-Tyne
NE3 1PH (Tel: 091-284 0480)

Sandwell CAC
Boulton Road
West Bromwich
West Midlands B70 6NN
(Tel: 021-553 0908)